# THE GUILD® SOURCEBOOK
# OF RESIDENTIAL ART 6

# THE GUILD® SOURCEBOOK OF RESIDENTIAL ART 6

Your Guide to the Artful Home

Guild Sourcebooks
Madison, Wisconsin

# THE GUILD® SOURCEBOOK
# OF RESIDENTIAL ART 6

Your Guide to the Artful Home

Guild Sourcebooks
An imprint of The Guild, Inc.
931 E. Main Street
Madison, Wisconsin 53703
TEL 800-930-1856
E-MAIL sourcebookinfo@guild.com

ADMINISTRATION
Toni Sikes, CEO & Founder
Michael Baum, President
Annik DuPaty, Manager of Sourcebook Sales
Elizabeth Tucker, Manager of Trade Relations
Jenna Brandt, Administrative Assistant

DESIGN, PRODUCTION & EDITORIAL
Jill Schaefer, Editorial Manager/Writer
Laura Grady, Project Designer/Production Artist
Barbara Hatley, Image Specialist/Production Coordinator
Laura Beausire, Writer
Melita Schuessler, Proofreader

ARTIST CONSULTANTS
Susan Buzby • Nicole Carroll • Laura Marth
Amy Lambright Murphy • Paul Murphy

SOURCEBOOK INTERNS
Miel-Margarita Paredes • Maggie Sasso • Ellen Siebers

Front cover: *Smoke-Fired Vessels Series 2* and *Three-Candle Candleholder (#2)* by Carol Green, see pages 108-109. *Espresso Cups and Saucers* by Laura Zindel, see page 86. Other Guild artists shown (clockwise from left): Mary Lynn O'Shea, Janna Ugone, Brad Reed Nelson, and Michael Cohn and Molly Stone. Photograph: Eric Ferguson.
Page 3: *Crow with Berry* by Joline El-Hai, see page 71. Photograph: Lance Wagner.
Opposite: Lighting by Hubbardton Forge, see page 74. Photograph: Jim Westphalen Photography.
Back cover: *Grafted* by Brian A. Hubel, see page 47. Photograph: Don Jones Photography.

Special thanks to our 2007 Review Committee:
Karen J. Darcy-Dominguez, Owner, Archisphere Design Studio LLC
Catherine Davidson, Owner, CR Davidson Art
Sharon Devenish, President, Devenish Associates, Inc.
Tom McHugh, AIA
Sean Sennott, Gallery Director, Gallery 323 at Rubin's

# A Reason for Art

Welcome to the sixth edition of *The Guild Sourcebook of Residential Art.* You're receiving this book because you've indicated an interest in including original art in your designs or projects. Each year, we take great care and delight in providing the tool for finding the nation's best commissionable artists and their work.

Still, in the hustle and bustle of day-to-day work, it's easy to forget the "whys" behind commissioning artwork. It's true that commissioning a work of art directly from an artist allows you and your client to design an environment to unique specifications, instead of making selections from limited (and often uninspired) off-the-shelf product lines.

But there's more to it than that.

Works of art, those pieces that say something surprising and true about who we are, merit more than "afterthought" status. An original, artist-made commission comes to life in its intended environment, revealing the soul of its maker as well as its owner. Inviting an artist to take part in your design process results in a rewarding and eye-opening journey for all involved.

As you turn—and return to—these pages in the year ahead, we hope you discover artists who can share and enrich your creative vision, artists who will expand your clients' sense of what's possible in the spaces where they live, work, and play.

Toni Sikes
Publisher

# contents

## 1

## Introduction

## 2

## Profiles

1. *Morning Glory* by Richard Hall Fine Art, see page 192. Photograph: Tom Jordan.  2. *Hydra* and *mirabel* by Steve "Spike" Finch, see page 105.

# 3

## Artist Gallery

# 4

## Resources

3. *Bird and Wall* by Jon Michael Route, see page 264.  4. *Boundless Spirit* by James T. Russell, see page 134. Photograph: Paul Moses.

# How to Use *The Guild Sourcebook of Residential Art 6*

## Your Direct Connection to Artists' Studios

The decision to live with art is a decision to live with things of enduring value. The paintings, prints, and photographs you place in your home—like the works of art in clay, fiber, metal, glass, and wood—enrich your life with a silent and strengthening presence, and with the joy of beauty and imagination.

Because original art can be costly compared to manufactured goods, and because each artwork is unique, shopping for art calls for research and initiative. Hence *The Guild Sourcebook of Residential Art.* This unique volume invites you to browse, buy, and commission works of art directly from the studios of exceptional contemporary artists.

Works are grouped in two main sections.

■ Furniture, Sculpture & Objects features furniture, lighting, architectural elements, and art objects in all media, as well as sculpture for pedestals and gardens.

■ Art for the Wall features paintings, photographs, prints, fiber art, and other works for the wall.

Full-color photographs make it easy to find the artists whose style appeals to you most, while complete contact information allows you to get in touch with those artists directly to purchase existing pieces or commission custom-designed works.

You need not be a designer to purchase works from artists included in this book. In fact, the only qualifications you really need are a sincere appreciation for the artists you call and a genuine interest in owning their work.

### Putting the Book to Work

We welcome you to browse *The Guild Sourcebook of Residential Art,* enjoying the artwork, the illustrated designer profiles, and the many suggestions for building a home rich in beauty

and creative energy. But there's more to this book than that. Every one of our featured artists invites you to call or e-mail to purchase pieces from their studio or to arrange a commission for a custom work of art.

Your call to any one of these artists can take you in many directions.

■ Artworks shown on these pages may be available for immediate purchase. Some of these works are from an artist's production line or created in limited editions; others are one-of-a-kind pieces.

■ The artist may have other available works on hand. If you live near the artist (see the Location Index), consider visiting the studio. If a studio visit isn't feasible, ask to see images; these can often be e-mailed for quick review.

■ Alternately, you could hire the artist to create a unique work that reflects your home, your aesthetic, and perhaps, some landmark event in your life or the life of

*Vase with Red Inlay* (left) and *Vase with Handles* by Carol Green, see page 108-109. Photograph: Jim Ream.

## Finding What You Need
### A Roadmap to this Book

Want to contact an artist featured in *The Guild Sourcebook of Residential Art*? Look for addresses, phone numbers, and other contact information at the tops of artists' display pages. Additional information about each artist can be found in the Artist Statements section in the back of the book; listings are in alphabetical order by the heading on each artist's page. This is where you'll find information about the artists' media and techniques, their range of products, and their notable awards or commissions.

If you know what type of artwork you want to purchase or commission, a search by section will help you find results quickly. You'll find a list of sections in the Table of Contents. Likewise, if you know the name of the artist you want to work with, you can easily search using the Index of Artists & Companies, found in the back of the book. If you would like to work with an artist in your area, check the Location Index.

Curious about an artist's work? Don't hesitate to contact that artist directly; he or she will be delighted to hear from you. And for more information about these and other artists who create works for home environments, visit the The Guild's Custom Design Center, a featured service of www.guild.com.

someone you love. For help in commissioning artworks, consider the services of The Guild's Custom Design Center. You can reach the CDC from The Guild's home page (www.guild.com), or call CDC staff at 1-877-565-2002.

When viewing an artist's page, keep in mind that while the projects shown are representative of the artist's work, they don't demonstrate the full extent of the artist's capabilities. If you like a certain style but want something other than the works pictured here, call the artist and talk it over. He or she may be intrigued at the prospect of exploring new forms.

Above: *Silk Road Weaves Rug* by Barbara Jacobs, see page 88.

# Commissioning Artwork

There's something exhilarating about engaging an artist to create a unique artwork for your home. Custom-designed (or "commissioned") works of art reflect your personal taste and vision more deeply than "off-the-shelf" art. At the same time, they can significantly enhance the value of your home.

Commissioned works of art may or may not be expensive, depending upon the scope of the project, but they will always require your personal involvement. If you enjoy that involvement, art commissions are the ultimate way to buy original art. Custom-designed artworks—whether movable, as with a painted portrait, or permanently attached to the structure of your home, as with a tile fireplace surround—can become instant family treasures, adding deeply to the heritage of who you are.

## Choosing an Artist

The most important step you'll take when planning a commission is choosing an artist. What makes a good choice? Someone whose previous art projects appeal to you. Whose previous clients are enthusiastic. Who has undertaken similar projects in the past and delivered completed work within the agreed-upon budget and schedule.

And how do you find this individual?

*The Guild Sourcebook of Residential Art* is a wonderful place to start. Every one of our featured artists accepts commissions for custom-designed artwork, and the contact information included with their individual display pages will put you in touch with them directly. You may also want to talk with friends who have hired artists for commissions similar to yours, or visit artists' studios and art fairs to talk with candidates in person.

Above: *Winter in Berlin* by Libby Ware, see page 285. Photograph: Art Pierson. Opposite: *Horse Shadows* (detail) by Adam Jahiel, see page 229.

Once your A-list is narrowed down to two or three names, it's time to schedule meetings to discuss the project, either face-to-face (for local artists) or by phone. As you talk, try to determine the artist's interest in your project, and pay attention to your own comfort level with the artist. Try to find out whether the chemistry is right—whether you have the basis to build a working relationship—and confirm that the artist has the necessary skills to undertake your project. Be thorough and specific when asking questions. Is the artist excited about the project? What does he or she see as the most important issues or considerations? Will your needs be a major or minor concern? Evaluate the artist's style, approach, and personality.

If it feels like you might have trouble working together, take heed. But if all goes well and it feels like a good fit, ask for a list of references. These are important testimonials, so don't neglect to make the calls. Ask about the artist's work habits and communication style, and—of course—about the success of the artwork. You should also ask whether the project was delivered on time and within budget. If you like what you hear, you'll be one important step closer to hiring your artist.

## The Contract: Putting It in Writing

It's a truism in any business that it's cheaper to get the lawyers involved at the beginning of a process than after something goes wrong. In the case of custom-made works of art, a signed contract or letter of agreement commits the artist to completing his or her work on time and to specifications. It also assures the artist that he or she will get paid the right amount at the right time. That just about eliminates the biggest conflicts that can arise.

Contracts should be specific to the job. If your commission is for a photograph of a beloved country home, a sales slip noting down payment and delivery date should do the trick. If, on the other hand, you've hired a muralist to paint an *Alice in Wonderland* scene in the kids' playroom, a more detailed document will be needed.

Customarily, artists are responsible for design, production, shipping, and installation. If someone else is to be responsible for installation, be sure you specify who will coordinate and pay for it. With a large project, it's helpful to identify the tasks that, if delayed for any reason, would set back completion of the project. These should be discussed up front to ensure that all parties agree on requirements and expectations.

## Expect Professionalism

Once you've selected the artist, careful planning and communication can help ensure a great outcome. If this is an expensive or complicated project, you may want to request preliminary designs at this time. Since most artists charge a design fee whether or not they're ultimately hired for the project, start by asking for sketches from your top candidate. If you're unhappy with the designs submitted, go to your second choice. If, on the other hand, the design is what you'd hoped for, it's time to finalize your working agreement with this artist. As you discuss contract details, be resolved that silence is not golden and ignorance is not bliss! Discuss the budget and timetable, and be sure that these and other important details are spelled out in the contract. Now is the time for possible misunderstandings to be brought up and resolved—not later, when the work is half done and deadlines loom.

## Payment Schedule

The more skill you need and the more complex the project, the more you should budget for the artist's work and services. With larger projects, payments are usually tied to specific milestones; these serve as checkpoints and assure that work is progressing in a satisfactory manner, on time and on budget. Payment is customarily made in three stages, although—again—this will depend on the circumstances, scope, and complexity of the project.

The first payment for a large-scale commission is usually made when the contract is signed. It covers the artist's time and creativity in developing a detailed design specific to your needs. For larger projects, you can expect to go through several rounds of trial and error in the design process, but at the end of this stage you'll have detailed drawings and, for three-dimensional work, an approved maquette (model). The cost of the maquette and the design time are usually factored into the artist's fee.

The second payment is generally set for a point midway through the project and is for work completed to date. If the materials are expensive, the artist may also ask that you advance money at this stage to cover his or her costs. If the commission is canceled during this period, the artist keeps the money already paid for work performed.

Final payment is usually due when the work is finished or, if so arranged, installed. Sometimes the artwork is finished on time but the building is delayed (as so often happens with new construction); in this case, the artist should be paid upon completion but still has the obligation to oversee installation.

## Where to Find Help

If your project is large and expensive, or if it needs to be carefully coordinated with other aesthetic and functional aspects of your home, consider hiring an art consultant. The consultant can help with complicated contract arrangements and make certain that communication between the artist and professionals such as architects, interior designers, and engineers is clear and complete.

For some people, the process of commissioning a work of art involves a degree of involvement that they just don't want to take on. If that describes you, rest assured—you may still find that treasured work of art! Many artists have a wide selection of completed works on hand in their studios, giving you the option to purchase something ready-made and immediately available. If you find something great among the artist's inventory, don't hesitate to buy it. The piece you choose will still be unique, and it will still reflect your personal aesthetic sense. Your goal should be to develop an individual approach to enjoying art . . . and that includes your comfort level with how you purchase it.

Above: Wavy etched texture by Nancy Gong, see page 95.

Custom-designed artworks—whether movable, as with a painted portrait, or permanently attached to the structure of your home, as with a tile fireplace surround—can become instant family treasures, adding deeply to the heritage of who you are.

Above: *A Parenthetical Thought* by Myra Burg, see pages 244-246.

15

# Determining Value

Let's face it. When we find art that appeals to us, our reaction is immediate. We fall in love with it first—and then think about the pragmatic aspects of buying or owning it. But before you buy that painting or art quilt, it's important to ask some hard-nosed questions. Do I want to live with this work for years to come? If I buy it, where will I place it? And, equally important: Is the piece worth the asking price?

Here at The Guild, we help thousands of customers purchase original art each year. We also interact with hundreds of artists. Based on what we've learned, we can suggest some guidelines for assessing the value of a work of art.

## Cost and Value

One criterion that all experts and collectors agree upon is this: buy art that you love; all other considerations are secondary. While we agree with the spirit of this suggestion, we also think you'll make better and more confident purchases if you conduct basic research into the artist's background and stature.

## Pricing

The cost of a work of art is often related to the experience of the artist. Those who have worked in their fields for many years command higher prices than relative newcomers. The same is true for artists whose work is included in museum collections or publications, or who have mounted one-person shows. These are landmark events; they demonstrate respect for the artist on the part of curators, publishers, and gallery managers, and they have a cumulative effect on the artist's prices.

Whether or not a work of art seems expensive, it's good to remember that value and price are different qualities. The value of artwork is perceived and subjective, while the price is set and, usually, firm.

## Education

An artist's academic record sheds more light on his technical background and skills than on his natural talent. Museums and institutions consider an artist's schooling important, particularly when selecting emerging artists to participate in shows. Your choice of an etching or of tile for a fireplace surround, however, should not be based on which institution granted the artist a master's degree—or even whether the artist holds that degree at all. Some of our most esteemed artists developed their skills as apprentices or within an artists' community rather than at an institution.

## History of Exhibitions

More than schooling, an artist's credibility is reflected in the number and range of shows that have exhibited his work. This is a very important reference point for value.

Above: *June #10-05* by Chin Yuen, see page 207. Photograph: Saskia Soderman.  Opposite: Interior design by Tony Raffa, see page 28. Photograph: Rex Spencer.

Emerging artists compete to participate in group shows at local and regional galleries. Artists who are more advanced in their careers mount one-person shows.

When reviewing an artist's resume, pay close attention to the dates and locations of exhibitions.

- How long has the artist been exhibiting?
- Has the work been exhibited regionally, nationally, or internationally?
- Are the exhibition sites well known?
- Has the artist received awards?

## Editorial Reviews

Reviews in journals, magazines, and newspapers are another benchmark of value. Art critics act as interpreters, and their reviews not only evaluate the quality of artworks, but also place them in the context of history and genre. A strong endorsement by a respected critic can have a significant influence on an artist's career.

## Collections

It can be interesting to learn which private, public, and corporate collections include works by a particular artist. It can also be affirming to learn that others share your passion for a particular artist. With established artists, it becomes substantially more important to know who owns their work. If the work is part of a museum collection, for example, this adds to its value. Likewise, ownership by prestigious collectors and corporations can have a significant influence on price.

## Career Overview

Artists go through periods of development influenced by the world around them, producing works that explore particular techniques and themes of influence. When you meet artists or gallery curators, ask them to comment on the artist's body of work. How long has the artist been developing a particular theme or using a specific technique? How refined are the themes and techniques? Is the artist highly prolific? The answers to these questions will provide insight into the artist's depth of experience; in that way, they may influence the value you place on the work.

## The Value of Passion

Although the factors discussed here relate to marketplace value, they should also be considered as you think about the value you and your family place on a work of art. That said, we cannot emphasize too strongly that your passion for a work of art should always drive your purchase.

Buying art for your home involves a different set of standards than those faced by a major collector or museum. The right surroundings and appropriate placement in your home environment are much more important than investment appeal or a history of shows at major museums. Original art has an aesthetic and emotional impact on your home. This is one area where we urge you to lead with your heart.

# The Guild's Online Services

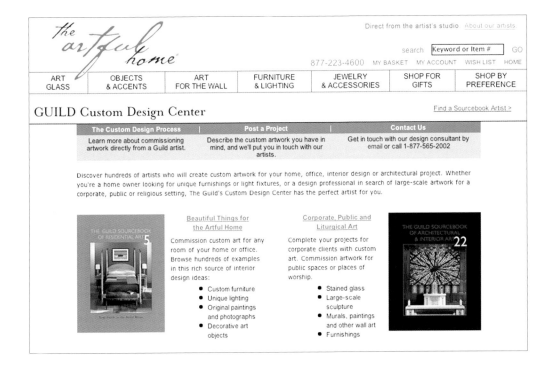

If you are an architect, an interior designer, an art consultant, or a professional in a related trade, a trip to The Guild's website, www.guild.com, can ease the task of finding the perfect artists for your design projects. Perhaps you are trying to locate an artist to personalize a new home or mark a family milestone with a custom work of art. Or maybe you have clients who need an artful solution for a specific design problem or to fill a particular space. In any of these cases, you will find that The Guild's online resources are deep and varied.

## ArtfulHome.com

In your search for artwork, make www.artfulhome.com, our retail site, your first stop. Among the thousands of works of art available for immediate purchase, you may find just the right piece for your project.

## Trade Professional Benefits

It pays to register as a trade professional at The Guild's website, www.guild.com/trade. Registration is free of charge, and it opens the door to a host of services designed to help you meet the needs of your clients successfully. As a registered trade professional, you will have access to areas of the www.guild.com website that have been created especially for you.

Benefits of registration include:

■ **An exclusive trade discount** – 15% off all original art at www.artfulhome.com

■ **Guild Sourcebooks** – Our annual desktop directories of commissionable artists

■ **Custom Design Center** – Direct e-mail access to commissionable artists online

■ **Post-a-Project** – Instantly broadcast your commission opportunities to our artists

■ **Web Portfolios** – Save portfolios of artwork under consideration for projects

To register as a trade professional on our website, simply go to www.guild.com/trade.

# From Commission to Completion

A customer in Diablo, California, was faced with a design challenge when she started looking for a dining table for her contemporary home. "I needed a custom table to fit in my new breakfast nook," she told us. "The breakfast nook is part of the contemporary open kitchen that we have, and I would like the table to be a unique addition that will bring in the glass, brushed stainless, and wood elements of the existing kitchen. From a functional standpoint, I need the table to easily slide out for bench access."

The client mentioned that she liked the work of Guild artist Eric Ziemelis, so our design consultant immediately contacted the artist about creating this custom piece.

Eric was able to provide the client with a rendering of the proposed design [see right], which is part of his usual design process. "Three-dimensional renderings have enabled to me to show the client what I'm envisioning in advance," the artist notes, "and it's easy to make changes to those renderings based on the client's wishes." With the client's approval of this rendering in hand, Eric was able to create a dream table for this homeowner.

Be sure to visit The Guild's Custom Design Center—or call one of our design consultants—to learn how artists like Eric Ziemelis can bring the imagination and color of original art into your own artful home.

---

# The Custom Design Center

Should you decide to broaden your search, you can browse examples of work by The Guild's sourcebook artists in the Custom Design Center at www.guild.com. The Custom Design Center is the gateway to commissionable artists and their work. Hundreds of examples of completed works of art provide inspiration for your design projects. Once you find something appropriate, you can commission artwork directly from that artist.

## Post a Project

The Custom Design Center also has a Post a Project feature that lets you broadcast project specifications by filling out an online form. Simply describe what kind of artwork you have in mind, as well as any project constraints. Guild staff will share your project details with qualified artists, then forward their proposals directly to you.

## Design Consultation Services

If you prefer to explore your project ideas over the phone, please call 1-877-565-2002. A Guild design consultant will be happy to help you refine your specifications and recommend artists for your project. Our consultant will work closely with you to select an artist, provide images of an artist's work, address your questions, and help you fine-tune your project requirements. Once you have made the decision to move forward, you may collaborate directly with the selected artist, sharing ideas and developing prototypes to arrive at a final design and price.

# Fabulous and Familiar

## Three Professionals on Designing an Artful Home

Every house is, at least, a shelter from the elements, a human nest or den, a more-or-less protective box in which we sleep and eat and carry on the mechanical details of living.

But an artful home is something else entirely.

To the notion of simple shelter we add the emotional content of home—a place where we belong—as well as a creative dimension that reflects who we are and what we value. A truly artful home nourishes our soul and satisfies our psyche. Life-size, it is a kind of sculpture we are delighted to inhabit, providing the perfect stage for the drama of our lives. As such, it is a place of repose and stimulation, comfort and inspiration.

Creating an artful home can be as simple as bringing a perfect little bouquet of wildflowers into the kitchen or displaying a beloved child's drawing in a place of honor. But it can also be as dauntingly complicated as building a house, from vague but passionate ideas to blueprints, and empty site to finished construction.

Usually, we don't need much help to pick a bouquet of flowers. But there are other times in creating an artful home that we would like vision and knowledge beyond our own as we try to create an environment that looks fabulous and feels familiar.

The very best design professionals at work today—architects, interior designers, builders, and the artists with whom they collaborate—bring their artistic sensibilities, skills, and experience together as they help create homes that not only surpass their clients' dreams, but also reflect a distinctive sense of unique and individual style.

Please join a handful of top design professionals in the pages that follow as they both show and tell how they help their clients create an artful home. You will be inspired by their words and their work.

Opposite: Paintings (from left) by: Laddie Dill and T.L. Lange. Photograph: © Benjamin Benschneider / *The Seattle Times*.

# KENDALL MARCELLE

Fort Lauderdale, FL

"I really have a passion for what I do," interior designer Kendall Marcelle admits, "and I have a lot of fun doing it." That enthusiasm and commitment to excellence shine through in the attention she lavishes on each artful detail of the spaces she creates.

Her firm, Kendall Marcelle Design Associates, founded in Florida in the early 1990s, focuses on high-end residential projects. Marcelle's versatility allows her to design in either traditional or contemporary idioms, but regardless of the style, she always encourages her clients to explore original art. "I love to use art," she admits. "It adds a lot of personality."

To homeowners who are wary of collecting, Marcelle counsels, "Don't be afraid of it. Try it! Start in a small way, with a local artist, or even at a local craft show." An avid collector herself, she notes that "art is a lot more attainable than people think. I've found original art in everything from flea markets to very expensive galleries."

Choosing the right art pieces for a private home is an opportunity for collaboration. "There's a lot of emotion in art," Marcelle notes, "and that's why unless I've worked with a client a lot and really know their tastes, I don't like to necessarily go out and just buy. I usually like for them to be involved."

"We concentrate so much on furniture, which is important for comfort and style, but in the end it is the art, fine rugs, accessories, and sculpture that really speak to you," she notes. "The sofa and chairs become background." Drawing on wisdom steeped in experience, Marcelle concludes, "Buy art for the art of living with it."

Joe Lapeyra, Lepeyra Photography

▾ Kendall Marcelle took this standard cherry builders kitchen, and with just a few added touches, elevated it to an artful room. "Pewter checkerboard tiles, in flat and polished finishes, replaced the standard four-inch tile backsplash, which was a simple change, but very effective," the designer notes. Using this contrasting color in the tile, in addition to some well-placed lighting and accessories and "you have a statement rather than a mold."

The unique, hand-shaped papier-mache vessels on the counter add texture, soft lines, visual interest, and a touch of whimsy to an otherwise symmetrical room.

Joe Lapeyra, Lepeyra Photography

▲ The living room of this art-filled high-rise condominium in Aventura, Florida, stylishly fulfills the needs of an active young family.

Kendall Marcelle explains, "When you buy condominiums here, it's basically just a shell." The space was softened by installing six floating sculptural boxes, which cling to the ceiling and conceal electrical wiring for lighting fixtures. Marcelle custom-designed an ample set of soft furnishings and a user-friendly cherry coffee table to accommodate frequent visitors.

A bold oil painting, *Red Poppies for a Blue Lady*, by Linda Prudhommes, sets the tone for the room. The work's brilliant colors appealed to the clients, and the subject matter resonated in a family graced with three little girls. Marcelle light-heartedly refers to the room as "a woman's domain."

The clients tried four or five different paintings in the space before they made their final decision. Marcelle explains the captivating immediacy of the artwork: "In contemporary spaces I love to use over-scaled and even exaggerated pieces. You feel it. You're there."

A bronze horse sculpture by Carlos Matas rests on a pedestal nearby, casting an appealing shadow on the wall.

The joined family and breakfast areas of the same residence reflect a sophisticated take on family comfort with a sizzle of creative flair. The cherry red sofa sectional and child-pleasing ottoman create a welcoming environment and are enhanced by pieces from the client's art collection.

A radiant bouquet of gladioli, painted by Mark Kaplan, sends an explosion of color into the space, balancing smaller works by Marc Chagall between the ocean-side windows. Marcelle applauds her client's approach to selecting artwork, which she characterizes as, "We love it; it makes us feel good."

*See more projects by Kendall Marcelle Design Associates, Inc. at www.kendallmarcelle.com.*

Joe Lapeyra, Lepeyra Photography

# LISA LODESKI

Aliso Viejo, CA

Trained as an art historian with a curatorial background, Lisa Lodeski is a natural when it comes to educating clients about art. Her art consulting business, Lisa Lodeski Fine Arts, emerged in 1997 in San Francisco before moving to southern California's Orange County and, more recently, expanding into Hawaii.

Lodeski's success relies on sensitivity to the needs of her clients. "I'm primarily a matchmaker between the artist and the patron," she notes. "I work for the client rather than the artist. My responsibility is to lead my clients through the selection process and prevent them from making choices they may regret later," Lodeski says. "I'm their guide."

Collectors who seek Lodeski's expertise represent a broad range of interests and experience. "Some clients are extremely serious, building collections that eventually might be donated to a museum or published, or they may loan pieces for exhibition. Those types of collections usually have a focal point, and each artwork purchased relates in some way to the ideas expressed across the collection. Often I am searching for particular works to fill in the gaps in a collection." Such intensity, Lodeski adds, is rare.

"That's the smallest percentage of residential placement. Most people are looking to buy simply what they like, artworks that they want to live with, where the energy from the work is adding to the living environment."

For new collectors, Lodeski's consulting process resembles a private tutorial during which the client is encouraged to develop a discerning eye. First, Lodeski gains an appreciation for the reason or purpose underlying the collection, then she provides background information on the mysteries of the art market and describes the distinctions between decorative and fine art. In subsequent meetings, Lodeski and her clients sift through images, or travel together to museums, exhibitions, studios, and auction houses in search of artworks that resonate on a personal level with the client.

"When you're collecting artwork that you want to live with and that you love, you're working on an emotional level," Lodeski explains. If a client is seriously considering purchasing a piece of art, she asks them one simple question: "Is your heart pounding faster?"

Ever the astute matchmaker, Lisa Lodeski believes that if a client thinks the artwork is "sort of" interesting or that it might increase in value later, it's better to pass. "That's not reason enough to buy it."

*More information about Lisa Lodeski Fine Arts can be found at www.llfa.net.*

▲ The airy, light-filled living room of this waterfront home in Newport Beach, California, showcases the owners' art collection. Lodeski recalls the three-year process of educating the design-savvy clients (a contractor and interior designer) while they worked toward making several important acquisitions. "They wanted to learn. They looked at thousands of pieces as they developed their individual tastes. In the end, they selected primarily non-Western artworks," she explains. "In this case we were looking at mostly Latin American works, from pre-Colombian to contemporary."

Two arresting images inhabit the space like resident spirits. A striking figurative work by contemporary Mexican painter Guiller-

mo Ceniceros fixes the viewer in her gaze on the left side of the fireplace, and is counterbalanced by the ghostly, semi-abstract painting by Spain's Lita Cabellut on the right.

A trio of sculptural pieces is placed in compelling juxtaposition atop the console. From left, an ancient Etruscan vase sits beside a delicate wood sculpture by contemporary Japanese artist Kawashima Shigeo, while a pre-Colombian tripod vessel from Costa Rica strikes a pose on the right.

An antique Chinese rendering of a kneeling Bactrian camel rests upon the coffee table in the center of the room, enriching the cultural mix.

## designer profile

# TONY RAFFA

Houston, TX ■ Highlands, NC

Tony Raffa is a master of balance. Though his tastes have a widely eclectic range, his skillfully orchestrated interiors achieve an artful equilibrium between bold and neutral, contemporary and antique.

Artistic talent is a common thread running through Raffa's family. His mother was an accomplished painter, and his aunt was a noted interior and textile designer. Tony laughingly recalls his nascent design instincts: "I knew in fourth grade that I was going to do this. As a kid I used to rearrange my siblings' bedrooms and make them crazy."

Raffa launched his own firm, Raffa Design Associates, in Houston in 1989. Specializing in residential interiors, Raffa currently splits his time between offices in Houston and Highlands, North Carolina.

Describing his style, Raffa explains, "It's very eclectic; it's focused more around art than about anything else, really." Living in art-filled spaces comes naturally. "I have that passion for collecting art, and I love looking at the art that we've acquired," he confesses. "I've been lucky that a lot of my clients have had that same appreciation."

In fact, the client's art collection often provides the inspiration for Raffa's design concept. "If I don't start with the art, it's usually with a Persian rug. For me, those are the two starting points for designing a room. In many cases it's the focal point for the room, a lot of times it also determines the color and pattern of the room as well—or it can set the tone or the mood."

Raffa has a gift for blending diverse furniture and artistic and decorative elements into a coherent interior that looks

Rex Spencer

Rex Spencer

natural and not forced. With such a well-trained eye, he can trust his instincts. "I've been able to mix art styles in the same space over the years. I think that good art is good art."

*For more information about Tony Raffa, visit Raffa Design Associates at www.raffadesignassociates.com.*

◄ The sitting and dining rooms of Tony Raffa's former Houston home illustrate the designer's easy mix of styles.

Without a formal fireplace, this converted ranch home lacked a central design feature, so Raffa cleverly substituted an antique chest of comparable size and stature. A whimsical painting by contemporary Mexican artist Jose Antonio Gurtubay adds a jolt of blue above, while a blown glass piece in swirls of orange and red and a playful paper sculpture sit atop the chest.

Flashes of red from the designer's collection of hearts add notes of excitement around the room, culminating in the series of three heart-motif prints by Houston artist Dan Allison. Flaunting convention, Raffa chose a dazzling antique Baccarat chandelier to illuminate a glass table supported by a humble, retrofitted aluminum planter.

▲ In designing his own Highlands, North Carolina, great room, Raffa chose sumptuous rusticity over country cliché.

He happily notes that other than the two hair-on-hide club chairs, which flank a self-designed oxidized metal and locust wood fireplace, nothing else in the room matches. Still, as Raffa observes, "The room seems balanced to me. What helps is that the scale of the objects varies."

Neutral wall colors amplify the impact of the rug and the artwork. "There are lots of art pieces and artifacts to look at as you spend more time in the room," Raffa explains. The glowing red tones and surreal geometry of contemporary Houston artist Renzo Barchi's depiction of a seated man draws attention upward, echoing the color and angular motifs of the kilim below.

A landscape painting by local North Carolina artist Jon Houglum hangs above the mantel and is joined on the left by an attenuated ceramic sculpture of a female form by Cathy Broski.

Raffa's personal collection of religious art and artifacts, along with a small painting by his mother, adorns the display areas surrounding the built-in knotty pine television cabinet.

# The Portrait of a Collector

## An Interview with Larry Winn, Seattle, WA

When it comes to collecting art, a design professional can provide invaluable assistance and connections not always available to the average collector. But that's not to discount the abilities and passion of a homeowner, who may have clear ideas about the style and placement of art for his or her home. Such is the case with Larry Winn, founder of Grand Image, Ltd., an art publishing company. Larry talked with us about the how and why of collecting original art—for others and in his own home.

*When did you begin collecting art?*

Thirty years ago. I was just starting in the art business and getting acquainted with painters and the art scene and styles. I'm self-educated; as the years progressed, my aesthetic sensibility was developed through enormous exposure to the "art world" and just imagery in general.

*Then and now, what drives you to buy art?*

It's so hard to describe. It's just a feeling that you really,

really like this so much you want it in your presence at all times. It's kind of a compulsion, and it becomes, like most compulsions, stronger and stronger as the years go by.

Collectors are really hard to define; they come from all walks of life. It's hard to pinpoint what makes a collector except for one thing: They all really have a kind of obsession.

*Where do you find the art for your home?*

Literally everywhere. I go to galleries all the time, and wherever I travel. I also read a boatload of art and design magazines. I'm constantly looking; I can't help but look. I am an image junkie, there's no question about it.

I like things big, so most of what I buy has a tendency to be on a larger scale. The initial impact is just so much more. I have a couple of walls where I can handle some very, very large pieces. Indeed, my home was designed with that in mind.

*How would you classify your collection?*

Great collections are ones that have a real specific focus. I would classify my collection as a lot of good paintings, a few great, and some eclectic things that may be perceived as ephemera or craft. It can go from furniture to first edition books to photography.

I'm most drawn to modern art. To a lot of people, it's a very misunderstood movement, but it's very beautiful and innovative, and it encompasses a lot of esoteric things besides just actual paint on canvas.

*Contemporary art can sometimes be challenging. How do you live with it?*

It's very easy for my wife, Susan, and I to live with it. There's a reason why the art attracts you to begin with, and the more you live with your paintings, you get to know them better and you see other things about them. It's like a relationship.

All works of art have personality traits, and some are very, very bad, and some are dark, and some are sweet, and some are annoying. Some are just wonderful because they encompass line and grace and beauty and color and space and all those things that when thrown in the gumbo of a painting bring out a "wow" in you.

*What does your company, Grand Image, set out to do?*

We deal primarily in paintings and editioned prints. We try to handle the highest-level artwork that we can possibly offer at price points the average person can afford.

I am definitely a populist. We've all been in these vast white galleries and been more than a little bit nervous. I think to some degree, though, it's not always the case; there's a lot of intellectual intimidation that goes on in that game, and there doesn't need to be.

*What advice would you offer new collectors?*

The more they look and the more they're aware of what's out there, the better their eyes are going to be and the better they can trust their own judgment and their instincts. They should buy what they love.

Get to know a particular arena, focus on something that really turns you on and stay with it. It's a lot easier to learn that way because the art market is so broad.

*How does artwork contribute to the atmosphere of a home?*

Putting aside a bed to sleep on and a table to eat on, I think art is by far the most important thing that one can have in the home. People buy something and they hang it up, and they just can't believe what a change it's made in terms of their attitude and how they feel about their place and how it's changed their environment, and in some cases, their lives.

Think about it—if you walk into a house and the walls are covered with great art, are you really looking at anything else?

Home accents by Millea Furnishings, see pages 54-55. Photograph: Anthony Scaglione.

# FURNITURE, SCULPTURE & OBJECTS

# SCOTT E. ARMSTRONG

ARROWLEAF STUDIO ▨ 150 SOUTH JONES STREET ▨ POWELL, WY 82435 ▨ TEL 307-754-8019
E-MAIL ARROWLEAFSTUDIO@HOTMAIL.COM ▨ WWW.ARROWLEAFSTUDIO.COM

Top left: *Antelope Table*, figured cherry veneer and ebonized maple, 30"H x 40"W x 17"D. Top right: *Gambrel Writing Table and Stool, Ribbon Mirror*, avodire veneer and ebonized maple, 42"W x 29"H x 20"D. Bottom: *Nelson Dining Set*, ribbon sapele veneers and solids, 29"H x 120"L x 42"W. Photographs: Elijah Cobb.

# BOYKIN PEARCE ASSOCIATES

DAVE BOYKIN ■ 1875 EAST 27TH AVENUE ■ DENVER, CO 80205
TEL/FAX 303-294-0703 ■ E-MAIL DAVE@BOYKINPEARCE.COM ■ WWW.BOYKINPEARCE.COM

Top: *Curved Face Buffet*, pommele sapele, wenge, and mahogany, 32"H x 49"W x 17.75"D.  Photograph: Jim Staton.
Bottom: *Pool Table*, quilted makore, mahogany, and ebony.  Photograph: Ron Ruscio.

# BRADFORD WOODWORKING ■ PAMELA HILL QUILTS

BRAD SMITH ▨ PO BOX 157 ▨ WORCESTER, PA 19490 ▨ TEL 610-584-1150 ▨ BRAD@BRADFORDWOODWORKING.COM
PAMELA HILL ▨ 8500 LAFAYETTE STREET ▨ MOKELUMNE HILL, CA 95245 ▨ TEL 209-286-1217 ▨ PAMELA@PAMELAHILLQUILTS.COM

Highpost bed and bedside tables by Brad Smith, bed: cherry, ash, poplar, and cast steel, available in queen or king sizes, tables: cherry,
oak, and walnut, each: 28"H × 21"W × 18"D. *Coperta I v.3 Art Quilt* by Pamela Hill, dupioni silk and cotton batting, 112"L × 96"W.
Other Guild artists shown (clockwise from left): Janna Ugone, Holly Wallace, Ken Elliott, Patricia Dreher, and Keith and Valerie Raivo. Photograph: Eric Ferguson.

# ALI CARTER

CEDARS OF HIRAM ▨ 13102 STILLWATER ROAD ▨ WATERPORT, NY 14571 ▨ TEL 585-682-5505
FAX 585-682-0148 ▨ E-MAIL ANCIENTCEDAR@YAHOO.COM ▨ WWW.CEDARSOFHIRAM.COM

Top: *Yates Library Bench*, apple wood and sandstone, 24" × 78" × 18". Photograph: Idris Salih.
Bottom: *Writing Desk*, ebony, poplar, antique window, and glass balls, 36" × 62" × 29". Photograph: Clarke Conde.

# DAVID J. LUNIN FURNITURE MAKER

DAVID J. LUNIN ■ 1134 ELIZABETH AVENUE ■ LANCASTER, PA 17601 ■ TEL 717-293-1504
E-MAIL DAVE@DJLFURNITUREMAKER.COM ■ WWW.DJLFURNITUREMAKER.COM

Top left: *Running Table.*   Top right: *WINDsor Table.*   Bottom: *Kneeling Coffee Table.*   Photographs: David Gentry.

# PETER DELLERT

DELLERT FURNITURE ▧ 174 SARGEANT STREET ▧ HOLYOKE, MA 01040 ▧ TEL 413-534-5253
FAX 413-534-5253*51 ▧ E-MAIL PFDELLERT@AOL.COM ▧ WWW.DELLERTFURNITURE.COM

Top: *Canyon Dining Table and Chairs,* table: live-edged, bookmatched curly maple, ebonized cherry, and dyed curly maple, 30" x 87" x 39"; chairs: curly maple, curly maple veneer, and ultra suede, 37" x 18" x 17." Bottom: *Canyon Coffee Table,* live-edged, bookmatched Swiss pear and ebonized cherry, 18" x 58" x 32." Photographs: John Polak.     39

# BRADLEY EHRSAM

5412 CALICO COURT ■ McFARLAND, WI 53558
TEL 612-327-5758 ■ E-MAIL BRADEHRSAM@GMAIL.COM ■ WWW.BRADLEYEHRSAM.COM

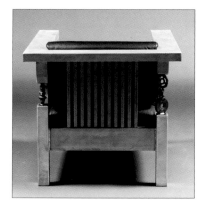  

Top left: *Motorcycle Mission Chair*, aluminum, steel, and leather, 30"H x 41"W x 38"D. Photograph: David Fick. Top center: *Wedding Night Stands*, stainless steel and wood, each: 25"H x 17"W x 14"D. Photograph: Jim Wildeman. Top right: *T-Rod End Table*, tricycle and motorcycle parts. Photograph: James H. Young. Bottom: *Motorcycle Mission Couch*, aluminum, steel, and leather, 30"H x 82"W x 38"D. Photograph: David Fick.

# CONSTANTINE FEDORETS

UGOL INC. WOODWORKING ■ 560 MINERAL SPRING AVENUE ■ PAWTUCKET, RI 02860
TEL 401-378-7583 ■ E-MAIL UGOLINC@GMAIL.COM ■ WWW.CONSTANTINESINTERIORS.COM

Top left: *Writing Desk*, cherry with koa and English sycamore inlay, 30"H × 55"W × 24"D. Right: *Clovez Bubiuga Cabinet*, bubiuga with cherry and ebony inlay, 77"H × 23"W × 6"D. Bottom left: *Crab Box*, curly maple and walnut, 5.25"H × 9.5"W × 5"D.

# JEFF FREEMAN

SIDE EFFECTS ■ TEN BREWER AVENUE ■ BAR HARBOR, ME 04609 ■ TEL 207-669-2356
E-MAIL DEADCARP@JEFFFREEMANART.COM ■ WWW.JEFFFREEMANART.COM

Top left: TIG-welded aluminum slat chair. Top right: TIG-welded aluminum base with polished concrete top.
Bottom: Credenza, TIG-welded aluminum. Photographs: Kevin Bennet.

42

# KEVIN GILL

KEVIN GILL STUDIOS ■ TEL 888-466-2899
E-MAIL KEVIN@KEVINGILLSTUDIOS.COM ■ WWW.KEVINGILLSTUDIOS.COM

Top left: *Phoenix Console Table*, walnut and emberwood, 32"H × 30"W × 10"D. Top right: *Deco Hall Table*, cherry and lacewood, 34"H × 42"W × 15"D.
Bottom: *Flip-Top Chess & Backgammon Table*, curly and flatsawn maple and figured yellow birch, 29"H × 32"W × 32"D. Photographs: Jim Dugan.

# DON GREEN

GREENTREE HOME ▪ 22 PROSPECT STREET ▪ DELHI, NY 13753 ▪ TEL 607-746-7095
FAX 607-746-3368 ▪ E-MAIL INFO@GREENTREEHOME.COM ▪ WWW.GREENTREEHOME.COM

Top: *Ava Console Table*, cherry, avodire, and ebonized wood in a basket-weave inset top.
Bottom: *Lady Edith's Bench*, ebonized mahogany and brown leather. Photographs: Drew Harty.

# GREG ARCENEAUX CABINETMAKERS, INC.

GREG ARCENEAUX ■ 703 WEST 26TH AVENUE ■ COVINGTON, LA 70433 ■ TEL 985-893-8782
TEL 985-626-2469 ■ FAX 985-867-3711 ■ E-MAIL GREGARCENEAUX@AOL.COM ■ WWW.GREGARCENEAUX.COM

*Painted Gold Leaf Cocktail Table*, interpretive piece designed Creole style with cabriole leg, scalloped apron,
and natural wood or painted finish (distressed or natural), 18"H x 34"W x 34"D. Photographs: Lakeside Camera & Images.

45

# JOHN HEIN

105 FEATHERBED LANE ■ HOPEWELL, NJ 08525 ■ TEL 609-466-8122
E-MAIL JHEIN@PLUTO.NJCC.COM ■ HTTP://PLUTO.JNCC.COM/~JHEIN

*Sikes Writing Desk*, 1989, wenge, cardinal wood, Gonçalo alves, and Queensland walnut.  Photograph: Brent Nicastro.

# BRIAN A. HUBEL

HUBEL HANDCRAFTED ▩ 1311 NORTH CORONA STREET ▩ COLORADO SPRINGS, CO 80903
TEL 719-667-0577 ▩ TEL 719-651-7789 ▩ E-MAIL HUBELHI@EARTHLINK.NET ▩ WWW.HUBELHI.COM

Top: *Grafted*, 2007, Santa Fe, NM, claro walnut, 17"H × 58"W × 11"D. Bottom left: *Sterling*, 2000, Colorado Springs, CO, claro walnut and ebony, 48"H × 12.5"W × 11"D. Bottom right: *Five Years in Time*, 2001, Colorado Springs, CO, bubinga with quilted maple, 74"H × 15"W × 12"D. Photographs: Don Jones Photography.

# RAY KELSO

TREEBEARD DESIGNS, INC. ■ 720 BLACK ROCK ROAD ■ COLLEGEVILLE, PA 19426
TEL 610-933-1080 ■ TEL 610-420-6614 ■ E-MAIL RAYKELSO@EARTHLINK.NET ■ WWW.RAYKELSO.COM

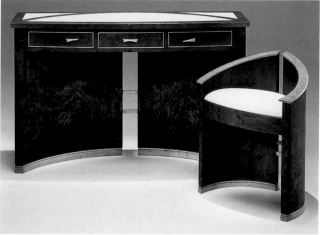

Left: *Video* cabinet, walnut and curly cherry, 43"H × 30"W × 18"D. Top right: Stools, walnut, cherry, and apple, 24"H × 14"W × 14"D and 18"H × 12"W × 12"D. Bottom right: Writing table and stool, walnut, walnut burl veneer, curly maple, and leather, table: 30"H × 48"W × 15"D, stool: 27"H × 22"W × 15"D. Photographs: Tom Crane Photography.

# JOHN KINGSLEY

JOHN KINGSLEY FURNITURE ■ 619 COMFORT ROAD ■ ITHACA, NY 14850
TEL/FAX 607-272-2146 ■ E-MAIL JKFURNITURE@AOL.COM

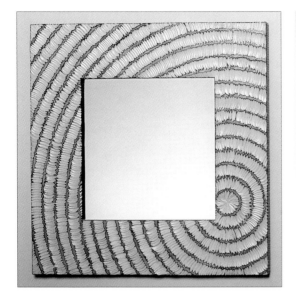 

Top left: *Granny Smith Mirror,* 2006, mahogany, milk paint, and lacquer finish, 20" × 20" × 1". Photograph: Cascadilla Photography. Top right: *Circles Mirror in Buttermilk,* 2006, mahogany, milk paint, and lacquer finish 30" × 30" × 0.75". Photograph: Cascadilla Photography. Bottom: *Blue Console Table,* 2005, cherry, milk paint, and lacquer finish, 23" × 52" × 16". Photograph: Eric Ferguson. Other Guild artists' work shown (clockwise from top left): Nicholas Kekic, Mitch Levin and Susie Levin, Patrick Meyer, Judith Weber, and Cheryl Williams.

# DAN KLEIN

KLEIN WOODWORKING, INC. ■ 574 BOSTON AVENUE ■ MEDFORD, MA 02155
TEL 781-395-8131 ■ E-MAIL DJKLEIN@RCN.COM ■ WWW.KLEINWOODWORKING.COM

Top left: *Zipper Table*, bubinga slab and black lacquer on maple, 29"H x 44"W x 84"L. Top right: *Wave Chair*, mahogany, bubinga veneer, and ultrasuede, 51"H x 18.5"W x 20"D.
Bottom: *Madrone Sideboard*, cherry, madrone burl veneer, and black lacquer on ash, 37"H x 17"D x 64"L. Photographs: Jeffrey Dodge Rogers.

# THOMAS F. LEDERER

LEDERER STUDIO ■ 24059 WEST MAIN STREET ■ COLUMBUS, NJ 08022 ■ TEL 609-324-0900
TEL 609-760-4877 ■ FAX 609-499-4339 ■ E-MAIL LEDERERSTUDIO@YAHOO.COM ■ WWW.LEDERERSTUDIO.COM

Top: *Pelin and Granite Credenza,* 2006, breakfront mahogany credenza with pelin burl panels, inset cocobolo moldings,
and blue pearl beveled granite top, lacquer finish, 36"H x 84"L x 22"D.  Bottom: *Corkscrew Willows Entertainment Center,* 2002, tiger maple
with hand-carved Swiss pear door panels and handles, rosewood moldings, and cherry base moldings, lacquer finish, 54"H x 144"L x 30"D.

# Scott C. Reuman

*"I'm an architect and my husband is a builder, so we're very particular about what we like. But we knew Scott personally, and he took our basic requirements and measurements for the piece, listened to our ideas, and then came up with a beautiful design. Not only is the design great, but the craftsmanship is just superb. We're really thrilled with it!"*

— Homeowner

*Blossom Bar* ■ 2004 ■ Boulder, CO ■ Honduras mahogany, bird's-eye maple, textured glass, patinated copper, and Lyons sandstone ■ 96" x 108" x 26" ■ See more work of Scott's work on page 99.

# MARK LEVIN

PO BOX 109 ■ SAN JOSE, NM 87565-0109 ■ TEL 505-421-3207
E-MAIL MLEVIN@PLATEAUTEL.NET ■ WWW.MARKLEVIN.COM

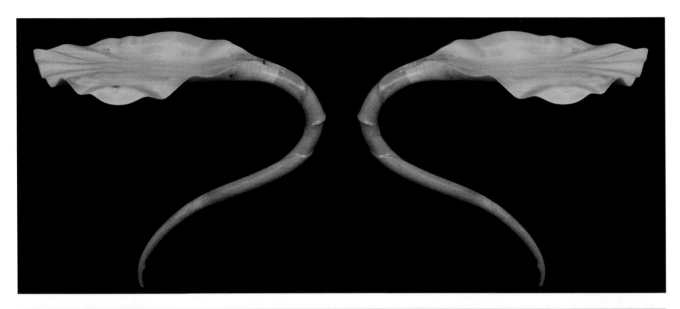

Top: *Autumn Leaf Shelves*, alder; 38"H x 45"W x 22"D.  Bottom: *Handel Flower Petal Desk #3 of 6*, walnut, 30"H x 70"W x 37"D.  Photographs: Margot Geist.

# MILLEA FURNISHINGS

ANNA MILLEA ▪ 4728 McPHERSON AVENUE ▪ ST. LOUIS, MO 63108 ▪ TEL 314-367-4200
FAX 314-367-4201 ▪ E-MAIL ANNA@MILLEAFURNISHINGS.COM ▪ WWW.MILLEAFURNISHINGS.COM

*Triptych Mirrors*, acrylic and lacquer on birch, total size with 5'' frame: 45" × 25" × 5"; *Trio Candle Stands*, acrylic and lacquer on birch, 8"–16"H; *Leather Table Runners*, acrylic on leather
with painted wooden and leather tassels, 90"L × 16"W; *Leather Placemats*, acrylic on leather, 13" × 17".  Photograph: Anthony Scaglione.

54

# MILLEA FURNISHINGS

ANNA MILLEA ▨ 4728 McPHERSON AVENUE ▨ ST. LOUIS, MO 63108 ▨ TEL 314-367-4200
FAX 314-367-4201 ▨ E-MAIL ANNA@MILLEAFURNISHINGS.COM ▨ WWW.MILLEAFURNISHINGS.COM

Left: *Makoto*, acrylic on canvas, 30"H × 60"W; cube end/storage table, acrylic and lacquer on birch, 23"H × 15"W × 19"D; *Leather Pillows*, acrylic on leather, various sizes;
*Zig Zag Coffee Table with Nested Foot Stools*, acrylic and lacquer on birch, 18"H × 40"W × 24"D. Right: *Tapered Floor Lamp*, acrylic and lacquer on birch, 72"H × 12"-square base;
*Leather Pillows*, acrylic on leather, various sizes; *Leather Storage Ottoman with Serving Tray*, acrylic and lacquer on birch and leather, 16"H × 20"W × 20"D. Photographs: Anthony Scaglione.

# PAULUS FINE FURNITURE

PAULUS WANROOIJ ■ 73 CHOPPS CROSS ROAD ■ WOOLWICH, ME 04579
TEL/FAX 207-443-3751 ■ E-MAIL PAULUS@PAULUSFURNITURE.COM ■ WWW.PAULUSFURNITURE.COM

Top left: *Sunburst Bed* (detail), cherry and curly maple. Top right: *Oceana End Table*, curly birch and sapele.
Bottom left: *Writing Desk* (detail), curly walnut and curly maple. Bottom right: Carved coffee table base, ash.

# MICHAEL PLATT

1319 CEDAR AVENUE ■ BOULDER, CO 80304 ■ TEL 303-443-4080 ■ FAX 303-443-5630
E-MAIL MICHAEL@PLATTSTUDIOS.COM ■ WWW.PLATTSTUDIOS.COM

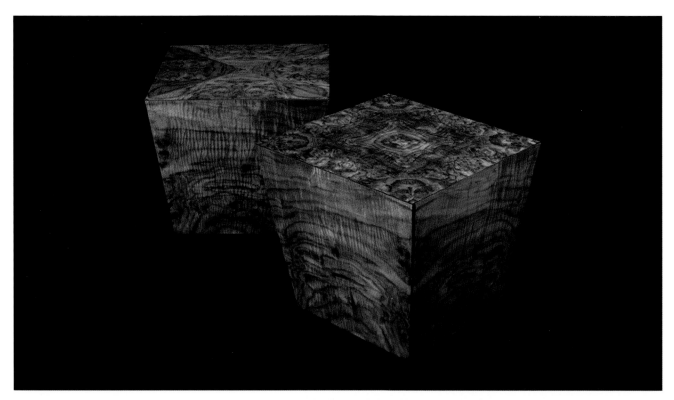

Top: *Coffee Table Cubes*, 2002, walnut burl, 16"H x 21" x 21".
Bottom: Bench, 2004, cherry and stainless steel, 16"H x 48" x 16". Photograph: Mark Ivins.

# DAVID RICHARDSON

DAVID RICHARDSON INC. ■ 1 FATHER DEVALLES BOULEVARD ■ FALL RIVER, MA 02723 ■ TEL 508-676-1760
E-MAIL DCRICHARDSON@COMCAST.NET ■ WWW.DAVIDRICHARDSONINC.COM

Top: *Naoshima Writing Desk*, 51"H × 34"L × 22.5"W.
Bottom: *Red-Winged Blackbird Splay Leg Table*, 19"H × 20"L × 14.5"W.  Photograph: Steve Marcel.

# ROB HARE, FURNITURE MAKER

ROB HARE ▨ 130 CARNEY ROAD ▨ ULSTER PARK, NY 12487 ▨ TEL 845-658-3584 ▨ FAX 845-658-3572
E-MAIL INFO@ROBHARE-FURNITUREMAKER.COM ▨ WWW.ROBHARE-FURNITUREMAKER.COM

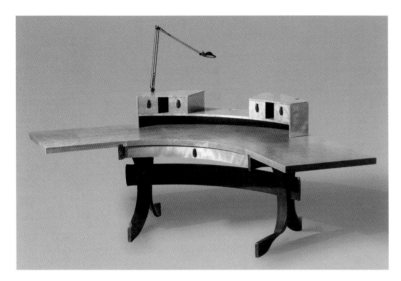

Top left: *Corner Desk*, 2004, cherry and forged steel, 3'H × 8'W × 4'D.  Right: *Narrow Sideboard*, 2004, cherry and forged steel, 7'H × 2.75'W × 1.75'D.
Bottom left: *Arm Chair*, 2007, claro walnut and forged steel, 3.25'H × 2.75'W × 3'D.  Photographs: Chris Kendall.

# Peter Dellert

John Polak

"*We designed the room around the medicine cabinet, which we fell in love with and purchased at the Philadelphia Furniture Show. After two years we finally realized the natural thing to do was have Peter design our bathroom vanity to complement it. Peter studied the room and came up with the design for the vanity. It was just what we were looking for: understated, elegant, and substantial.*"

— Homeowner

*Sleep/Dream Cabinet* and vanity ■ 2000 and 2002 ■ Falmouth, MA ■ cabinet: painted butternut, ebonized cherry, and patinated copper; vanity: cherry and patinated copper ■ cabinet: 32" x 5" x 20"; vanity: 30" x 24" x 20" ■ See more of Peter's work on page 39.

# ROBERT MANN ORIGINALS

ROBERT MANN ■ 63645 E. POSADA STREET ■ TUCSON, AZ 85739 ■ TEL/FAX 520-818-2225
TEL 877-825-5074 ■ E-MAIL BOB@ROBERTMANNORIGINALS.COM ■ WWW.ROBERTMANNORIGINALS.COM

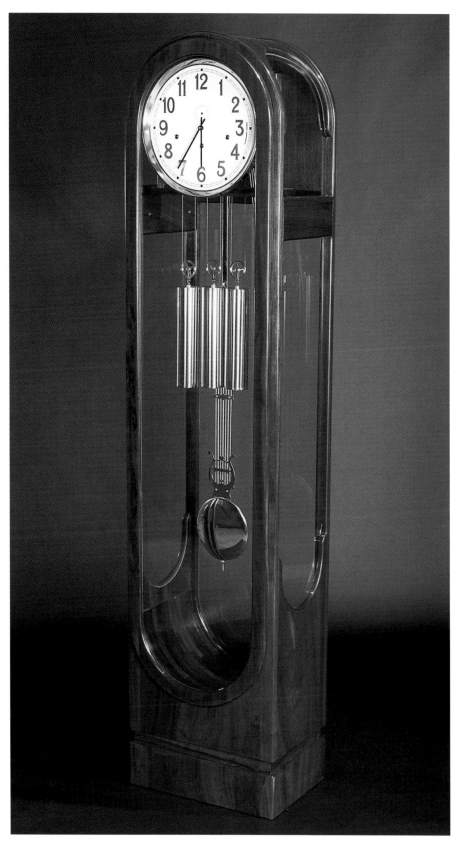

*Exotic Wooden Floor Clock*, 2004, African paduk, 78"H x 18.5"W x 12"D.  Photograph: Bruce Schockett.

U.S. patent #D496,287

# PHILIP SIMS

TETRAHEDRON ■ 320 21ST AVENUE NORTH ■ HOPKINS, MN 55343
TEL 612-599-0912 ■ E-MAIL TETRAHEDRON@QWEST.NET ■ WWW.TET-DESIGN-WORKS.COM

Top left: *Dek*, stainless steel and teak, 29.5"H x 46"L x 25"D.  Top right: *Sarah*, steel, stainless steel, and aluminum, 29.5"H x 42".  Bottom left: *Swept Around*, aluminum, 29.5"H x 42".  Bottom right: *Nesting Legs*, stainless steel and bloodwood, 25.5"H x 65"L x 14"D.  Photographs: Sean Fitzgerald.

# CHARLES TODD

MT. AIRY CUSTOM FURNITURE, INC. ▥ 7054 GERMANTOWN AVENUE ▥ PHILADELPHIA, PA 19119
TEL 215-264-2062 ▥ TEL/FAX 215-248-4391 ▥ E-MAIL CTODDMACF@HOTMAIL.COM ▥ WWW.TODDFURNITURE.COM

Display case, 2006, Philadelphia, PA, mahogany and Australian lacewood, 78"H × 38"W × 24"D.

# DARRIN VANDEN BOSCH

VB WOODWORKS ■ PO BOX 255 ■ GORE, VA 22637 ■ TEL 540-858-3555
FAX 540-858-2598 ■ E-MAIL VBWOODWORK@AOL.COM ■ WWW.VBWOODWORKS.COM

Left: *Obvious*, 2006, curly cherry, curly maple, and walnut, 60.5" x 17 x 10.5".
Top right: Prairie-style coffee and end table set, 2005, curly walnut and curly cherry, coffee table: 20.5" x 54" x 22", end table: 27.5" x 21" x 21".
Bottom right: Purpleheart console table, 2006, purpleheart and bird's-eye maple, 32" x 46" x 13". Photographs: John Westervelt.

# BILHENRY WALKER

BILHENRY GALLERY ■ 4038 NORTH SIXTH STREET ■ MILWAUKEE, WI 53212 ■ TEL 414-332-2509
FAX 414-332-2524 ■ E-MAIL BILHENRY@EXECPC.COM ■ WWW.BILHENRYGALLERY.COM

Top: *Captain's Chair* and five-leg card table, 2007, aluminum, 0.5" plate glass, pebble-steel vinyl fabric, table: 30" × 42" × 42", chair: 34" × 27" × 22".
Bottom left: Bar table and bar chair, 2007, aluminum, 0.75" plate glass, LED lights, pebble-steel vinyl fabric, table: 40" × 24" × 24", chair: 42" × 20" × 20".
Bottom right: *Diamond Spine Chair*, 2006, aluminum, microsuede fabric, 45" × 23" × 28".

# TIMOTHY WHITE

SPELLBOUND FURNITURE WORKS ▇ 337 BUCKLEY DRIVE #3 ▇ PO BOX 2215 ▇ CRESTED BUTTE, CO 81224
TEL 970-349-7292 ▇ E-MAIL SPELLBOUNDFURNITURE@MINDSPRING.COM ▇ WWW.SPELLBOUNDFURNITUREWORKS.COM

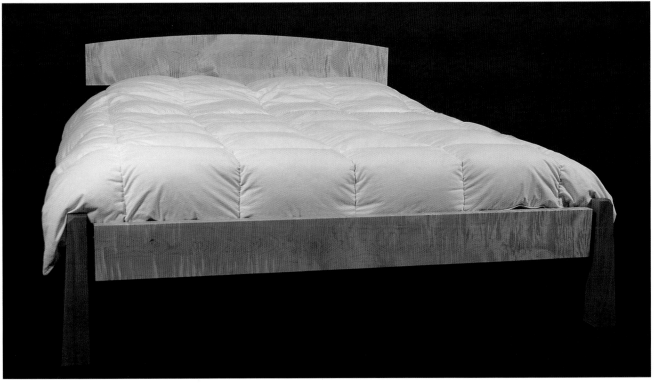

Top: *Symmetry Bench*, 2006, elm, wenge, ebonized ash, and stainless steel, 18.5"H × 41.75"W × 14"D.
Bottom: *Bed*, 2006, curly soft maple, cherry, and stainless steel, 33.5"H × 67.5"W × 87.75"D.

# LIGHTING

# BEL VETRO

LISA BLALOCK AND PAULO DELIMA ▨ 271 WESTERN AVENUE #203 ▨ LYNN, MA 01904
E-MAIL INFO@BELVETRO.BIZ ▨ WWW.BELVETRO.BIZ

Top: *Reticello Pendant*, 9"H x 21"W. Bottom left: *Stratus Fountain Chandelier*, 55"H x 38"W.
Bottom right: *Windchime Chandelier*, 65"H x 18"W.

# DEBORAH A. BRUNS-THOMAS

BEELINE STUDIO ▓ 1007 BLUE SCHOOL ROAD ▓ PERKASIE, PA 18944
TEL 215-527-5586 ▓ E-MAIL DABTSTUDIO@AOL.COM ▓ WWW.BEELINESTUDIO.NET

Top left: *Gradation,* tea bag paper, copper, and wood, 24" × 9" × 10".  Right: *Pleated Design,* tea bag paper, copper, and wood, 65" × 12" × 12".
Bottom left: *Puzzler Series,* tea bag paper, copper, and wood, 21.5" × 8" × 8". Photographs: Jack Ramsdale.

# DICKINSON DESIGNS

ANNE DICKINSON ■ THE FIRE WORKS STUDIOS ■ 38 HARLOW STREET ■ WORCESTER, MA 01605
TEL 508-451-7988 ■ FAX 501-694-5230 ■ E-MAIL INFO@DICKINSON-DESIGNS.COM ■ WWW.DICKINSON-DESIGNS.COM

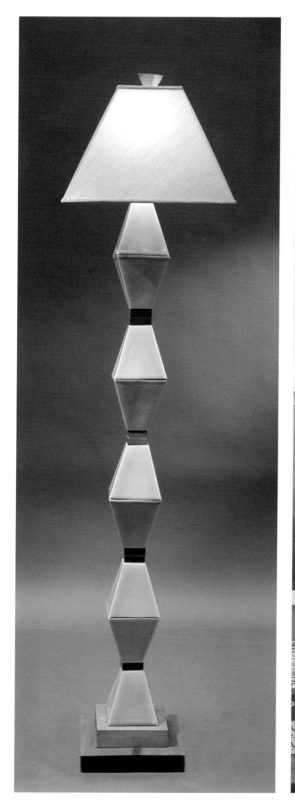

Left: *Pyramid Floor Lamp*, porcelain and birch, 55"H.  Photograph: Paul Jeremias.
Right: *Harlow Table Lamp*, porcelain and walnut, 30"H.

# JOLINE EL-HAI

BELLA LUZ STUDIO ■ 3737 NE 135TH STREET ■ SEATTLE, WA 98125 ■ TEL 206-364-8053
FAX 206-364-7235 ■ E-MAIL GLASS@BELLALUZ.COM ■ WWW.BELLALUZ.COM

Top left: *Crow with Berry,* 2005, fused, painted, and leaded glass, wood, 13" × 12" × 5". Photograph: Lance Wagner. Top right: *Ready for Flowers,* 2000, fused, painted, and leaded glass, wood, 13" × 12" × 5". Photograph: Jeff Curtis. Bottom left: *Apple Tree,* 2007, painted and leaded glass, wood, and copper. Wood design and fabrication: Jeff Wasserman. Photograph: Jeff Curtis. Bottom right: *Youth Unfurling,* 2007, fused, painted, and leaded glass, wood, 29" × 20" × 6". Wood design and fabrication: Jeff Wasserman. Photograph: Jeff Curtis.

# Dave Boykin

*"This table was commissioned by a couple with a large extended family, including a number of children. Their requirement was that the table seat everyone and double as a good surface for art projects with the kids. The heart of the table is the magnificent book-matched sapele slabs that make up the top. I like to think that the tree is now honored by the family in a special way."*

— Dave Boykin, artist

Bridges family dining table ■ 2005 ■ Littleton, CO ■ sapele slab wood ■ 102"L x 72"W ■ See more of Dave's work on page 35.

Ron Ruscio

# HIGH BEAMS LTD.

TRENNY ROBB ■ ROBERT MICHAUD ■ 29 MICHAUD DRIVE ■ SUTTON, VT 05867
TEL 802-467-3943 ■ E-MAIL HIGHBEAMS@SUTTONVT.NET ■ WWW.HIGHBEAMS.COM

*Large Jetson Table Lamp with Circled Leaf Design* and amber mica shade with real beech leaves; *Littlest Candle Travel Lamp* with natural mica shade and real poplar leaves; *Pumpkin Lamp* with watermelon shade; *Copper Rose Leaf Chandelier* with vintage glass piece; *Jetson Twisted Round Standing Lamp* with natural mica and real comfrey leaves. Photograph: Steven Legge.

# HUBBARDTON FORGE

154 ROUTE 30 SOUTH ■ CASTLETON, VT 05735 ■ TEL 800-826-4766
FAX 802-468-3284 ■ E-MAIL INFO@VTFORGE.COM ■ WWW.VTFORGE.COM

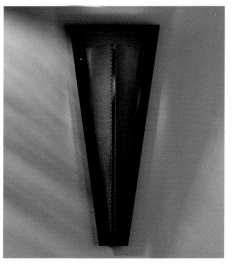

Left: *Almost Infinity*, hand-forged wrought iron floor lamp, 57"H.  Top right: *Steppe*, hand-forged wrought iron semi-flush with art glass, 12"H × 21"W × 9"D.  Center right: *Lunae*, hand-forged wrought iron table lamp with art glass, 15.25"H.  Bottom right: *Tapered Edge with Steel Back*, hand-forged wrought iron sconce, 19.5"H × 8.25"W × 3.75"D.

# WILLIAM LESLIE

PAPER SUN LIGHTSCULPTURE ■ 1397 TEMPLE HEIGHTS DRIVE ■ OCEANSIDE, CA 92056 ■ TEL 760-724-0319
E-MAIL WMLESLIE77@COX.NET ■ WWW.PAPERSUNLIGHTSCULPTURE.COM ■ WWW.LIGHTHEARTSCULPTURES.COM

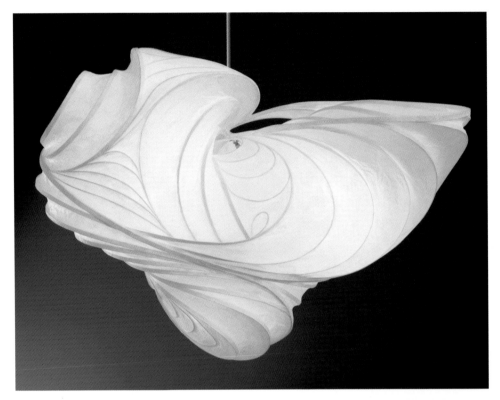

Top: *Cloud*, 2007, paper, wood, and polyvinyl resin chandelier, 46"Dia.
Bottom: *Dragon's Claw*, 2006, paper, wood, and polyvinyl resin wall sculpture, 11'H × 7'W × 2'D.

# RICK MELBY

RICK MELBY STUDIOS ■ 143 LOGAN AVENUE ■ ASHEVILLE, NC 28806
TEL 828-232-0905 ■ E-MAIL RICKMELBY@HOTMAIL.COM ■ WWW.RICKMELBY.COM

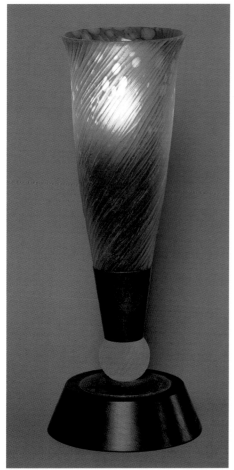

Top left: *Sconce*, 2006, copper, perforated brass, Strauss crystal, dichroic glass, glass jewels, and wood, 11"H × 6"W × 7"D. Right: *Leaf Sconce with Spirit Bowl*, 2007, sconce: water-jet cut plate glass (fused, etched, and slumped), slate, and brass, 11"H × 8"W × 5"D, bowl: water-jet cut plate glass, fused, etched, and slumped, 16"Dia. × 3.5"D. Bottom left: *Twisted*, 2006, diamond-cut and etched blown glass, and wood, 17"H × 5"Dia. Photographs: Michael Mauney.

# HOME ACCENTS

# ERIC ABRAHAM

ERIC ABRAHAM'S FLYING PIG STUDIO & GALLERY ■ 123 SOUTH MAIN STREET ■ LUCAS, KS 67648
TEL 785-525-7722 ■ TEL 785-477-0740 ■ E-MAIL EABRAHAM@WTCIWEB.COM ■ WWW.ERICABRAHAM.NET

Top: *Was Humpty Pushed or Did He Fall? Only That Local Gang, the King's Men, Know,* porcelain with graphite and prismacolor with plexiglass mirror, 29"H.
Bottom: *The Flying Pig Kids Are Starring in the Theatre of Your Life!,* porcelain with graphite and prismacolor with glass mirror, 24"H.

# SONYA LEE BARRINGTON

837 47TH AVENUE ▧ SAN FRANCISCO, CA 94121 ▧ TEL 415-221-6510
E-MAIL SONYA@SONYALEEBARRINGTON.COM ▧ WWW.SONYALEEBARRINGTON.COM

*Crazy Bed Quilt*, 72" x 72", recycled wool patchwork, hand quilted and embroidered, wool backing and batting.
Assorted pillows, recycled wool patchwork, hand quilted and embroidered, wool backing. Photograph: Gregory Case.

# Rob Lorenson

"We first saw Rob's work at a gallery in Florida. Our daughter lives in Boston, so on a trip to visit her, we made arrangements to visit Rob's studio, where we learned all about the creation of his work. I told him what I was looking for, and he sent us a sketch of the piece, which we liked very much. Rob was very easy to work with, and we're delighted with the piece. We've gotten many nice compliments from a wide range of passers-by."

— Terri Union, homeowner

*Stainless Taper* ■ 2007 ■ Fayetteville, NC ■ stainless steel ■ 72" x 40" x 40" ■ See more of Rob's work on page 138.

# CARLSON GLASSWORKS

KURT AND LINDA CARLSON ■ 4951 SUNNYSIDE ROAD ■ MIDDLESEX, NY 14507
TEL/FAX 585-554-6019 ■ E-MAIL CARLSONGLASS@USADATANET.NET ■ WWW.CARLSONGLASSWORKS.COM

Top left: *Green Lamp*, blown and hot-sculpted electric lamp, 15" × 6" × 7". Top center: *Blue Crackle Sconce*, blown and hot-sculpted glass, 12" × 6" × 7".
Top right: *Red Lamp*, blown and hot-sculpted electric lamp, 15" × 6" × 7". Bottom: *Decanter Set*, blown and hot-sculpted glass, decanter: 18"H.

# HUCK FISHER METALWORKERS

LAURA FISHER ■ CHRISTOPHER HUCK ■ SCOTTSDALE, AZ ■ TEL 480-946-3384 ■ OAXACA, MEXICO
TEL 011-52-951-0846 ■ E-MAIL INFO@HUCKFISHER.COM ■ WWW.HUCKFISHER.COM

*Heron Marsh Triptych*, private collection, Debary, FL, hand-painted mild steel with mirror, 3.5'H x 5'W. Photograph: Jace Delgado.

# MORAG

MORAG DESIGNS LLC ■ 5801 KINGSFORD ■ PARK CITY, UT 84098 ■ TEL 435-655-7746
FAX 435-615-8842 ■ E-MAIL MORAGTOTTEN@HOTMAIL.COM ■ WWW.MORAGDESIGNS.COM

Top: *Summer Colors*, Fojtik residence, Park City, UT, 40" × 63".
Bottom: *Spring Circuits* (detail), 28" × 33". Photographs: Steve Rutherford.

# OLD ELLICOTT FORGE, LTD.

PAUL MATTHAEI ■ 1519 BREHM ROAD ■ WESTMINSTER, MD 21157 ■ TEL 410-840-2876 ■ FAX 410-386-9152
E-MAIL PMATTHAEI@OLDELLICOTTFORGE.COM ■ WWW.OLDELLICOTTFORGE.COM

Top left: *Lily Pad Candleholder*, 2002, steel, 13" x 10". Right: *Sun, Moon, and Stars Mirror*, 2002, stainless steel, 54" x 30" x 4.5". Bottom left: *Desk Chair*, 2004, steel, 38" x 18" x 16".

# ROBBIE STUDIO

R.H. SANDERS ■ PO BOX 42 ■ OGDENSBURG, NY 13669
TEL 315-393-1302 ■ E-MAIL ROBBIESTUDIO@GMAIL.COM

*Candelabra Dream*, forged steel, 17"H x 12"Dia.  Photographs: Allen Photography.

# LAURA ZINDEL

LAURA ZINDEL CERAMICS ■ 339 COOLIDGE HIGHWAY ■ GUILFORD, VT 05301
TEL 802-254-8930 ■ E-MAIL ZINDEL@PRODIGY.NET ■ WWW.ZINDELCERAMICS.COM

Top: *Sea Horse and Coral Small Oval Platter,* 10"H x 14"W. Bottom: *Jelly Fish, Shells, and Urchin Large Deep Bowl,* 4.5"H x 12"W x 12"D,
*Sandollar, Cedris Urchin, Starfish, and Urchin Small Bowls,* 3.5"H x 5"W x 5"D. Photographs: John Polak.

# FLOOR COVERINGS

# BARBARA JACOBS COLOR AND DESIGN

BARBARA JACOBS ■ 53 FRAIRY STREET ■ MEDFIELD, MA 02052 ■ TEL 508-359-5753 ■ FAX 508-861-0120
E-MAIL BJACOBS@INTEGRALCOLOR.COM ■ WWW.INTEGRALCOLOR.COM ■ WWW.SILKROADWEAVES.COM

Hand-knotted Tibetan rugs, wool and silk. Top: *FLORA/Herbal Toss, Springing II,* silk: lightest color, 80 knots/sq. in., shown: 5' × 7'. Bottom: ELEMENTS, wool background, loop textured areas, silk lines, and spot colors, 100 knots/sq. in., shown: close-up detail of four colorways, sample section size: 12" × 18", full size design: 5.5' × 5.5' (not shown). Photographs: Robert Nash.

# PATRICIA DREHER

800 HEINZ #2 ■ BERKELEY, CA 94710 ■ TEL 510-849-2036
E-MAIL INFO@PATRICIADREHER.COM ■ WWW.PATRICIADREHER.COM

Top: *Maple Leaves*, 4' × 6'. Photograph: Eric Ferguson. Bottom: *Festival*, 5' × 7'.
High-grade canvas floorcloths painted with acrylics and non-yellowing varathane.

# Barbara Jacobs

*"Our experience working with Barbara to modify one of her original designs, Herbal Toss, to our needs, was very exciting. We loved the entire process, from the initial discussion through the installation, and we receive enthusiastic compliments about it from everyone who visits our home."*

— Homeowner

*Silk Road Weaves, FLORA* collection ■ 2007 ■ Walpole, MA
Himalayan wool and Chinese silk ■ 5' x 7' ■ See more of Barbara's work on page 88.

# OUT OF THE MAINSTREAM DESIGNS

CHRISTINE L. KEFER ▪ 107 SOUTH SECOND STREET ▪ GENEVA, IL 60134
TEL 630-232-2419 ▪ E-MAIL C.KEFER@ATT.NET ▪ WWW.OUTOFTHEMAINSTREAMDESIGNS.COM

Left: Three-ply handwoven wool tapestry rug, 3' x 5', reversible.  Top right: Three-ply handwoven wool tapestry (detail).
Bottom right: Three-ply handwoven wool rug, 8' x 2.5', reversible.  Photographs: Jay King.

# SHARI CORNISH CREATIVE

SHARI CORNISH ■ PO BOX 1310 ■ 81 RIVERSIDE TERRACE ■ HARDWICK, VT 05843 ■ TEL 802-472-5920
TEL 323-422-5887 ■ FAX 802-472-9414 ■ E-MAIL SHARI@SHARICORNISH.COM ■ WWW.SHARICORNISH.COM

Top left: *Pie and Coffee*, knotted 100% New Zealand wool, 6' × 4'. Top right: *S Curve*, knotted 100% New Zealand wool,
72" × 48", custom sizes available. Bottom: *Fall Back*, floor/wall/tabletop art, pigment-painted industrial felt, 2' × 3', custom sizes available.

# ARCHITECTURAL ELEMENTS

# Nancy Gong

*"Many of the windows in our home were created by Nancy. You can't walk into our house without noticing them. Each window is different, but they all give you a sense of peace and tranquility. Nancy is just a phenomenal artist."*

— Homeowner

*River of Dreams* ■ 1998 ■ Victor, NY ■ glass and lead ■ each: 25"H x 28"W ■ See more of Nancy's work on page 95.

Tim Wilkes

# NANCY GONG

GONG GLASS WORKS ■ 42 PARKVIEW DRIVE ■ ROCHESTER, NY 14625 ■ TEL 585-288-5520
FAX 585-288-2503 ■ E-MAIL NGONG@ROCHESTER.RR.COM ■ WWW.NANCYGONG.COM

Top left: Bryce & Doyle kitchen (detail), hand-chipped art glass breakfast bar. Top right: Art Glass accent counter top for Bryce & Doyle, view from above. Brackets by Paul Knoblauch.
Bottom left: *Fresh Air*, art glass entry with a peep hole, inspired by retreats in Colorado and the Bahamas, private residence. Bottom right: *Fresh Air* (detail).

# KATHY BARNARD STUDIO

KATHY BARNARD ■ 1605 LOCUST STREET ■ KANSAS CITY, MO 64108 ■ 816-472-4977
E-MAIL KATHY@KATHYBARNARDSTUDIO.COM ■ WWW.KATHYBARNARDSTUDIO.COM

*Reflections of Tuscany*, wine tasting room and theater divider, Heinegar residence, Kansas City, MO, opalescent stained art glass panel, 5' x 8'. Photographs: Lea Murphy.

# KATHY BARNARD STUDIO

KATHY BARNARD ■ 1605 LOCUST STREET ■ KANSAS CITY, MO 64108 ■ 816-472-4977
E-MAIL KATHY@KATHYBARNARDSTUDIO.COM ■ WWW.KATHYBARNARDSTUDIO.COM

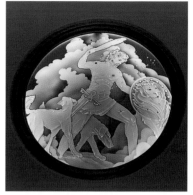

Left: Entry and living room, Heinegar residence, Kansas City, MO, edge-lit, carved, etched and airbrushed crystal glass, each: 4'Dia.
Right (from top): *Orion–Winter; Pegasus–Spring; Signus–Summer; Ursa Major, "The Big Dipper"–Fall.* Photographs: Lea Murphy.

# BILL MASTERPOOL

LA BELLA FERRO DESIGNS LLC ■ 1060 ERNST ROAD ■ FALLON, NV 89406 ■ PO BOX 745 ■ FALLON, NV 89407
TEL 775-423-7402 ■ FAX 775-423-1905 ■ E-MAIL WMASTERPOOL@CHARTER.NET

Mosaic fireplace and candelabra, metal. Photograph: Jeff Ross Photography.

# SCOTT CAMPBELL REUMAN

CONUNDRUM DESIGNS, INC. ■ 7425 MAGNOLIA ROAD ■ NEDERLAND, CO 80466 ■ TEL/FAX 303-442-0406
E-MAIL SCOTTREUMAN@CONUNDRUMDESIGNS.COM ■ WWW.CONUNDRUMDESIGNS.COM

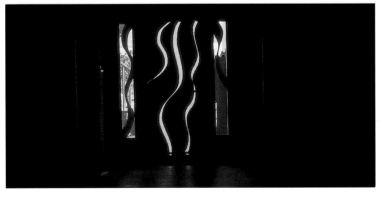

*River Series™ Golden River Door*, mahogany and dyed inlaid resin with mahogany sidelight sculptures, door: 84" x 36", sidelight sculptures each 84" x 12" x 6".

# KEN ROBY

VILLAGE BLACKSMITH INC. ■ 11193 TAYLOR MAY ROAD ■ AUBURN, OH 44023
TEL 440-543-4977 ■ FAX 440-543-0529 ■ E-MAIL KGROBY@MSN.COM ■ WWW.VILLAGEBLACKSMITHINC.COM

Railings in private residences, hand-forged iron. Photographs: Itamar Gat, Eyes of the World Photography.

# STANTON GLASS STUDIO, LLC

BRYANT STANTON ▥ 322 ROGERS HILL ROAD ▥ WACO, TX 76705 ▥ TEL 800-619-4882
FAX 254-829-2521 ▥ E-MAIL INFO@STANTONGLASS.COM ▥ WWW.STANTONGLASS.COM

Top: Stained glass and iron dome, private residence, 12' Dia. Bottom left: Stained and painted
leaded glass parlor transom. Bottom right: Custom stained glass bath window 12' x 4'.

# UNITED ARTWORKS

ANDREW WERBY ■ 8730 E STREET ■ OAKLAND, CA 94621 ■ TEL 510-568-4298
E-MAIL A.WERBY@COMCAST.NET ■ WWW.UNITEDARTWORKS.COM

Top: Brass exterior lock plate with sage leaf pattern.  Bottom: Carved wood panel with openwork sea fan pattern.

# OBJECTS

# JAN BILEK

THE NATURE OF CLAY ■ 1500 JACKSON STREET NE ■ MINNEAPOLIS, MN 55413
TEL 651-341-9205 ■ E-MAIL JAN@JANBILEK.COM ■ WWW.JANBILEK.COM

Top left: *Gourd Still Life*, wheel-thrown and altered porcelain, fired to a cone 9 in oxidation, 11" x 9" x 9". Top right: *Flower Bowl*, wheel-thrown and altered porcelain, fired to a cone 9 in oxidation, 9" x 9" x 3". Bottom left: *Berry Bottles*, wheel-thrown and altered porcelain, fired to a cone 9 in oxidation, 5" x 4" x 4" each (or 5" x 14" x 9" as three). Bottom right: *Squash Bottle*, wheel-thrown and altered porcelain, fired to a cone 9 in oxidation, 11" x 5" x 5". Photographs: Dave Ginsberg.

# STEVE "SPIKE" FINCH

EXOTIC VESSELS ▪ 789 17TH AVENUE ▪ MENLO PARK, CA 94025
TEL 650-292-0455 ▪ E-MAIL SPIKE@EXOTICVESSELS.COM ▪ WWW.EXOTICVESSELS.COM

Left: *Pure Elegance Series #2*, Italian alabaster, Italian agate, copper, and ebony, 10.75"H × 8"Dia. Top right: *Hydra* (left), Brazilian sopastone and Madagascar rosewood, 7.75"H × 4.75"Dia. and *Mirabel* (right), Brazilian sopastone, Madagascar rosewood, and Canarywood, 5"H × 4.75"Dia. Bottom right: *Flowering Lily*, sculpture, Brazilian soapstone, Italian alabaster, and ebony wood, 11.5"H × 18.5"Dia.

105

# RONALD R. FRANKLIN

ATELIER DU LAC LTD ■ 5338 ORANGE GROVE ROAD ■ HILLSBOROUGH, NC 27278
TEL 919-929-6185 ■ E-MAIL ATELIERDULAC@HOTMAIL.COM

Top left: *Song*, raku clay, 8"H × 8"W. Top right: *Memory*, raku clay, 8"H × 8"W.
Bottom: *Hallowed Supplements*, raku clay with wood, 5"H × 10"W × 4"D.

# GLASSICS

SHERRY SALITO-FORSEN ■ 204 AVENIDA SIERRA ■ SAN CLEMENTE, CA 92672
TEL 949-498-6489 ■ E-MAIL GLASSICS1@COX.NET ■ WWW.GLASSICSART.COM

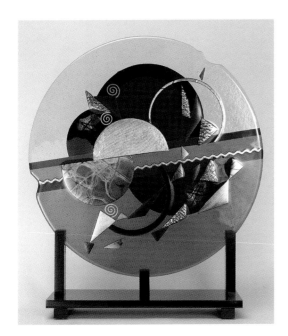

Top left: From *The Journey* series, 26"H × 23"W.  Right: *Serenity*, 34"H × 17"W.
Bottom left: From *The Journey* series, 26"H × 23"W.  Photographs: Rick Lang.

# CAROL GREEN

CAROL GREEN STUDIO ■ ELBURN, IL ■ TEL 630-365-1238 ■ FAX 630-365-1337
E-MAIL CAROL@CAROLGREEN.COM ■ WWW.CAROLGREEN.COM

*Gourd with Contorted Filbert*, wheel-thrown mica-impregnated earthenware, copper, and cast bronze, 16" x 8" x 8".

# CAROL GREEN

CAROL GREEN STUDIO ■ ELBURN, IL ■ TEL 630-365-1238 ■ FAX 630-365-1337
E-MAIL CAROL@CAROLGREEN.COM ■ WWW.CAROLGREEN.COM

Top left: *Candle Branch Pair,* cast bronze, and patina, 3.5" × 7" × 1.5", 3" × 6" × 3". Top right: *Gourd with Double Wandering Vine,* wheel-thrown mica-impregnated earthenware, copper, and cast bronze with patina, 11" × 11" × 11". Bottom: *Triple Candle Branch II,* cast bronze and patina, 3" × 13" × 11".

# JOEL HUNNICUTT

410 EAST RALEIGH STREET ■ SILER CITY, NC 27344
TEL 919-742-3168 ■ E-MAIL JOELHUNNICUTT@EARTHLINK.NET

Left: *Tall Vase with Open Segment Neck.* Right: *Bottleform.* Photographs: Jason Dowdle.

# IPSO FACTO PRODUCTIONS

GREG FIDLER ■ 349 SPRING CREEK ROAD ■ BAKERSVILLE, NC 28705
TEL/FAX 828-688-2973 ■ E-MAIL GREGFIDLER@MSN.COM ■ WWW.GREGFIDLERGLASS.COM

Top: *Chocolate,* opal green form studies, tallest form 28".
Bottom left: *Luna Green Form Studies.* Bottom right: *Luna Green Form Studies.* Photographs: Tom Mills.

# Cheryl
# Williams

*"I commissioned this piece for my second home in Oregon. It is the focal point of the sitting room. We have collected Cheryl Williams's work over the years and are very excited about her larger sculptures, which I have placed in my office as well."*

— Edward Alpern, homeowner

*Wow* ■ 2007 ■ Ashland, OR ■ ceramic ■ 17"H x 16"W ■ See more of Cheryl's work on page 153.

Barbara Bobes

# JOHN CHILES GLASS

JOHN CHILES ■ 690 ROUTE 73 ■ ORWELL, VT 05760 ■ TEL 802-948-2209
E-MAIL JOHN@HUBGLASS.COM ■ WWW.JOHNCHILESGLASS.COM

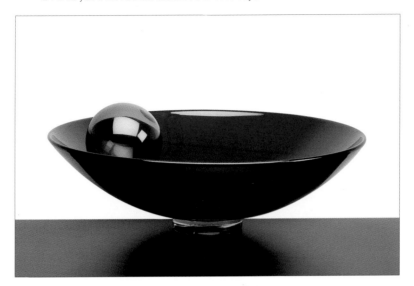

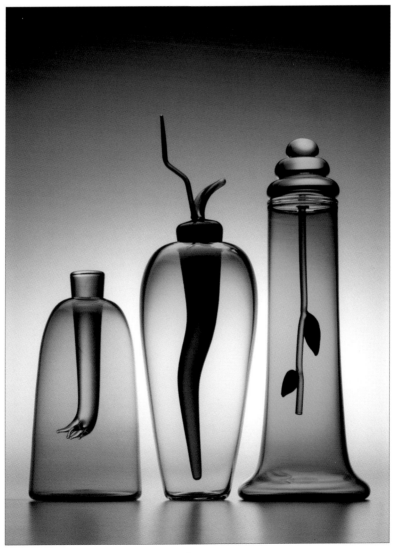

Top: *Gravity Bowl.* Bottom: *Organic Bottle Series.* Photographs: May Mantell.

# MELODY LANE

18E BROCKETTS POINT ROAD ■ BRANFORD, CT 06405 ■ TEL 203-481-3182
FAX 203-432-8939 ■ E-MAIL MELODY.LANE@YALE.EDU ■ WWW.MELODYLANESTUDIO.COM

Top left: *Flame Window Sculpture*, clay and glass on metal stand, 26.5"H × 20.5"W × 1"D. Top right: *Heptagon Window Sculpture*, clay and glass on metal stand, 20"H × 16"W × 1"D. Bottom: *Rose Square Table*, clay and glass on metal base, 20"H × 18"W × 18"D. Photographs: Bob Barrett.

# SUSAN MADACSI

MADACSI METALWORK ■ 22 BAYVIEW ■ STONINGTON, CT 06378 ■ TEL 860-857-8768
FAX 860-535-3214 ■ E-MAIL SMADACSI@EARTHLINK.NET ■ WWW.MADACSIMETALWORK.COM

Top: *Wabi Saki Totems*, forged steel and enamel paint, 34"H. Bottom left: *Wabi Sabi Vessel*, forged steel and enamel paint, 16"Dia.
Bottom right: *Wabi Saki Platter*, forged steel with enamel paint, 14"Dia. Photographs: RJ Phil.

# Steven Whyte

*Structure* ■ 2006 ■ Monterey, CA ■ bronze ■ 37" x 13" x 10"

See more of Steven's work on page 150.

*"We worked with Steven Whyte on the development of a collection of his work for our home. He helped us select edition pieces that complemented our living space, and worked with us on the creation of unique sculptures made especially for our home's space, architectural style, and our personal preferences. The resulting collection is a point of great pride for us, and working with Steven was both convenient and inspiring."*

— Lynn Mitchell, homeowner

# JENNIFER C. McCURDY

PO BOX 138 ■ VINEYARD HAVEN, MA 02568 ■ TEL 508-627-0443
FAX 508-696-0262 ■ E-MAIL JEN@JENNIFERMCCURDY.COM ■ WWW.JENNIFERMCCURDY.COM

Top left: *Coral Vessel*, 7" × 7" × 7". Right: *Yin-Yang Egg on Stand*, 19" × 6" × 6".
Bottom left: *Vortex Vessel*, 10" × 7" × 7". Photographs: Katherine Rose.

117

# NINA PALADINO AND MICHAEL K. HANSEN

CALIFORNIA GLASS STUDIO, INC. ■ 1815 SILICA AVENUE ■ SACRAMENTO, CA 95815 ■ TEL 916-925-9322
FAX 916-925-9370 ■ E-MAIL PALADINOHANSEN@GMAIL.COM ■ WWW.PALADINOHANSEN.COM

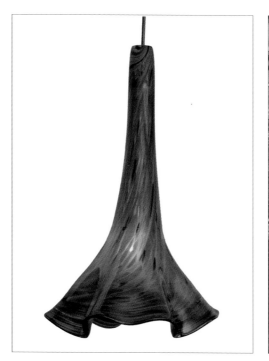

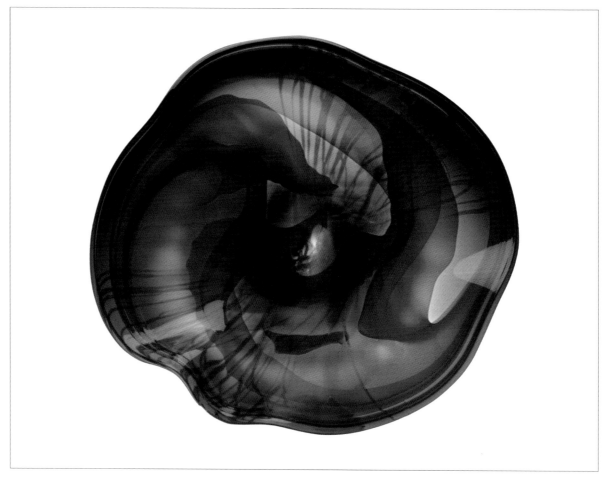

Top left: Pendant, 12"H x 5"Dia. Top right: Kitchen pendant lighting and *Morning Glory Freeform Bowl*.
Bottom: *Sunset Freeform Bowl*, 26"Dia. x 6"D. Photograph: Dave Brooks. Custom colors and sizes to suit your décor.

# RAKU VESSELS

HEATHER McQUEEN ■ GREG MILNE ■ 1800 WEST CORNELIA ■ CHICAGO, IL 60657
TEL 773-248-8616 ■ FAX 773-334-6545 ■ E-MAIL INFO@RAKUVESSELS.COM ■ WWW.RAKUVESSELS.COM

Top left: *Small Partial Arc Vessel*, 20"H × 18.5"W × 15.5"D.  Right: *Tall Partial Arc*, 36"H × 17.5"W × 25"D.
Bottom left: *Saturn Vessel*, 33"H × 20"W × 20"D.  Photographs: Dan Merlo.

# TAYLOR BACKES ■ TIBITU

WILLIAM DEXTER ■ SECOND AND WASHINGTON STREET ■ BOYERTOWN, PA 19512
TEL 610-367-4600 ■ FAX 610-367-4601 ■ E-MAIL WILL@DEJAZZD.COM ■ WWW.TAYLORBACKES.COM

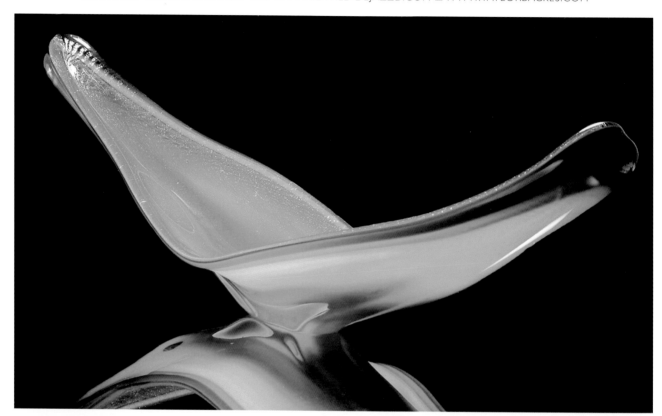

Top: *Green Boat*, 2007, blown glass/dichroic, 8" × 38" × 6".  Bottom: *Tidal Waters©*, 2006, cardiac waiting room, north wing of Reading Hospital, PA, two matching installations of blown glass, 12" × 96" × 22".

# MIA TYSON

11002 DOGLEG TRACE ■ TEGA CAY, SC 29708 ■ TEL 803-548-4534 ■ TEL 704-293-8183
FAX 803-548-4534 ■ E-MAIL MIA.TYSON@MIATYSON.COM ■ WWW.MIATYSON.COM

Top: *Sculptural Pitcher*, red earthenware with black glaze and freehand sgraffito, 26"H x 19"W x 6"D.  Bottom: *Window Sculpture*, red earthenware with black glaze and freehand sgraffito, 26"H x 19"W x 6"D.  Both pieces available in 32"H and 20"H sizes.  Photographs: Villa Photography.

# CANDONE M. WHARTON

111 BROAD AVENUE ■ DAYTONA BEACH SHORES, FL 32118
TEL 407-687-8555 ■ FAX 386-304-1543 ■ E-MAIL IBZ27@AOL.COM ■ WWW.CANDONE.COM

Left: *Torre Roja*, ceramic, 20" × 8" × 5". Top right: *Castillo Dorado*, 2006, hand-built raku-fired vessel, gold luster glazes, 17" × 15" × 15".
Bottom right: *Castillo Azul*, 2006, hand built from slabs and carved coils, copper crackle and gold raku glazes, 14" × 6" × 6". Photographs: Jerry Anthony.

# SCULPTURE

# ALEX ANAGNOSTOU GLASS STUDIO

ALEX ANAGNOSTOU ■ TEL 416-668-4411 ■ E-MAIL INFO@ALEXANAGNOSTOU.COM ■ WWW.ALEXANAGNOSTOU.COM

Left: *Golden Spiral, Filaments* series, 9'H × 33"Dia. Photograph: Kevin Hedley. Top right: *Golden Spiral* (detail). Center right: *Ovoid Forms*, blown glass with glass threads, aluminum base, 7" × 6" × 8" and 12" × 6" × 8". Bottom right: *Cell Division*, blown glass with glass threads and interior blown bubble, aluminum pins, wood, 7"H × 6"W × 30"L. Photograph: Kevin Hedley.

# DONNA BRANCH

TARA GLASSART STUDIO ■ 7621 LAKESHORE DRIVE ■ McCALLA, AL 35111
TEL 205-477-6661 ■ E-MAIL DONNABRANCH@TARAGLASSART.COM ■ WWW.DONNABRANCH.COM

Left: *Relic of a Memory No.1*, 2006, glass, cast, carved with battuto, sandblasted, acid-etched, steel frame, 16.5"H x 14"W x 14.5"D,
lampworked glass twigs may vary in dimension, limited edition of twenty-five. Right: *Ode to the Ancients: No. XXV*, 2006, glass, cast,
carved with battuto, sandblasted, acid-etched, steel frame, 8.25"H x 8.5"W x 6.5"D, limited edition of twenty-five. Photographs: Ralph Anderson.

# JEANINE BRIGGS

PO BOX 475441 ■ SAN FRANCISCO, CA 94123
TEL 415-567-4662 ■ E-MAIL ARTLINKS@PACBELL.NET

Left: *Earth Mother*, discarded leather and wood, 60" x 24" x 24".
Right: *Mélange*, discarded metal on wood with insulation foam, 47.5" x 13" x 4.5". Photographs: Maximage.

# ANDREW CARSON

ANDREW CARSON WIND SCULPTURE ■ 1531 NE 89TH STREET ■ SEATTLE, WA 98115 ■ TEL 206-524-9782
TEL 206-349-0552 ■ FAX 425-952-8170 ■ E-MAIL CARBETT@MAC.COM ■ WWW.WINDSCULPTURE.COM

Top left: *Bronze Sun Glass Balls,* Seattle, WA. Top right: *Leafy Phoenix* (detail). Bottom: *Lyon,* 8' wheel fountain, Woodway, WA.

127

# PATRICK W. DOYLE

PO BOX 1462 ■ FORT BRAGG, CA 95437 ■ TEL 707-367-4509 ■ TEL 707-964-4286
E-MAIL PWD@MCN.ORG ■ WWW.PWDFINEWOODWORKING.COM

Top left: *The Secret*, 2006, virgin redwood burl. Photograph: David Russell. Right: *Kelpish Veil* of *Source* (view 1 of 4 sides), 2007, virgin redwood burl, 86" × 44" × 32". Bottom left: *Double Tear Leaf Table*, 2007, virgin redwood burl, 27" × 55" × 24". Photographs: Larry Wagner.

# ERIC EHLENBERGER

GLASSLIGHT STUDIO ■ 2601 CHARTRES STREET ■ NEW ORLEANS, LA 70117
TEL 504-943-7446 ■ E-MAIL NEON@EHLENBERGER.COM ■ WWW.EHLENBERGER.COM

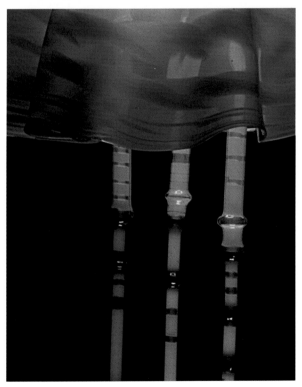
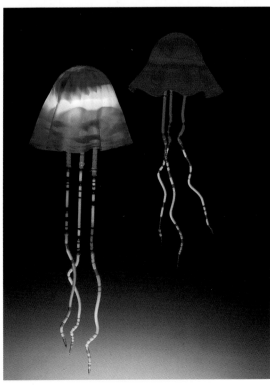

*Jellyfish*, blown glass and neon, sizes variable, each approx: 42" x 16" x 16".

# BARRY ENTNER

BARRY ENTNER SCULPTURE ■ 41 VIOLET HILL ROAD ■ RHINEBECK, NY 12572
TEL 845-876-3077 ■ FAX 845-876-3077 ■ E-MAIL BENTNERGLASS@AOL.COM ■ WWW.BARRYENTNER.COM

Left: *Corona Series*, steam-blown glass on stainless steel armature, 6'H x 34"W x 34"D.  Photograph: Bob Barrett.  Top right: *Corona Series*, steam-blown glass on stainless steel armature, 3'H x 34"W x 34"D.  Photograph: Realf Schermer.  Bottom right: *Flora Sconce*, steam-blown glass on brushed steel wall mount, 20"H x 16"W x 8"D.

# LINDSAY FEUER

LINDSAY FEUER STUDIO ■ TEL 215-688-0873
E-MAIL LINDSAY@LINDSAYFEUER.COM ■ WWW.LINDSAYFEUER.COM

Top left: *Hybrid 'Bi-Flora' No. 4*, hand-built porcelain, 10"H × 5"W × 6"D. Top right: *Hybrid 'Cluster' No. 7*, hand-built porcelain, 19"H × 12"W × 11"D. Bottom: *Hybrid 'Flora' No. 5*, hand-built porcelain, 8"H × 9"W × 7"D. Photographs: John Carlano.

# HARRINGTON SCULPTURE

JESSE C. HARRINGTON ■ 3510 SCOTTS LANE SUITE 3015 ■ PHILADELPHIA, PA 19129 ■ TEL 267-979-3800
FAX 610-933-0244 ■ E-MAIL JESSE@HARRINGTONSCULPTURE.COM ■ WWW.HARRINGTONSCULPTURE.COM

Top left: *Miguell Antonio Horn*, 2006, plaster of paris, 16"H x 7"W x 9"D. Top right: *Torso*, 2006, Indiana limestone, 21"H x 11"W.
Bottom: *Sorrow*, 2004, Carrera marble, 20.5"H x 26"L x 16"D.  Photographs: Sara Evans.

# DORI JALAZO

DORI JALAZO VISIONS ▩ 505 KEMP ROAD WEST ▩ GREENSBORO, NC 27410
TEL 336-299-2517 ▩ E-MAIL DORI@DORIJ.COM ▩ WWW.DORIJ.COM

Left: *Beloved,* from the *Shekinah* series.  Right: *Strength and Compassion,* from the *Shekinah* series.  Photographs: Anthony Cornelison.

# JAMES T. RUSSELL SCULPTURE

JAMES T. RUSSELL ■ 1930 LOMITA BOULEVARD ■ LOMITA, CA 90717 ■ TEL 310-326-0785
FAX 310-326-1470 ■ E-MAIL JAMES@RUSSELLSCULPTURE.COM ■ WWW.RUSSELLSCULPTURE.COM

*Boundless Spirit*, 2006, polished stainless steel, 40" x 19" x11". Photograph: Paul Moses.

# BARRY WOODS JOHNSTON

SCULPTURE WORKS, INC. ■ 2423 PICKWICK ROAD ■ BALTIMORE, MD 21207 ■ TEL 410-448-1945
FAX 410-448-2663 ■ E-MAIL BARRY@SCULPTORJOHNSTON.COM ■ WWW.SCULPTORJOHNSTON.COM

*Ballerina,* 1988, bronze, 32.5" × 42" × 18" without base, edition of eight, also available in large: 5.3' × 6.6' × 3' or small: 14" × 17" × 4.5" without base, awarded Best in Show for the 1990 National Arts Club Annual.

135

# BARBARA KOBYLINSKA

1236 SOUTHFIELD PLACE ■ VIRGINIA BEACH, VA 23452
TEL 757-463-0605 ■ E-MAIL B@KOBYLINSKA.COM ■ WWW.KOBYLINSKA.COM

Top (from left): *Red Beauty*, 2006, 80" × 16"; *Ornamental Rossette*, 2002, 60" × 22"; *Golden Tree*, 2005, 68" × 19"; *Wild West*, 2005, 78" × 15". Bottom left (from left): *Blue Hen*, 2006, 65" × 21"; *Sprouting Bud*, 2003, 84" × 16"; *Great Predator*, 2005, 78" × 15". Bottom right (from left): *Fire Bird*, 2006, 67" × 22"; *Spiky Lady*, 2003, 77" × 25"; *Brown Pelican*, 2007, 65" × 16".

# KRAMER SCULPTURES INC.

BORIS KRAMER ■ 3370 DUSTAN STREET ■ VINELAND ON, L0R 2E0 ■ CANADA ■ TEL 866-733-3434 ■ TEL 905-562-3025
FAX 905-563-0721 ■ E-MAIL INFO@KRAMERSCULPTURES.COM ■ WWW.KRAMERSCULPTURES.COM

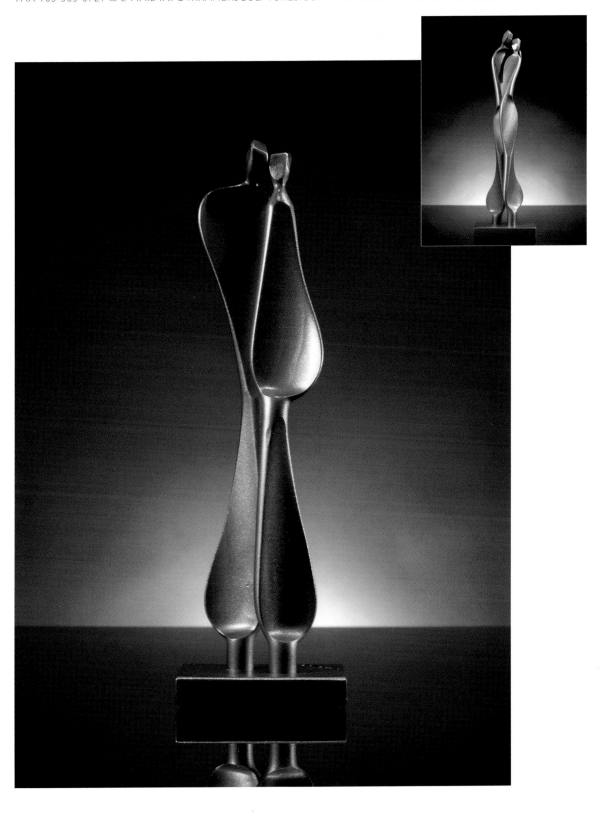

*Quiet Encounter,* low carbon steel, available up to 94"H.  Inset: *Intimacy,* low carbon steel, available up to 94"H.

137

# ROB LORENSON

SEVEN COOMBS STREET ■ MIDDLEBORO, MA 02346 ■ TEL 508-454-5478
FAX 508-531-6128 ■ E-MAIL RLORENSON@BRIDGEW.EDU ■ WWW.ROBLORENSON.COM

Top left: *Red Boxer*, 2007, painted aluminum, 32" x 48" x 48". Top right: *Pulsar*, 2006, stainless steel, 85" x 96" x 96".
Bottom left: *Syosset Series #10*, 2007, painted aluminum, 96" x 72" x 32". Bottom right: *Solar Flare*, 2005, stainless steel, 96" x 70" x 60".

# JIM MALKOWSKI

8485 SOUTH 44TH STREET ■ FRANKLIN, WI 53132 ■ TEL 414-421-0112 ■ TEL 262-857-3600
FAX 212-857-9546 ■ E-MAIL MALKOJF@YAHOO.COM ■ WWW.JMALKOART.COM

*Sun Catcher*, 2007, bronze on stone base, 35"H (without base).

# PETER W. MICHEL

PETER W. MICHEL, SCULPTOR ■ 36 KELLOGG STREET ■ CLINTON, NY 13323 ■ TEL 315-853-8146
TEL 315-663-5308 ■ FAX 315-859-1480 ■ E-MAIL PETER@PETERMICHEL.COM ■ WWW.PETERMICHEL.COM

Top: *Transactions of the Mind Series* (left to right): *Dancing*, 20.25"H x 10"W x 5.25"D, *Mindfolk*, 21"H x 9.25"W x 5.75"D, *Dozing*, 17.5"H x 8.75"W x 5.25"D,
and *Wake Up*, 20.25"H x 9.5"W x 5.25"D, 1996, painted wood.  Bottom left: *Two are Halves of One*, 2006, painted wood, 15.5"H x 6"W x 6.5"D.
Bottom center: *Fathers and Sons*, 1999, painted wood, 24"H x 23.5"Dia.  Bottom right: *Family Celebration*, 2006, painted wood, 12.5"H x 9"W x 9.5"D.

# LEE MILTIER

701 BANCROFT WAY ■ BERKELEY, CA 94710 ■ TEL 510-649-1977 ■ FAX 510-649-1123
E-MAIL LEE@PHOTOSYNTHESIS.CC ■ WWW.PHOTOSYNTHESIS.CC

*Energy Bottles,* 2007, 66"–75".

# AMY J. MUSIA

LONE STAR STUDIO ■ PO BOX 18064 ■ EVANSVILLE, IN 47719 ■ TEL 812-985-7523
TEL 812-459-8833 ■ E-MAIL A.MUSIA@ATT.NET ■ WWW.AMYMUSIA.COM

Top: *Nymphaea*, 2004, collection of Edward and Julie Meade Johnson, MA, wood with 24K gilding, 36"H × 34"W × 16"D. Bottom left: *Good Morning, Glory*, 2006, wood, 50"H × 24"W × 12"D. Bottom right: *Dreams, Loves, Beliefs*, 2006, wood with copper, silver, and 24K gold gilding, 40"H × 24"W × 24"D.

# ANNIE PASIKOV

30 STAGECOACH TRAIL ■ LYONS, CO 80540 ■ TEL 303-823-6757 ■ FAX 303-823-8033
E-MAIL ANNIESCULPTS@MSN.COM ■ WWW.STONESCULPTURES.NET

Left: *Awaiting the Dawn*, 2001, bronze cast from marble sculpture, 47". edition of twenty-one. Photograph: Marie Commiskey.
Top right: *Sacred Fire*, 2003, calcite, 26" × 28". Photograph: Norman L. Koren. Bottom right: *Fly With Me*, 2001, alabaster, 8" × 21" × 6".

# JEFF PENDER

TEL 704-779-0533 ■ TEL 704-660-9165 ■ E-MAIL JEFF@JEFFPENDER.COM ■ WWW.JEFFPENDER.COM

Left: *Entity's Eye 1*, stoneware, earthenware, wood stain, glaze, terra sigillata, 24.5"H × 10"W × 9.5"D.
Right: *Ancestors Metamorph 2*, stoneware, wood stain, luster, 17"H × 8"W × 4"D. Photographs: Mitchell Kearney.

# BINH PHO

WONDERS OF WOOD ■ 48 WEST 175 PINE TREE DRIVE ■ MAPLE PARK, IL 60151 ■ TEL 630-365-5462
TEL 630-728-5464 ■ FAX 630-365-5837 ■ E-MAIL TORIALE@MSN.COM ■ WWW.WONDERSOFWOOD.NET

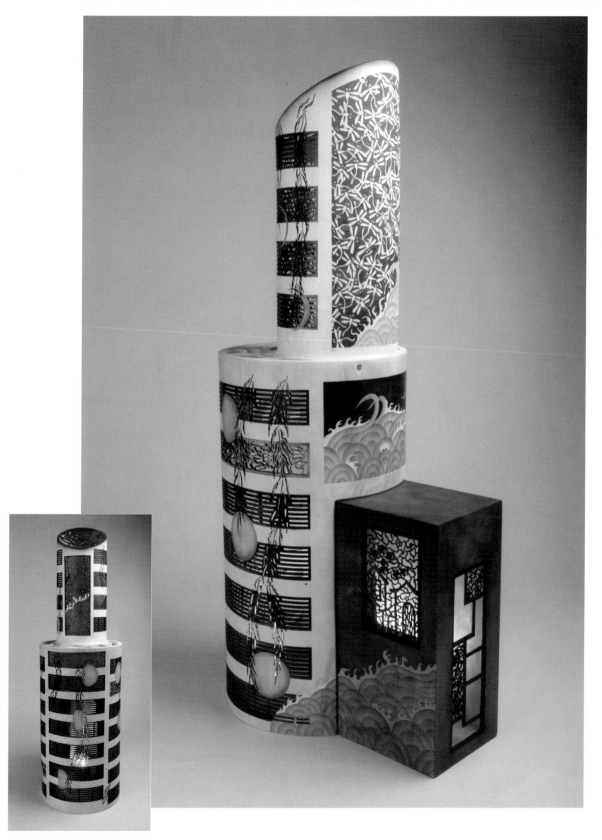

*Waiting for the Moon to Go Away,* 2006, York residence, Lighthouse Point, FL, box elder and acrylic paint, 31"H x 16"W x 12"D.

# DIANA REUTER-TWINING

PO BOX 552 ■ ALDIE, VA 20105 ■ TEL 703-327-5333 ■ FAX 703-327-4274
E-MAIL DREUTERTWI@AOL.COM ■ WWW.BRONZED.NET

*Rufus*, 24"H x 20"L x 9"W.  Photograph: Brandon Webster.

# LOIS S. SATTLER

LOIS SATTLER—CERAMICS ■ 3620 PACIFIC AVENUE ■ MARINA DEL REY, CA 90292
TEL 310-821-7055 ■ FAX 310-821-3012 ■ E-MAIL CLAGRLLOIS@AOL.COM

 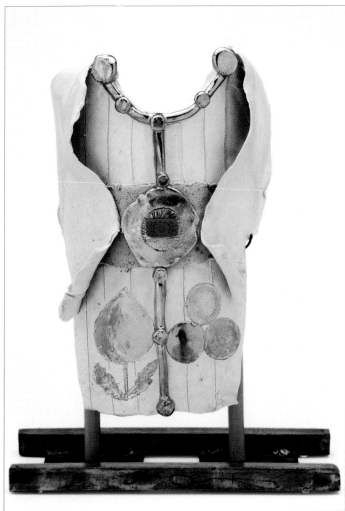

Left: *Red Kimono,* 2006-2007, Los Angeles, CA, porcelain embellished with mixed media on metal stand with bamboo, 18" x 8".
Right: *Celedon Kimono,* 2006-2007, Los Angeles, CA, porcelain embellished with mixed media on metal stand with bamboo, 18" x 8". Photographs: Alan Shaffer.

147

# TED SCHAAL

FINE ART BRONZE ▩ 1633 SOUTH ESTRELLA AVENUE ▩ LOVELAND, CO 80537
TEL 970-461-2007 ▩ E-MAIL TED@SCHAALARTS.COM ▩ WWW.SCHAALARTS.COM

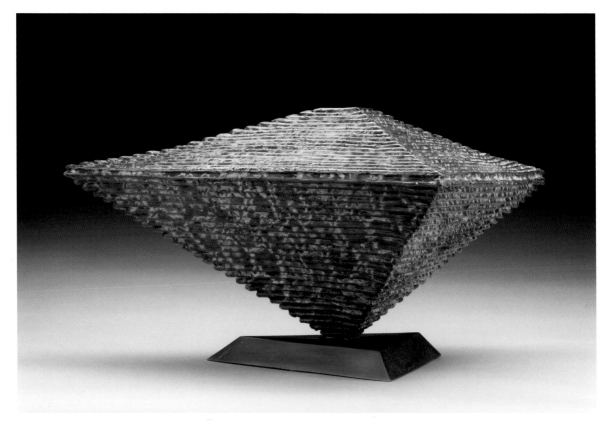

Top: *Equilibrium*, 2006, bronze, 10" × 12" × 12".
Bottom: *Spaciana*, 2006, bronze, 10" × 42" × 8".

# GEORGE SCHROEDER

SCHROEDER ART ▪ 257 WEST TURBO ▪ SAN ANTONIO, TX 78216 ▪ TEL 210-601-2508
TEL/FAX 210-341-3317 ▪ E-MAIL GEORGE@SCHROEDERART.COM ▪ WWW.SCHROEDERART.COM

Top left: *Passage,* 2005, private collection, bronze and limestone, 102"H × 73"W × 28"D. Photograph: Chris Cooper.
Top right: *Neptula,* lamp sculpture, 2006, private collection, bronze, steel, and glass, 32"H × 18"Dia. Photograph: Ansen Seale.
Bottom: *Mercury,* sculpture bench, 2007, private collection, hand-formed polished aluminum, 20"H × 78"L × 30"W. Photograph: Ansen Seale.

# STEVEN WHYTE SCULPTURE STUDIOS

STEVEN WHYTE ■ PO BOX 148 ■ CARMEL-BY-THE-SEA, CA 93921 ■ TEL 831-620-1917
TEL 831-521-6045 ■ E-MAIL SCULPTU@EARTHLINK.NET ■ WWW.STEVENWHYTESCULPTOR.COM

Left: *Nurture, Stance* series, bronze, 21" × 8" × 8", edition of forty-eight. Top right: *Dancing Bacchante 1, Bacchanlia* series, bronze, 19" × 12" × 8", edition of forty-eight. Bottom right: *#4 Rhiannon, Six Inch Square* series, bronze, 6" × 6" × 6", edition of forty-eight.

# CHARLES STRAIN

7600 WEST CARR LANE ▪ HARRISBURG, MO 65256 ▪ TEL 573-874-3174 ▪ TEL 573-268-1173
E-MAIL CSTRAIN@HOWARDELECTRICWB.COM ▪ WWW.CHARLESSTRAIN.COM

Left: *Duo*, 2004, bronze, 72" × 36". Top right: *Visionary*, 2006, bronze, 36" × 15".
Center right: *Flames*, 2006, bronze, 12" × 7". Bottom right: *Model*, 2007, bronze, 36" × 21". Photographs: Sheri Bryan.

151

# DARREL TRACY

143 NORTH CHATHAM AVENUE ■ SILER CITY, NC 27344 ■ TEL 919-704-5216
E-MAIL QUAKERCRAFTS@EMBARQMAIL.COM ■ WWW.DARRELTRACY.NET

Left: *Cascade Spirit House*, 12"H. Top right: *White-Oak Mountain Home*, 30"H.
Bottom right: *Tenakee Cabin*, 12"H. Photographs: Jason Dowdle.

# CHERYL WILLIAMS

PO BOX 1283 ■ ASHLAND, OR 97520 ■ TEL/FAX 541-482-0609 ■ TEL 541-531-3677
E-MAIL CWILLIAMS@SANDPOINT.NET ■ WWW.CHERYLSWILLIAMS.COM

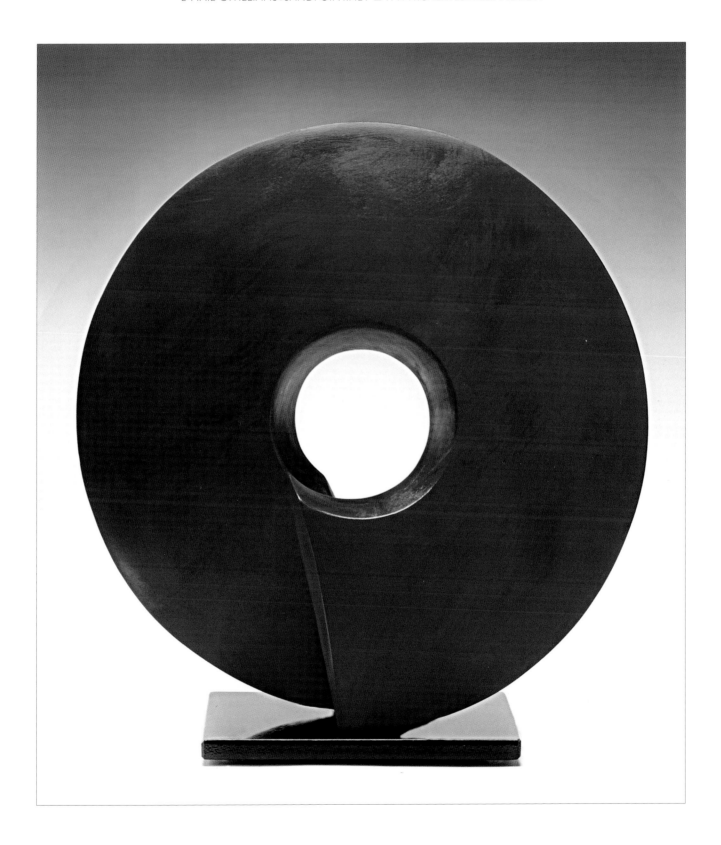

*Wow*, ceramic, 17" x 17". Photograph: Stuart Gray.

# JEANNINE YOUNG

PO BOX 520876 ■ SALT LAKE CITY, UT 84152-0876 ■ TEL 801-467-6692
E-MAIL JYSCULPTURES@MSTAR.NET ■ WWW.JEANNINEYOUNG.COM

*Grace*, 2007, bronze, 35"H x 13"W x 11"D, edition of twenty-five.  Photograph: David Hawkinson.

# WILLIAM ZWEIFEL

MIDLAND STUDIO ■ N7652 PLEASANT LAKE ROAD ■ ELKHORN, WI 53121 ■ TEL 414-659-2313
FAX 262-742-2313 ■ E-MAIL WEZ@MIDLANDSTUDIO.COM ■ WWW.MIDLANDSTUDIO.COM

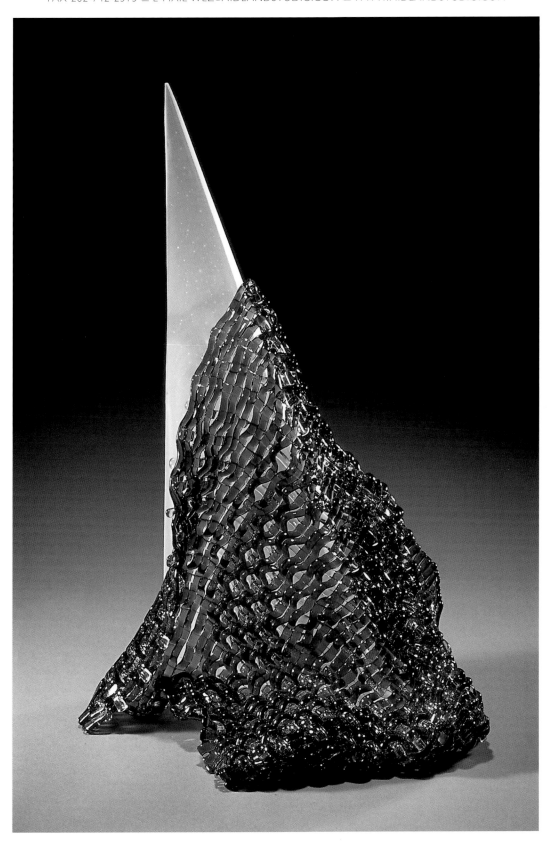

*Drift*, 2006, cast and woven glass, 18"H x 12"W x 8"D. Photograph: Larry Sanders.

*November #1-05* (left) and *June #10-05* (right) by Chin Yuen, see page 207. Photograph: Saskia Soderman.

# ART FOR THE WALL

# CHRISTINE BRENNAN

175 NORTH PUEBLO AVENUE ■ OJAI, CA 93023 ■ TEL 805-640-8329
E-MAIL RUN-AMOK@SBCGLOBAL.NET ■ WWW.CHRISTINEBRENNAN.NET

Top: *Untitled, #PA696*, oil on board, 36" x 36".  Bottom left: *Untitled, #PA700*, oil on board, 11" x 11".
Bottom right: *Untitled, #699*, oil and gold leaf on board, 16" x 16".

# URSULA J. BRENNER

URSULA J. BRENNER FINE ART, INC. ■ 948 BUTTERFLY COURT ■ CINCINNATI, OH 45231-5801
TEL 513-300-9997 ■ FAX 513-521-0584 ■ E-MAIL UJBRENNER@FUSE.NET ■ WWW.URSULABRENNER.COM

Top left: *Transitions I*, 2006, painting, 30" × 30", also available as a giclée print. Top right: *Transitions II*, 2006, painting, 30" × 30", also available as a giclée print.
Center: *Geometry*, 2007, painting on canvas, 22" × 60". Bottom: *Fleeting Moments*, 2007, painting on canvas, 22" × 60". Photographs: Robin Imaging.

# BETTY BUTLER ■ ITALA LANGMAR

RESPONSIVE ART ■ 9175 GROSS POINT ROAD #177 ■ SKOKIE, IL 60077
TEL 847-347-3144 ■ E-MAIL RESPONSIVEART@COMCAST.NET ■ WWW.RESPONSIVEART.COM

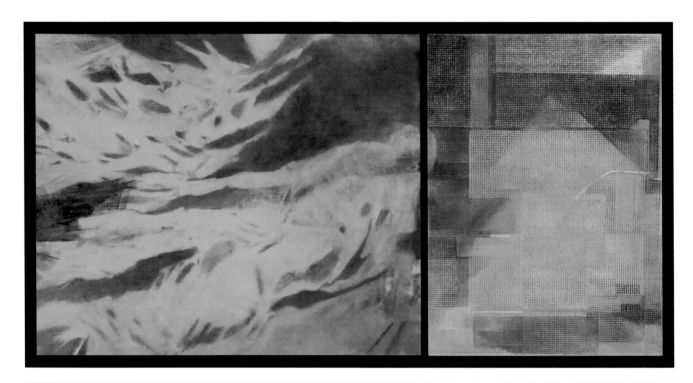

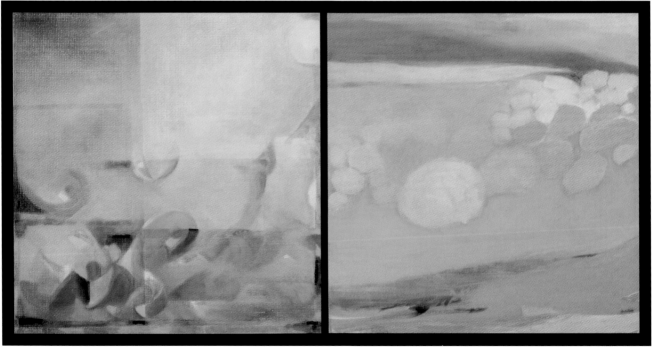

Top: *Cobalt Clouds* (left), by Betty Butler, acrylic, 24" x 30", *Response* (right), by Itala Langmar, mixed media, 24" x 18".
Bottom: *Caressing the Horizon* (left), by Itala Langmar, mixed media, 30" x 30", *Response* (right), by Betty Butler, acrylic, 30" x 30".

*Love, Dreams & Struggle*, 2007, acrylic on canvas, 30" × 24". Limited editions available.

# CARRIE CRANE

214 MILE HILL ROAD ■ BOYLSTON, MA 01505 ■ TEL 508-869-2633 ■ TEL 508-450-5516
E-MAIL CRANE.CARRIE@GMAIL.COM ■ WWW.CARRIECRANE.COM

Top: *The Overlook*, acrylic on panel, 16" x 16". Bottom: *October Bridge*, acrylic on panel, 16" x 16". Photographs: Winthrop Studios.

# KINGA CZERSKA

1404 THIRD AVENUE NORTH #15 ■ SEATTLE, WA 98109 ■ TEL 206-369-4824
E-MAIL KINGA_CZERSKA@HOTMAIL.COM ■ WWW.KINGACZERSKA.COM

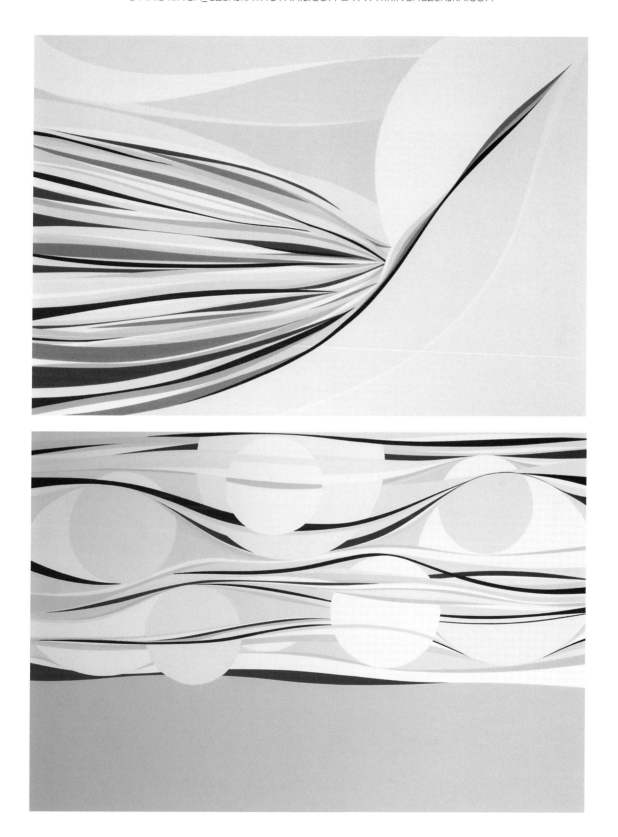

Top: *Embrace*, acrylic on wood panel, 40" × 60" × 2".
Bottom: *Metamorphosis*, acrylic on wood panel, 40" × 60" × 2".

# LILLIANA S. DIDOVIC

GORDAN ART STUDIO ■ 7513 SHERWOOD ROAD ■ PHILADELPHIA, PA 19151 ■ TEL 215-878-9128 ■ TEL 610-585-2146
E-MAIL GORDAN89@MSN.COM ■ E-MAIL LILLIANA@LILLIANADIDOVIC.US ■ WWW.LILLIANADIDOVIC.US

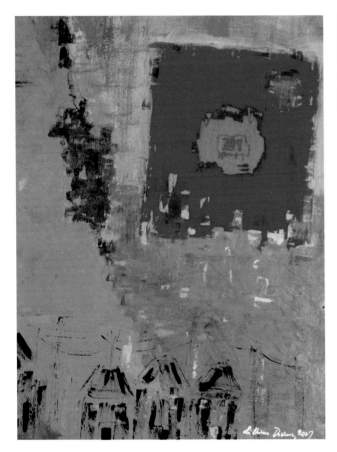 

Left: *North*, acrylic on canvas, 30" x 24". Right: *Sunset at the City*, acrylic on canvas, 20" x 16".

# MARGARET DOBBINS

11871 BRIAR FOREST ■ HOUSTON, TX 77077 ■ TEL 281-496-7322
E-MAIL MSDOBBINS@PEOPLEPC.COM ■ WWW.MARGARETDOBBINS.COM

Top: *Distant Dreaming*, acrylic on wrapped canvas, 40" x 40". Bottom left: *Winter Trees*, acrylic on
wrapped canvas, 29" x 29". Bottom right: *Canyon Trees*, acrylic on wrapped canvas, 40" x 40". Photographs: Rick Wells.

# THE ELEPHANTWORKS STUDIO

MELISSA J. LEAYM-FERNANDEZ ■ 4230 FAIRWAY DRIVE ■ FORT GRATIOT, MI 48059 ■ TEL 810-385-8944
TEL 810-300-3456 ■ E-MAIL ELEPHANTWORKSTUDIO@SBCGLOBAL.NET ■ WWW.ELEPHANTWORKSTUDIO.COM

Top: *Linear Collection IV*, oil on canvas, 48" x 36", limited-edition print available, image 20" x 16". Photograph: Kole Montross.
Bottom: *Green Sea Turtle*, 16" x 20".

# NANCI ERSKINE

ERSKINE STUDIO ■ 201 SOUTH COLLEGE AVENUE #209 ■ FORT COLLINS, CO 80524 ■ TEL 970-224-2553
TEL 970-402-7621 ■ E-MAIL ERSKINE@PEAKPEAK.COM ■ WWW.ARTISTSREGISTER.COM/ARTISTS/CO3

 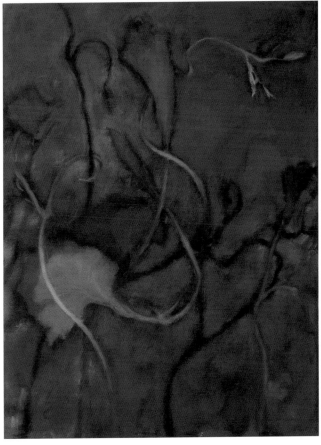

Top: *Floating World*, oil on canvas, 28" x 42".  Bottom left: *Morning Glory*, oil on canvas, 16" x 12".  Bottom right: *Night Bloom*, oil on canvas, 16" x 12".

# ERIN McGEE FERRELL

424 EAST THIRD STREET ■ MOORESTOWN, NJ 08057 ■ TEL 856-380-1301 ■ TEL 856-630-9832
FAX 856-380-2405 ■ E-MAIL ERIN@ERINMCGEEFERRELL.COM ■ WWW.ERINMCGEEFERRELL.COM

Top left: *Toy Store, Main Street America*, 2007, oil on canvas, 20" x 16". Top right: *Our Lady of Good Counsel*, 2006, oil on canvas, 32" x 28".
Bottom: *Sarcone's Bakery, Italian Market*, 2007, 24" x 30". Photographs: Profiles Printmaking, Philadelphia, PA.

# JOANNE FOX

480 GATE FIVE ROAD 260 A ■ SAUSALITO, CA 94965 ■ TEL/FAX 415-332-8133
E-MAIL FOXFOLD@SBCGLOBAL.NET ■ WWW.JOANNEFOX.NET

Left: *Home*, oil, 72"H x 54"W.  Right: *Tuscany Afternoon*, oil, 74"H x 54"W.  Photographs: Charles Kennard.

# FRANCESCO

GOODMAN ENTERTAINMENT, INC. ■ PO BOX 6583 ■ BRANDON, FL 33508-6010 ■ TEL 813-657-2500
TEL 813-215-3673 ■ FAX 813-662-5967 ■ E-MAIL GOODMANENTERTAIN@GMAIL.COM ■ WWW.KROSLAK-FRANCESCO.COM

*DaSola,* 2005, acrylic on canvas, 45" × 45".
Inset: *Apocalyptic Hooker,* 2007, acrylic on canvas, 36" × 24".

# CAROL GRIFFIN

185 EAST 85TH STREET #17 L ■ NEW YORK, NY 10028 ■ TEL 212-427-6847
FAX 212-534-2293 ■ E-MAIL GGRIFFIN2@NYC.RR.COM ■ HTTP://WEB.MAC.COM/CGRIFFIN6

Top: *Cypress Green Plaid*, gouache on paper, 9" x 9". Bottom: *Sienna Marble Plaid*, gouache on paper, 9" x 12". Photographs: Stuart Tyson.

# MARY HATCH

6917 WILLSON DRIVE ■ KALAMAZOO, MI 49009 ■ TEL 269-375-0376
E-MAIL MARY_HATCH@SBCGLOBAL.NET ■ WWW.MARYHATCH.COM

*Bouquet Day*, oil on canvas, 48" x 34".  Photograph: Lacey Vogt.

# STEPHEN HENNING

22399 OAK HILL ROAD NORTHWEST ■ EVANSVILLE, MN 56326 ■ TEL 218-948-2288
FAX 218-948-2344 ■ E-MAIL HENNING@GCTEL.COM ■ WWW.STEPHENHENNING.COM

Top: *Savannah Sunset,* acrylic on canvas, 49" x 69".
Bottom: *Between Hawk and Mallard,* acrylic on canvas, 36" x 66".

173

# DOUGLAS HYSLOP

2532 GREGORY STREET ■ MADISON, WI 53711
TEL 608-263-6560 ■ TEL 608-238-3186 ■ E-MAIL DBHYSLOP@WISC.EDU

Top left: *Pianist & Ballerina*, pencil and acrylic on canvas, 48" × 36". Top right: *Spanish Fan Dance*,
pencil and acrylic on canvas, 60" × 48".  Bottom: *Donkey Girl*, pencil and acrylic on canvas, 60" × 48".

# KAREN IGLEHART

WATER MOUNTAIN STUDIO ■ 14 RYANS HILL ROAD ■ LEVERETT, MA 01054
TEL 413-549-4788 ■ E-MAIL INFO@KAREN-IGLEHART.COM ■ WWW.KARENIGLEHART.COM

*Remembering Nova Scotia*, 2007, oil and graphite on canvas, 40"H x 30"W.  Photograph: Stephen Petegorsky.

# CAROLINE JASPER

CAROLINE JASPER STUDIO ■ 796 BOUNDARY BOULEVARD ■ ROTONDA WEST, FL 33947
TEL 941-698-0718 ■ FAX 941-698-0801 ■ E-MAIL JASPERINC@MINDSPRING.COM ■ WWW.CAROLINEJASPER.COM

Top: *Rush*, oil on canvas, 30" × 40", giclée prints available.
Bottom: *Light Links*, oil on canvas, 24" × 36", giclée prints available.

# NICOLETTE JELEN

PO 2778 49 BAYVIEW AVENUE ■ SAG HARBOR, NY 11963 ■ TEL 631-725-2385
TEL 631-793-3360 ■ E-MAIL NICOLETTE.JELEN@VERIZON.NET ■ WWW.NICOLETTEJELEN.NET

Top: *Mountain View,* 2007, oil on paper, image: 14" × 22", paper: 24" × 30".
Bottom: *The Inlet,* 2007, oil on paper, image: 26" × 34", paper: 30" × 40".

# HOLLY KATZ

429 GREENWICH STREET ▨ NEW YORK, NY 10013 ▨ TEL 212-431-9555
FAX 212-343-9194 ▨ E-MAIL HOLLYMEREDITHKATZ@YAHOO.COM

Top: *Red Sunset*, 2005, oil, 60" x 60".  Bottom left: *Untitled*, 1998, oil, 96" x 72".
Bottom right: *Adobe I*, 1998, oil, 85" x 76".  Photographs: Tom Ligamari.

# ANNE KESSLER

PO BOX 147 ■ POINTARENA, CA 95468 ■ TEL 707-882-3224
E-MAIL AKESS@MCN.ORG ■ WWW.ANNEKESSLERPASTELS.COM

Top: *Agua de Oro*, pastel on paper, 24" x 36".  Bottom left: *Light Over Water*, pastel on paper, 36" x 24".
Bottom left: *A Frog's Eye View*, pastel on paper, 24" x 18".  Photographs: Ron Bolander.

# Stephen Henning

*"Selecting artwork for someone's home is a daunting task for some clients, and working with an individual artist can sometimes be an even greater challenge for the average art buyer! It is so important to find a professional artist that can come into the home like Stephen Henning did, see the space, and then recommend pieces that not only enhance the space, but also truly become a part of the home."*

—Allison Geiger, Art Consultant, Buffalo Fish Fine Art, Willmar, MN

*Sylvan Glen* ■ 2003 ■ New London, MN ■ acrylic on canvas ■ 62" x 104" ■ See more of Stephen's work on page 173.

180

Allison Geiger

# KROSLAK

GOODMAN ENTERTAINMENT, INC. ■ PO BOX 6583 ■ BRANDON, FL 33508-6010 ■ TEL 813-657-2500
TEL 813-215-3673 ■ FAX 813-662-9536 ■ E-MAIL GOODMANENTERTAIN@GMAIL.COM ■ WWW.KROSLAK-FRANCESCO.COM

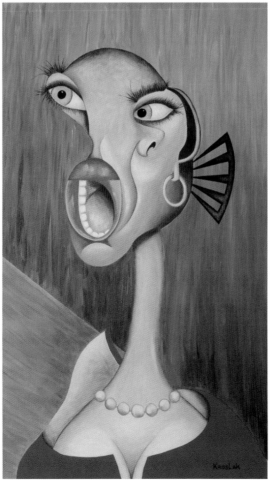

Top: *I Cried and No One Heard Me,* 2004, acrylic on canvas, 35" × 30".
Bottom: *Final Note,* 2005, acrylic on canvas, 32" × 20".

# MARLENE LENKER

LENKER STUDIO ■ 13 CROSSTREES HILL ROAD ■ ESSEX, CT 06426
TEL 860-767-2098 ■ E-MAIL LENKERART@PRODIGY.NET ■ WWW.MARLENELENKER.COM

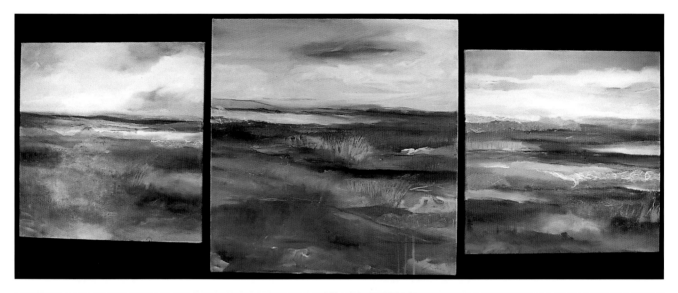

Top: *Meadow Spring*, canvas triptych, total size: 30" × 78", each panel: 24" × 24", 30" × 30", 24" × 24".

Bottom: *Sacred Journey*, canvas, 46" × 60".

# MICHELLE LINDBLOM

MICKART STUDIO ▥ 3316 HACKBERRY STREET ▥ BISMARCK, ND 58503
TEL 701-220-3808 ▥ E-MAIL MICKART@BIS.MIDCO.NET ▥ WWW.MICK-ART.COM

Top left: *Dancing Dialogues*, monotype, 24" x 18". Top right: *Release*, acrylic on canvas, 46" x 36".
Bottom left: *Circus Dialogue*, monotype, 24" x 18". Bottom right: *Rooted Dialogue*, acrylic on canvas, 34" x 30".

# LISA KESLER STUDIO

LISA KESLER ▓ 1801 WEST HENSLEY ROAD ▓ CHAMPAIGN, IL 61822
TEL 217-531-9956 ▓ E-MAIL KESLER.LISAK@GMAIL.COM ▓ WWW.LISAKESLER.COM

Top: *Morning Reverie*, 2007, acrylic on board, 10" × 30".
Bottom: *Meadow Repose*, 2007, acrylic on board, 10" × 30". Photographs: Bryan Heaton.

# CATHY LOCKE

STUDIO NORTH ▦ 560 TRUMBULL AVENUE ▦ NOVATO, CA 94947 ▦ TEL 415-893-9292
FAX 415-893-9464 ▦ E-MAIL CATHY@CATHYLOCKE.COM ▦ WWW.CATHYLOCKE.COM

*Yellow Light Orange Glads,* pastel, 30" x 20".   Photograph: Ming Studios.

# SHANNY LOTT

AUSTIN, TX ■ TEL 512-413-2061
E-MAIL SHANLOTT@TEXAS.NET ■ WWW.SHANNYSSTUDIO.COM

Top: *Number 3*, 2006, oils on canvas, 30" x 48".  Bottom: *1608 South Congress*, 2006, oils on canvas, 36" x 48".  Photographs: David Grimes.

# ELISE MILLS

ART BY ELISE ■ PO BOX 717 ■ RIDGEFIELD, CT 06877
TEL 914-841-1683 ■ E-MAIL ELISEMILLS@SNET.NET ■ WWW.ELISEMILLS.COM

Top left: *Transcendent Pond,* 2006, oil on linen, 30" × 30". Top right: *Wave of Light on Lily,* oil on linen, 40" × 40".
Bottom left: *Essence of the Reflective Flame,* oil on linen, 30" × 30".  Bottom Right: *Returning to the Path of Light,* 2007, oil on linen, 40" × 40".  Photographs: Color Group.

# BONNIE MINCU

20 EAST NINTH STREET #3J ■ NEW YORK, NY 10003 ■ TEL 212-614-7317
E-MAIL BONNIE@BONNIEMINCU.COM ■ WWW.MINCU-STUDIO.COM

Top: *Protection of the Castle*, 2006, New York, NY, oil on linen, 24" x 30".
Bottom: *Tuscan Hills Summer*, 2006, New York, NY, oil on panel, 24" x 36". Photographs: Osio Brown Editions.

# JILL MUSSER

SUNDANCE STUDIO ■ 1535 APPLE VALLEY ROAD ■ LYONS, CO 80540
TEL 303-823-5121 ■ E-MAIL JILLMUSSER@MAIL.COM ■ WWW.JILLMUSSER.COM

Top: *Leeks, Radishes and Purple Cabbage*, 2006, oil on canvas, 12" x 24". Center: *Granny Smiths and a Gala*, 2006, oil on canvas, 12" x 24". Bottom: *Lavender Garden*, 2006, oil on canvas, 36" x 48". Photographs: Ken Sanville.

# SRI PRABHA

TEL 510-517-4801 ■ E-MAIL SRI@SRIPRABHA.COM ■ WWW.SRIPRABHA.COM

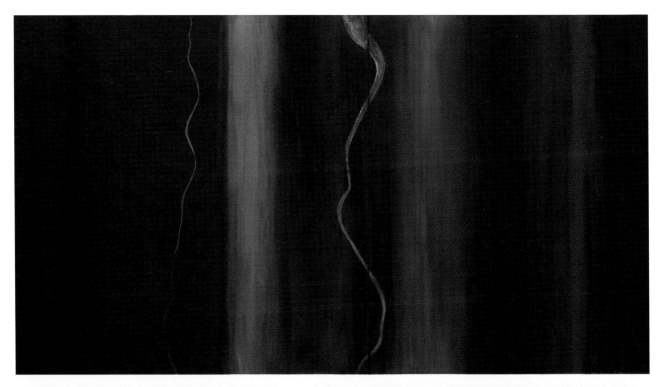

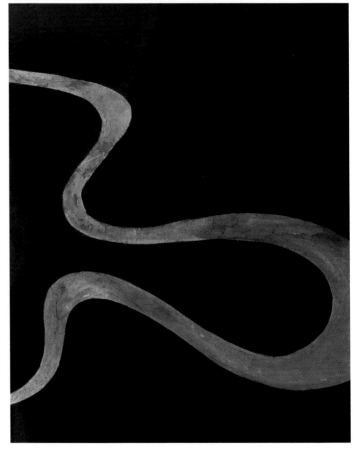

Top: *Inner Radiancy III*, 2007, acrylic and gold leaf on canvas, 30" x 54" diptych. Bottom left: *Inner Radiancy I*, 2007, acrylic and gold leaf on canvas, 60" x 40" diptych. Bottom right: *Stream of Consciousness II*, 2007, acrylic and gold leaf on canvas, 30" x 24". Select works available as giclées on paper or canvas.

# STEVEN RHUDE

STEVEN RHUDE FINE ART ■ 176 LINCOLN STREET ■ LUNENBURG, NS B0J 2C0 ■ CANADA ■ TEL 902-634-3870
TEL 902-640-3024 ■ E-MAIL STEVENRHUDE@NS.SYMPATICO.CA ■ WWW.STEVENRHUDEFINEART.COM

Top: *Fish House on a Road*, oil on canvas, 30" × 40".
Bottom: *Boat on a Road*, oil on canvas, 36" × 50".

# RICHARD HALL FINE ART

RICHARD HALL ■ 5130 EAST EMILE ZOLA AVENUE ■ SCOTTSDALE, AZ 85254 ■ TEL 602-819-7199
TEL 480-229-5755 ■ E-MAIL RICHARDHALLFINEART@COX.NET ■ WWW.RICHARDHALLFINEART.COM

*Morning Glory*, 2007, oil on canvas, 30" x 30".  Photograph: Tom Jordan.

# KIM RODY

FISHARTISTA® ■ 418 SE KRUEGER PARKWAY ■ STUART, FL 34996
TEL 772-223-7378 ■ E-MAIL KIM@RODY.COM ■ WWW.RODY.COM ■ WWW.FISHARTISTA.COM

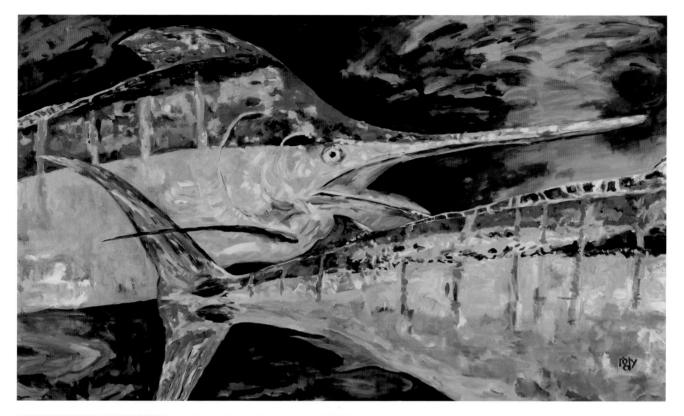

Top: *Tandem*, 2007, acrylic on canvas, 44" x 76". Photograph: Alan Carlisle.
Bottom: *Blue Striped Grunts*, 2003, acrylic on canvas, 43" x 76". Photograph: Robert Nelson.

# URSULA ROMA

LITTLE BEAR GRAPHICS ▪ 4236 BROOKSIDE AVENUE ▪ CINCINNATI, OH 45223
TEL 513-542-5722 ▪ TEL 513-885-5797 ▪ E-MAIL URSULAROMA@FUSE.NET ▪ WWW.URSULAROMA.COM

194                    *La Familia*, 36" x 36".  Photograph: Al Parrish.

# CAROLYN SCHLAM

CAROLYN SCHLAM STUDIO ◼ 534 NE 92ND STREET ◼ MIAMI SHORES, FL 33138 ◼ TEL 305-756-9330
TEL 786-897-2276 ◼ E-MAIL CAROLYNSCHLAM@AOL.COM ◼ WWW.CAROLYNSCHLAM.COM

Left: *Family Portrait,* oil on canvas, 56" x 50".  Top right: *Tango Dancer,* ink and crayon, 24" x 18".  Bottom right: *Red Ribbon,* ink and crayon, 24" x 18".

# YVETTE SIKORSKY

YVETTE SIKORSKY STUDIO ■ PO BOX 146 ■ MOHEGAN LAKE, NY 10547-0146 ■ TEL 914-737-5167

*Meditation II*, 2007, Weschester, NY, acrylic, 48" × 36".
Photograph: Howard Copland, Peekskill, NY 10566.

# SELENE SMERLING

32 NORTH DUTCHER STREET ■ IRVINGTON, NY 10533 ■ TEL/FAX 914-231-9265
E-MAIL SELENESMERLING@YAHOO.COM ■ WWW.SELENESMERLING.COM

*Dresden*, 2006, oil on paper, 30" × 22".  Photograph: John Maggiotto.

# SARAH SOLIE

TEL 920-366-7130 ■ E-MAIL SSOLIE@ATHENET.NET ■ WWW.SARAHSOLIE.COM

Top left: *Barn and Silo,* 2007, acrylic on board, 7" × 5". Top right: *Barn Near Plum City,* 2007, acrylic on board, 17" × 14".
Bottom: *Side of Barn,* 2002, acrylic on board. Photographs: Geoffrey Cook.

# STEPHANIE STANLEY

TEL 305-942-6628 ■ WWW.STEPHANIESTANLEY.COM

Top: *Lemon Yellow Sky,* oil, 30" × 48" × 1".
Bottom: *Blues,* 30" × 40" × 2".

# KRISTINE SULLIVAN

1562 MAIN ROAD ◼ GRANVILLE, MA 01034 ◼ TEL 413-357-6343
E-MAIL KRISTINE@KJSFINEARTS.COM ◼ WWW.KJSFINEARTS.COM

200

*Marcy's Scarf*, acrylic, 36" x 24".

# GWEN PEINE TOOMALATAI

TOOMALATAI STUDIO ▦ PO BOX 12787 ▦ OGDEN, UT 84412-2787 ▦ TEL 866-625-2824
FAX 801-782-6864 ▦ E-MAIL GWEN@TOOMALATAI.COM ▦ WWW.TOOMALATAI.COM

*Spring of Living Water*, oil on panel, 24" x 24". Photograph: Colton Rowland.

# STEPHANIE TORAL

STEPHANIE TORAL ART & DESIGN ■ 1235 WEST GOLF ROAD ■ LIBERTYVILLE, IL 60048
TEL/FAX 847-918-1988 ■ E-MAIL STEPHANIETORAL@COMCAST.NET ■ WWW.STEPHANIETORAL.COM

*The Four Seasons*, 2006, watercolor, series of four 10" x 7" paintings; prints also available.

# RACHEL TRIBBLE

1859 SW CRANE CREEK AVENUE ■ PALM CITY, FL 34990
TEL 772-708-8400 ■ E-MAIL INFO@RACHELTRIBBLE.COM ■ WWW.RACHELTRIBBLE.COM

Top: *Mexico*, 2004, watercolor, 14" x 10". Bottom: *Crescent*, 2004, watercolor, 14" x 10". Original artwork available in small, large, and mural sizes. Limited-edition giclée prints available in small and large sizes. Exclusive limited-edition mural-size giclée prints also available.

# JANE TROUP

1108 SOUTH PICKWICK AVENUE ■ SPRINGFIELD, MO 65804 ■ TEL 417-225-8556
TEL 417-865-3559 ■ E-MAIL JANETROUP@SBCGLOBAL.NET ■ WWW.JANETROUP.COM

*Tree of Life*, 2006, oil on canvas, 54" x 68".  Photograph: Rockafellow Photography.

# TUNSTULL

TUNSTULL STUDIO ■ 627 ROUTE 23 ■ CRARYVILLE, NY 12521 ■ TEL 518-851-3378
E-MAIL TUNSTULLSTUDIO@AOL.COM ■ WWW.TUNSTULLSTUDIO.COM

Top: *Summer Lights*, 24"H x 48"W.  Bottom: *Lady in Blue*, 30"H x 36"W.  Photographs: Nancy Donskoj.

# ELLEN WOODS

1219 ROAD 112 ■ CARBONDALE, CO 81623 ■ TEL 970-963-0398 ■ FAX 970-963-6057
E-MAIL ELLWOODS_@MSN.COM ■ WWW.ARTISTSREGISTER.COM/ARTISTS/CO723

Top: *Ranch Landscape*, oil on canvas, 48" x 42".
Bottom: *Composed Landscape*, oil on canvas, 48" x 48".

# CHIN YUEN

CHIN YUEN ART ■ 1112 RENO STREET ■ VICTORIA, BC V9A 4B6 ■ CANADA ■ TEL 250-381-1688
FAX 250-381-1687 ■ E-MAIL CHIN@CHINYUENART.COM ■ WWW.CHINYUENART.COM

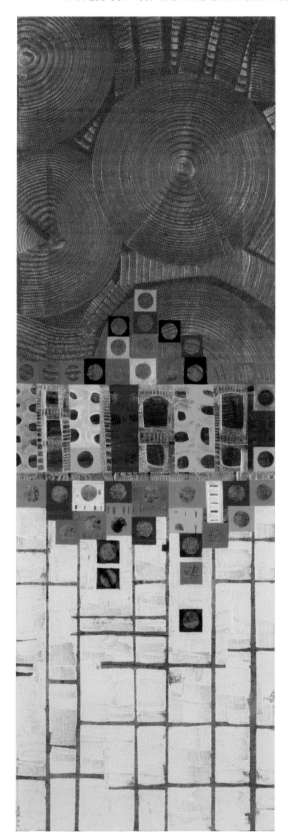 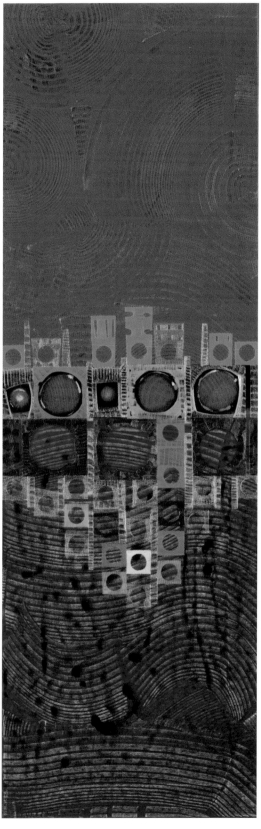

Left: *May #1 – 07*, acrylic on canvas, 36" x 12".
Right: *May #2 – 07*, acrylic on canvas, 36" x 12".  Photographs: Destrube Photography.

# KURT DANIEL ZIVELONGHI

5820 SPINNAKER COVE ROAD ▨ MIDLOTHIAN, VA 23112 ▨ TEL 804-739-7526
E-MAIL KURT_ZIVELONGHI@YAHOO.COM ▨ WWW.KURTDANIELGALLERIES.COM

Top: *Symphony in Red*, 2006, oil on canvas, 24" × 20".
Bottom: *Study for the Golden City*, 2006, pastel on paper, 12" × 19".

# PRINTS

# Shanny Lott

*"This painting evokes a surreal emotion. The dual image of boats and dolphins makes my brain dynamically flip-flop. I get pleasure visualizing each of the images."*

— Bob Paluck, homeowner

*Zilker Dolphins* ■ 2005 ■ Dallas, TX ■ oil on canvas with stainless steel frame ■ 39" x 104" ■ See more of Shanny's work on page 186.

Bob Paluck

# BARBARA K. BUER

5438 OXFORD DRIVE ■ MECHANICSBURG, PA 17055 ■ TEL 717-697-6505
TEL 941-575-0789 ■ E-MAIL FLWRBKB@AOL.COM ■ WWW.BKBFLORALART.COM

Top: *One White Peony*, giclée print of an original oil.
Bottom: *Fjord Patterns #1*, giclée print of an original oil.  Photographs: J. Arthur Davis.

# FRAN BULL

FRAN BULL STUDIO ■ PO BOX 401 ■ BRANDON, VT 05733
TEL 802-247-0125 ■ E-MAIL FRANBULL@FRANBULL.COM ■ WWW.FRANBULL.COM

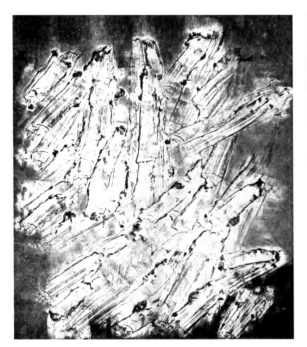

Top left: *Rastros 2* (negative), 2006, acrylic plate, handmade paper, paper: 27" × 25", plate: 19.5" × 17.5".
Top right: *Rastros 3a* (positive), 2006, acrylic plate, handmade paper, paper: 25" × 27", plate: 19.5" × 19.5". Bottom left: *Rastros 2a* (positive), 2006, acrylic plate, handmade paper,
paper: 25" × 27", plate: 19.5" × 19.5". Bottom right: *Rastros 4* (negative), 2006, acrylic plate, handmade paper, paper: 27" × 25", plate: 19.5" × 17.5". Photographs: Ernie Longey..

# FRAN BULL

FRAN BULL STUDIO ■ PO BOX 401 ■ BRANDON, VT 05733
TEL 802-247-0125 ■ E-MAIL FRANBULL@FRANBULL.COM ■ WWW.FRANBULL.COM

Top left: *Rastros 4a* (positive), 2006, acrylic plate, handmade paper, paper: 27" × 25", plate: 19.5" × 17.5".
Top right: *Rastros 6a* (positive), 2006, acrylic plate, handmade paper, paper: 25" × 27", plate: 19.5" × 19.5". Bottom left: *Rastros 5a* (positive), 2006, acrylic plate, handmade paper, paper: 27"× 25'', plate: 19.5" × 17.5". Bottom right: *Rastros 10a* (positive), 2006, acrylic plate, handmade paper, paper: 25" × 27", plate: 17.5" × 19.5". Photographs: Ernie Longey.

213

# CHERI FREUND

PIXEL ARTIST ■ 2207 NAPA TRAIL ■ WAUKESHA, WI 53188
TEL 206-850-0610 ■ E-MAIL CHERI@PIXEL-ARTIST.COM ■ WWW.PIXEL-ARTIST.COM

*Petal Swirl*, giclée on canvas, 30" × 30". Inset: *Carrie's String*, giclée on canvas, 36" × 36".

# MEREDITH MacLEOD

7712 HELLMAN ROAD ▪ CLINTON, WA 98236 ▪ TEL 360-579-3079 ▪ FAX 360-579-1060
E-MAIL CBAYTILE@WHIDBEY.COM ▪ WWW.MEREDITHMACLEODARTIST.COM

Top left: Hand-painted, fused glass tile, 10" × 8".  Right: *Motif #18* (detail), mixed-media print, 25.5" × 18".
Bottom left: *Motif #15*, mixed-media print, 25.5" × 18".

215

# MARLIES MERK NAJAKA

241 CENTRAL PARK WEST ■ NEW YORK, NY 10024 ■ TEL 212-580-0058
E-MAIL NAJAKA@GMAIL.COM ■ WWW.WATERCOLOR-PAINTINGS.COM

*Capistrano*, giclée on watercolor paper, image: 22" × 30", limited edition.

# PATTI MOLLICA FINE ART STUDIO

PATTI MOLLICA ■ 990 BRADLEY HILL ROAD ■ NYACK, NY 10960
TEL 845-405-1768 ■ E-MAIL PMOLLICA@OPTONLINE.NET ■ WWW.MOLLICASTUDIO.COM

*Soho Fire Escapes*, giclée on canvas, up to 6' × 4', original painting, oil on canvas, is available 48" × 36".

# JANE STERRETT

JANE STERRETT STUDIO ■ 536 GRAND STREET ■ HOBOKEN, NJ 07030
TEL 201-656-5979 ■ E-MAIL JANE@JANESTERRETT.COM ■ WWW.JANESTERRETT.COM

Top left: *Schoolyard Lily*, 2007. Top right: *Wild Iris*, 2007.
Bottom: *Sea Side Memories*, 2007. All available in various sizes as giclée prints.

# BARBARA ZINKEL

BARBARA ZINKEL EDITIONS ■ 333 PILGRIM ■ BIRMINGHAM, MI 48009
TEL 248-642-9789 ■ FAX 248-642-8374 ■ E-MAIL BZINKEL@AOL.COM

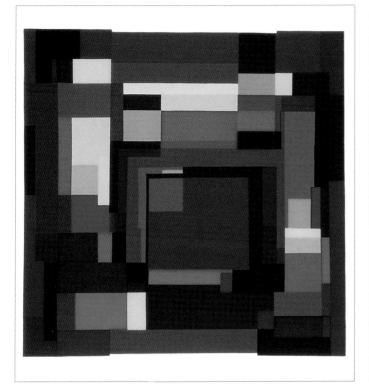

Top left: *Reflections*, serigraph print, 42"H × 40"W, edition of 250. Top right: *Wildwood*, serigraph print, 38"H × 32"W, edition of 250.
Bottom: *BZ-R104*, custom wool area rug, professionally hand-woven and hand-carved, 9.5' × 12', additional larger sizes available.

# Kristine Sullivan

"Kristine showed me this painting, and I just fell in love with it. We live in an antique house entirely covered in pumpkin pine. It's amazing how this wonderful, happy art just makes our days sunnier and brighter in New England. I think Kristine paints with a wonderful sense of color and humor."

— Homeowner

*Vertigo* ■ 2000 ■ Westfield, MA ■ gouache and oil pastels on paper ■ 54"H x 36"W ■ See more of Kristine's work on page 200.

# FINE ART PHOTOGRAPHY

# CÉSAR

CÉSAR PAREDES STUDIO ■ 601 NE 36TH STREET SUITE 2101 ■ MIAMI, FL 33137
TEL 786-522-8966 ■ E-MAIL CESAR@ZARPA.COM ■ WWW.ZARPA.COM

Top: *Crooked Lake 76A.*  Bottom left: *Water Lilly Blue 64.*  Bottom right: *Sea of Galilee 78B.*

# JOY DOHERTY

ORGANIC IMAGERY ■ 648 HYMETTUS AVENUE ■ ENCINITAS, CA 92024 ■ TEL 760-415-8285
FAX 760-942-0270 ■ E-MAIL JOY@ORGANICIMAGERY.COM ■ WWW.ORGANICIMAGERY.COM

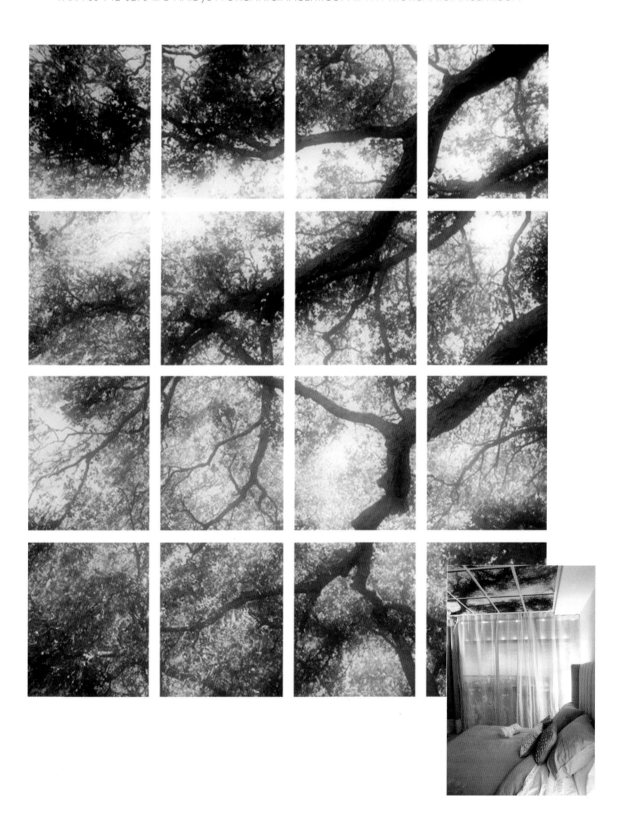

*Tree Canopy*, 2007, CityMark/Aperture Sales Office, San Diego, CA, photographic image on Sintra panels,
each panel: 21.5" x 26"; total size: 92" x 110". Available in panel sets of six, nine, twelve, or sixteen.

# KELLY FITZGERALD

KELLY FITZGERALD PHOTOGRAPHY ■ 1357 MONUMENT TRAIL DRIVE ■ CHULA VISTA, CA 91915
TEL 619-934-6608 ■ E-MAIL INFO@KELLYFITZGERALDPHOTO.COM ■ WWW.KELLYFITZGERALDPHOTO.COM

Top: *Bodie House*, 2006, limited-edition print from the *California Sierra* series.
Bottom: *Bank and Saloon*, 2006, limited-edition print from the *California Sierra* series.

# JOE GEMIGNANI

VISUAL IMPRESSIONS, INC. ■ MIAMI, FL ■ ASHEVILLE, NC ■ TEL 954-832-0800
TEL 954-328-9563 ■ E-MAIL GEMIG@BELLSOUTH.NET ■ WWW.VISUALIMPRESSIONSART.COM

Top: *Just Umbrellas*, 2006, Polaroid art, giclée print in sizes from 10" x 10" to 40" x 40".
Bottom: *Mother & Child*, 2006, Polaroid art, giclée print in sizes from 10" x 10" to 40" x 40".

The Guild® Sourcebook of Residential Art 6. © 2008 The Guild, Inc.

# HEMBROUGH GALLERY

DORIS K. HEMBROUGH ■ 103 WEST AMELIA ■ CASSVILLE, WI 53806 ■ TEL 608-575-7750
FAX 608-274-5845 ■ E-MAIL INFO@HEMBROUGHGALLERY.COM ■ WWW.HEMBROUGHGALLERY.COM

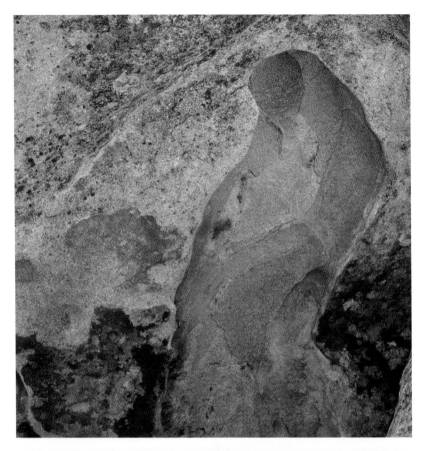

Top: *Idaho Woman*, photograph, 25" x 25".
Bottom: *Untitled*, New Mexico, photograph, 24.5" x 24.5".

# ELIZABETH HOLMES

333 EAST 23RD STREET 8LL ■ NEW YORK, NY 10010 ■ TEL 212-679-2433
E-MAIL EJHOLMES@RCN.COM ■ WWW.ELIZABETHJHOLMES.COM

Top: *Bird Watching*, hand-colored infrared photograph, 16" x 20" and 20" x 24".
Bottom: *Lifeguard Stand II*, hand-colored infrared photograph, 16" x 20" and 20" x 24".

# JL SULLIVAN PHOTOGRAPHY

JILL SULLIVAN ■ 100 SUNFLOWER TRAIL ■ PISGAH FOREST, NC 28768 ■ TEL 828-877-4121
TEL 828-553-7155 ■ FAX 828-877-4123 ■ E-MAIL JLS@JLSULLIVANPHOTO.COM ■ WWW.JLSULLIVANPHOTO.COM

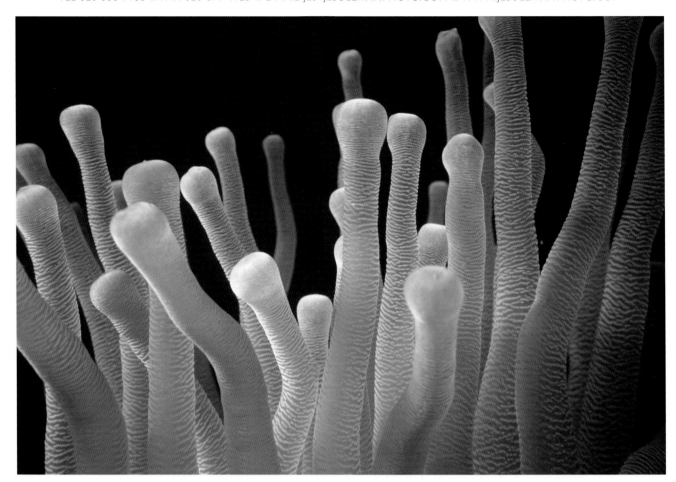

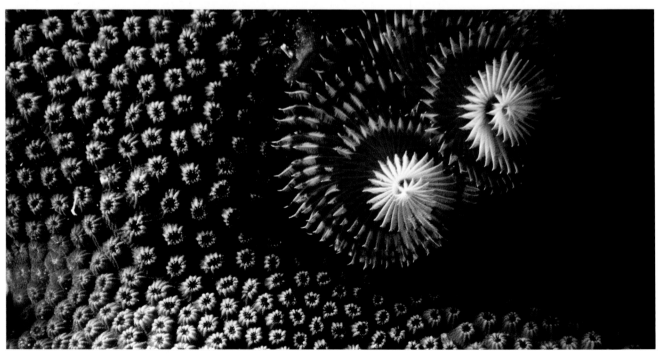

Top: *Alien Fingers*, archival fine art print from macro 35mm film.  Bottom: *Christmas Trees*, archival fine art print from macro 35mm film.
Archival fine art prints available in image sizes from 5" x 7" to 18" x 24", matted and framed to standard studio design or requested specification.

228

# ADAM JAHIEL

ADAM JAHIEL—PHOTOGRAPHER ■ PO BOX 501 ■ 90 NORTH PINEY ROAD ■ STORY, WY 82842
TEL 307-683-2862 ■ FAX 307-683-2730 ■ E-MAIL AJAHIEL@FIBERPIPE.NET ■ WWW.ADAMJAHIEL.COM

*Horse Shadows,* 1990, Spanish Ranch, NV, platinum print.

# JERRY MADER PHOTOGRAPHIC IMAGERY

JERRY MADER ■ TOLT RIVER STUDIOS ■ 8100 361ST AVENUE NE ■ CARNATION, WA 98014
TEL 425-333-6989 ■ E-MAIL JERRY@MADERPHOTO.COM ■ WWW.MADERPHOTO.COM

Top: *Amish Church Yard, Lancaster, PA*, silver gelatin print, 8" × 20". Bottom left: *Frosty Barn*, carbon image on fused and etched glass, 18" × 21". Bottom right: *Waukeena Falls, OR*, carbon image on fused and etched glass, 22" × 14".

# JOEL ANDERSON PHOTOGRAPHY

JOEL ANDERSON ▦ 337 WEST MIDDLE ROAD ▦ LYKENS, PA 17048 ▦ TEL 717-365-3376
E-MAIL JOEL@JOELANDERSONPHOTO.COM ▦ WWW.JOELANDERSONPHOTO.COM

Top left: *Mystic Forest*, 1996, New Mexico, type C sepia photograph, 20" × 24". Top right: *Base of Vernal Falls*, 1993, Yosemite, type C sepia photograph, 20" × 24".
Bottom left: *Nesting Birds*, 2005, Skelling Island, Ireland, type C color photograph, 20" × 20". Bottom right: *Double Arch Alcove*, 1996, Utah, type C color photograph, 20" × 20".

# KIM ELLEN KAUFFMAN

SYNECDOCHE STUDIO ■ 712 TERMINAL ROAD ■ LANSING, MI 48906
TEL/FAX 517-321-2815 ■ E-MAIL KIM@SYNECDOCHESTUDIO.COM ■ WWW.SYNECDOCHESTUDIO.COM

*Harmony*, from a series of limited-edition photo collages from multiple scans of original objects.

# JUDY MANDOLF

STUDIO ONE ■ 2945 DENVER STREET ■ SAN DIEGO, CA 92117 ■ TEL 619-276-5760
FAX 619-276-5787 ■ E-MAIL JUDYMANDOLF@YAHOO.COM ■ WWW.JUDYMANDOLF.COM

Top: *Winter Sun,* 2007, San Diego, giclée on wood panel, 24" x 36". Bottom left: *Lawn Bowling,* 2007, San Diego, giclée on wood panel, 24" x 36". Bottom right: *Sea Grass,* 2007, San Diego, giclée on wood panel, 24" x 36".v

# PJ BOYLAN PHOTOGRAPHY

PJ BOYLAN ▨ MILWAUKEE, WI ▨ TEL 414-530-0326 ▨ FAX 414-357-9499
E-MAIL MAIL@PJBOYLANPHOTOGRAPHY.COM ▨ WWW.PJBOYLANPHOTOGRAPHY.COM

234

Top: *Sanctum*, 2002. Bottom: *Mission Wall #4*, 2006. Photograph: Leo Tseng.

# RACHAEL WALLER PHOTOGRAPHY

RACHAEL WALLER ■ 35425 SIERRA VISTA DRIVE ■ AGUA DULCE, CA 91390
TEL 661-268-1379 ■ E-MAIL RACHAEL@INDIANSTUNTS.COM ■ WWW.INDIANSTUNTS.COM

Top: *Jule & Elvis*, black-and-white photograph, prints: 13" × 19", canvas: 18" × 36".
Bottom: *Back in Black*, black-and-white photograph, prints: 13" × 19", canvas: 16" × 24".

235

# LEITH A. ROHR

LEITH A. ROHR PHOTOGRAPHY ▦ 150 WEST MAPLE STREET #609 ▦ CHICAGO, IL 60610
TEL 312-587-7956 ▦ E-MAIL LAROHR@EARTHLINK.NET

Top: *Dawn, Washington Island, WI.*  Bottom: *Dream, Apollo Arch, Naxos, Greece.*

# DANIEL SROKA

DANIEL SROKA DESIGNS LLC ▩ 26 BLACKBERRY LANE ▩ MORRIS TOWNSHIP, NJ 07960
TEL/FAX 815-301-8836 ▩ E-MAIL DS@DANIELSROKA.COM ▩ WWW.DANIELSROKA.COM

Top: *Flight: Abstraction of a Maple Seed.*
Bottom: *Sun and Moon: Abstraction of Acorn Caps.*

# TRINITY SULLIVAN

TEL 208-757-9788 ■ E-MAIL TRIN@TRINITYSULLIVAN.COM ■ WWW.TRINITYSULLIVAN.COM

Top: *Earth*, 2007, from the *Ruggine Series*. Bottom: *Sky*, 2007, from the *Ruggine Series*.

# XAVIER NUEZ CONTEMPORARY PHOTOGRAPHY

XAVIER NUEZ ▇ PO BOX 1412 ▇ FREMONT, CA 94538
TEL 510-648-6810 ▇ E-MAIL X@NUEZ.COM ▇ WWW.NUEZ.COM

Top: *Alleys & Fire Escapes, no. 55, Blessed Light*, 1999, Toronto, ON, 12:30am, ultrachrome print, 32" x 40". Bottom left: *Alleys & Fire Escapes, no. 60, Canyons*, 2004, Chicago, IL, 10:30pm, ultrachrome print, 40" x 32". Bottom right: *Alleys & Fire Escapes, no. 50, Deliverance*, 1999, Toronto, ON, 10:00pm, ultrachrome print, 40" x 32".

239

# Patricia Dreher

*Lucca* ■ 2001 ■ Tiburon, CA ■ painted canvas floorcloth ■ main section: 12' x 16'
See more of Patricia's work on page 89.

*"In terms of what I've done to our residence in the last twenty years, this is our favorite decorative piece in the entire house. I get to walk on it every day and the maintenance is absolutely minimal. To collaborate with an artist who was willing to research the type of artwork we wanted and who could contribute her own artistic vision was just magical."*

— Homeowner

MIXED & OTHER MEDIA
WALL ART

# MAUDE ANDRADE

PO BOX 10472 ■ ALBUQUERQUE, NM 87184 ■ TEL 505-379-0208 ■ FAX 505-792-8064
E-MAIL MAUDEANDRADE@COMCAST.NET ■ WWW.MAUDE-ANDRADE.COM

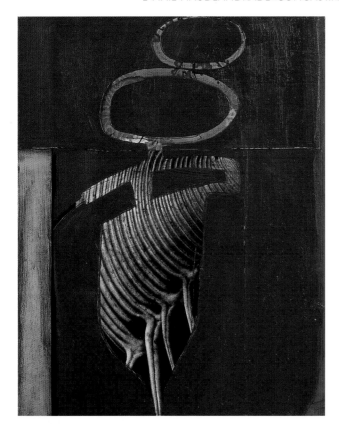 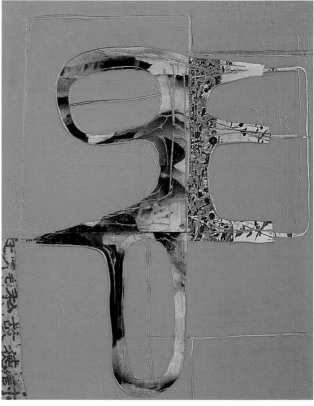

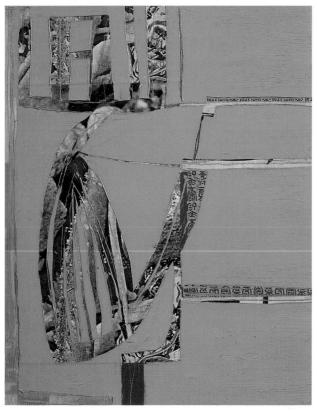 

Top left: *Night Swim*, mixed media on board, 10" × 8" × 2". Top right: *Waters Edge*, 10" × 8" × 2".
Bottom left: *Beach Rose*, 10" × 8" × 2". Bottom right: *Diatom*, 10" × 8" × 2". Photographs: Margot Geist.

# ART BY CARMEN

CARMEN GRAY ■ 10109 JACOB PLACE SUITE 203 ■ LAS VEGAS, NV 89144
TEL 702-419-2230 ■ FAX 702-202-3938 ■ E-MAIL CKIMAGE1@MAC.COM ■ WWW.CKIMAGE1.COM

Top: *Harmony II,* 2005, offices at The College Network, Las Vegas, NV, mixed media and acrylic on canvas, 36" x 48".
Bottom: *Untitled,* 2005, private residence, mixed media and acrylic on canvas, 36" x 60".  Photographs: Greg Preston.

# MYRA BURG

171 PIER AVENUE #353 ■ SANTA MONICA, CA 90405 ■ TEL 310-399-5040
TEL 310-780-0666 ■ E-MAIL MYRABURG@YAHOO.COM ■ WWW.MYRABURG.COM

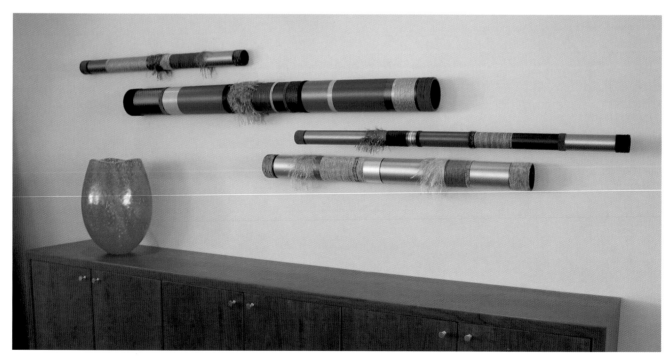

Top: left: *Quiet Oboes* in pick-up sticks configuration. Top right: *Quiet Oboes* in amber and cinnamon (detail), wrapped fiber over hollow core. Bottom: *Horizontal in Orange.*

Opposite page: *Quiet Oboes* in lipstick red and gold (detail). *Quiet Oboes* are available in any color, including custom, from 2" to 7" in diameter, and 2' to 7' in length, longer by request.

# MYRA BURG & LIZ CUMMINGS

171 PIER AVENUE #353 ■ SANTA MONICA, CA 90405 ■ TEL 310-399-5040 (MYRA)
TEL 877-249-2552 (LIZ) ■ WWW.MYRABURG.COM ■ WWW.LIZCUMMINGS.COM

Top: *Prismatic*, 60"H × 84"W.  Bottom left: *Interactive*, 60"H × 24"W.  Bottom right: *Inner Passion*, canvas total size: 60"H × 24"W.
Oil paintings with wrapped fiber over hollow core.  Photographs:  Barry Blau.

# DEBRA DRESLER

623 QUINLAN AVENUE NORTH ■ LAKELAND, MN 55043 ■ TEL 651-436-3663
FAX 651-436-3664 ■ E-MAIL DDRESLER@EARTHLINK.NET ■ WWW.DEBRADRESLER.COM

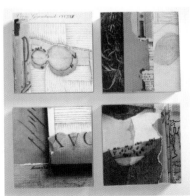
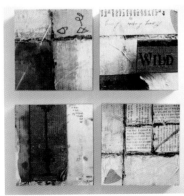

Top: *Be*, 2007, mixed media and acrylic paint, 16" × 20". Bottom: *Ladder* (left), *Lake* (center), and *Wild* (right), 2007, four canvas giclée archival prints on wood blocks, each block: 6" × 6" × 2", can be purchased individually or mixed and matched.

247

# K4 GLASSART

ALICIA AND BEATRIZ KELEMEN ■ 94 ANDERSON OAKS DRIVE ■ MARSHALL, NC 28753
TEL/FAX 828-649-1956 ■ E-MAIL KELEMENKUATRO@K4GLASSART.COM ■ WWW.K4GLASSART.COM

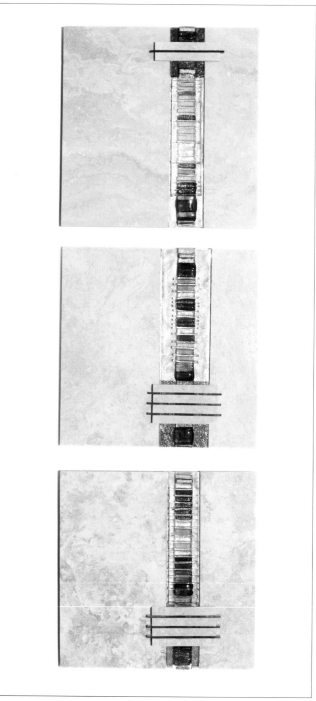

Left: *Maia*, mixed media, 29"H x 9"W. Right: *Arcoiris Triptych*, mixed-media wall piece, 36"H x 12"W. Photographs: Paul Jeremias.

# LINDA LEVITON

LINDA LEVITON SCULPTURE ▪ 1011 COLONY WAY ▪ COLUMBUS, OH 43235
TEL 614-433-7486 ▪ E-MAIL GUILD@LINDALEVITON.COM ▪ WWW.LINDALEVITON.COM

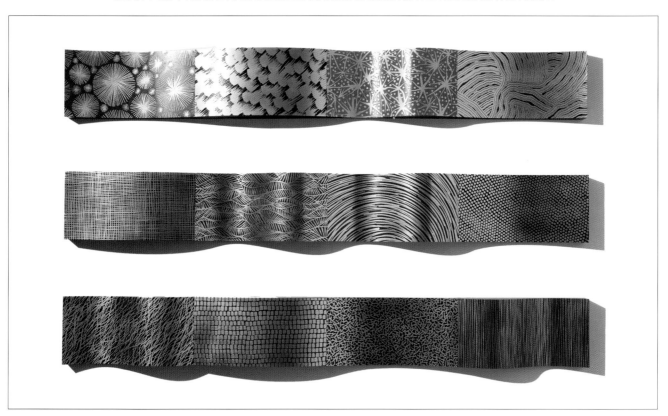

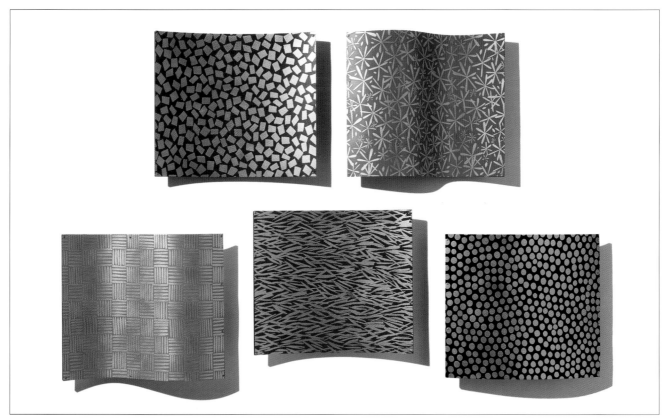

Top: *Patterns of Nature, Ribbon* series, copper, patina, paint, and wood, each ribbon: 7.75"H × 62"W × 4"D.
Bottom: *Patterns of Nature, Floating Wave* series, copper, patina, paint, and wood, each panel: 17"H × 21"W × 5"D. Photographs: Flashback Photography.

# ELISSA LIEBERMAN

LIEBERMAN STUDIO ▦ 12467 CARMEL CAPE ▦ SAN DIEGO, CA 92130 ▦ TEL 619-888-3793
TEL 858-792-5781 ▦ E-MAIL LISSYJILL@YAHOO.COM ▦ WWW.ELISSALIEBERMAN.COM

Left: *Wall of Faces*, 2007, mixed media, 60" × 36", each panel: 12" × 12". Top right: *Wedding Tree*, 2006, mixed media on canvas, 36" × 48".
Bottom right: *New Park Rule*, 2006, oil on canvas, 36" × 36". Photographs: RJ Pennell.

# BARRY MIDDLETON

WOODSONGS ■ 3066 SUNSET LANE ■ SCHENECTADY, NY 12303
TEL 518-357-4737 ■ E-MAIL KODIAKBARR@AOL.COM ■ WWW.YOURWOODSONGS.COM

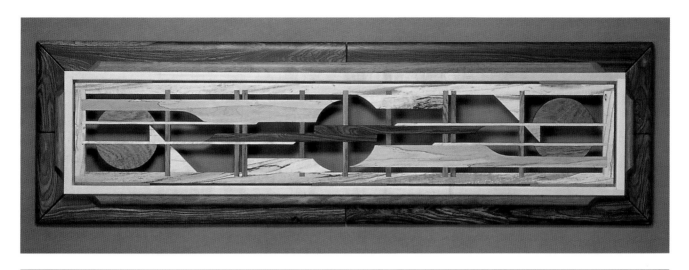

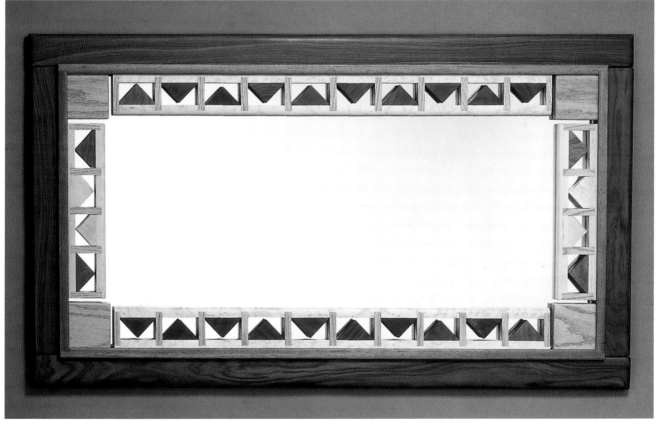

Top: *Sparrow*, wall sculpture, 2007, cocobolo, jatoba, and spalted maple.
Bottom: *Borders*, mirror, 2007, pauferro, cherry, bird's-eye maple.  Photographs: Stan Blanchard.

# Myra
## Burg

*"Myra's installation at the end of the hallway on a large wall is perfect. It is an attention-getter. The colors and textures are just right for our contemporary architecture. All our guests are intrigued by it and want to know how she did it. We love it!"*

— The Prebles, homeowners

*A Desert Bloom* ■ 2006 ■ Palm Desert, CA ■ wrapped fiber over hollow core ■ 7'H x 8'W x 15"D ■ See more of Myra's work on pages 244-246.

# RAVEN LUNATIC STUDIOS

KAMILLA WHITE ■ 829 NW 62ND STREET ■ SEATTLE, WA 98107
TEL 206-650-1263 ■ E-MAIL KAM@NEVERMORRIGAN.COM ■ WWW.NEVERMORRIGAN.COM

Top: *I Feel Pretty*, 2007, collage and colored pencil, 12" x 12". Bottom: *One Foot, Two Foot, Red Foot . . .*,
2007, collage and colored pencil, 16" x 20". Photographs: Art & Soul, Seattle, WA.

# RENEE DINAUER SCULPTURE

RENEE DINAUER ■ PO BOX 101032 ■ PALM BAY, FL 32910-1032 ■ TEL 321-223-1288
E-MAIL RDINAUER02@SPRINTPCS.COM ■ WWW.RENEEDINAUERSCULPTURE.COM

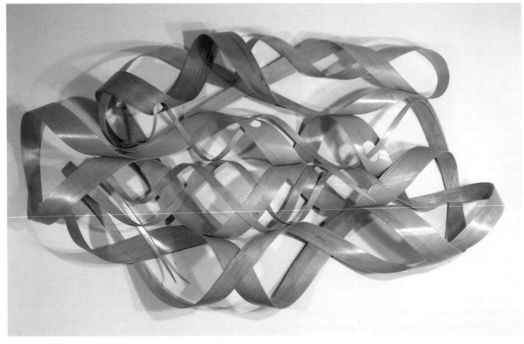

Top: *Crazola,* 2006, Houston, TX, wood sculpture, 39" x 48" x 9". Bottom: *Totally Blond,* Weston, FL, wood sculpture, 62" x 80" x 10".

# BETTE RIDGEWAY

RIDGEWAY STUDIO ■ SANTA FE, NM
E-MAIL BRIDGESFNM@AOL.COM ■ WWW.RIDGEWAYSTUDIO.COM

Top left: *Autumn Window.* Top center: *October.* Top right: *An Early Frost.*
Bottom: *Serengeti Storm,* acrylic with resin on steel.

# CRAIG ROBB

3470 SOUTH GRANT STREET ■ ENGLEWOOD, CO 80113
TEL 303-783-3659 ■ E-MAIL CRAIGER@4DV.NET ■ WWW.CRAIGROBB.COM

Top: *Rustle*, wood, steel, and root, 24" × 20" × 5".
Bottom: *Vapor*, wood, steel, cast iron, paper, graphite, and glass, 8" × 36" × 5".

# JUNO SKY

JUNO SKY STUDIO ▦ PO BOX 303 ▦ FINDLAY, OH 45839
TEL 419-422-7777 ▦ E-MAIL JUNOSKYART@AOL.COM ▦ WWW.JUNOSKYSTUDIO.COM

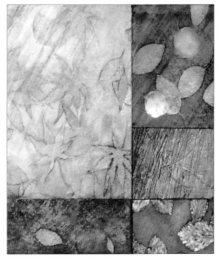

Top: *Seeking #4*, mixed media on canvas, 40" × 60".  Bottom left: *Brimming with Wonder #2*, mixed media on paper, 40" × 40".  Bottom center: *Foliage*, mixed media and gold leaf on paper; 20" × 20".  Bottom right: *Warm Breezes*, 2007, BVH Pavillion, three panels, each: 40" × 60".  Photographs: Adam Fulmer.

# MARY WILLIAMS

WILDWOOD ART ■ 7205 MIDDLEHAM PLACE ■ CASTLE ROCK, CO 80108 ■ TEL 303-688-2706
TEL 303-570-9435 ■ E-MAIL MWADART@COMCAST.NET ■ WWW.WILDWOODART.NET

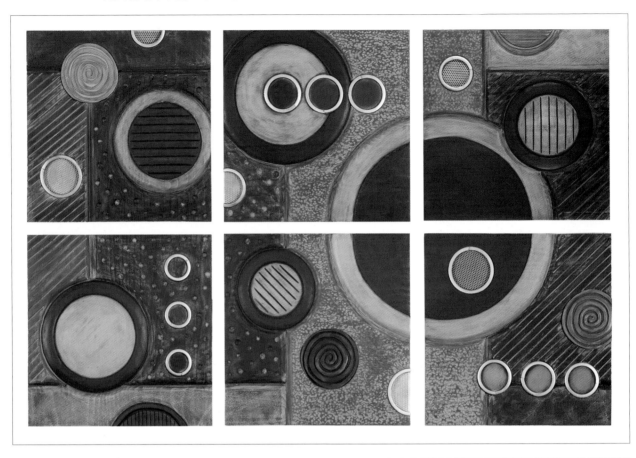

Top: *Beyond,* 2007, hand-carved poplar panels with acrylic and steel, 4' × 6'.
Bottom: *Eternal Renewal,* 2007, hand-carved poplar panels with acrylics, 3' × 5'.  Photographs: Dave Entrican.

# METAL WALL ART

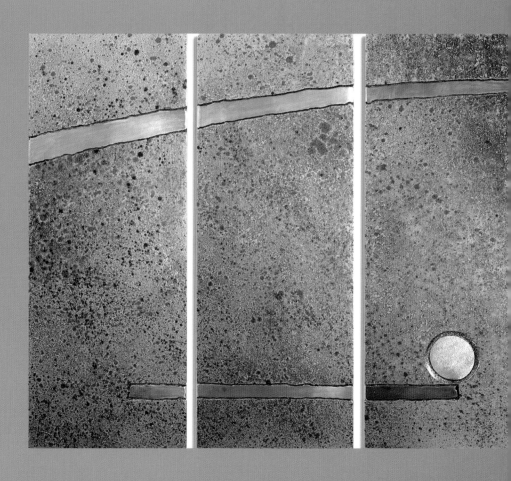

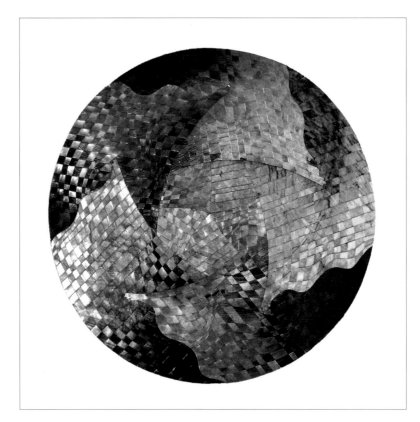

Top: *Peutad Mandala*, painted, woven copper layered on wood, 24"Dia.
Bottom: *Desert Shadows*, painted, woven copper folded on wood, 36" × 36" × 4".  Photograph: Kenneth Payne.

# JEAN MANDEBERG

114 SHERMAN STREET NW ■ OLYMPIA, WA 98502
TEL 360-943-5640 ■ E-MAIL JEANM44@EARTHLINK.NET

*Hopscotch*, private collection, found tin over wood, 22" × 17" × 1". Photograph: Roger Schreiber.

# SUSAN McGEHEE

METALLIC STRANDS ■ 540 23RD STREET ■ MANHATTAN BEACH, CA 90266
TEL 310-545-4112 ■ FAX 310-546-7152 ■ E-MAIL METALSTRANDS@AOL.COM ■ WWW.METALSTRANDS.COM

Top: *Shell Kimono*, 2007, 19" × 19" × 6". Bottom: *Beach Scrapbook Series: Manhattan Beach Pier*, 2007,
double-weave anodized aluminum wire and photo on canvas, 10" × 32" × 3". Photographs: Andrew Neuhart.

# BOB RICKARD

PO BOX 1360 ■ TAOS, NM 87571 ■ TEL 505-770-8287
E-MAIL BOB@BOBRICKARD.COM ■ WWW.BOBRICKARD.COM

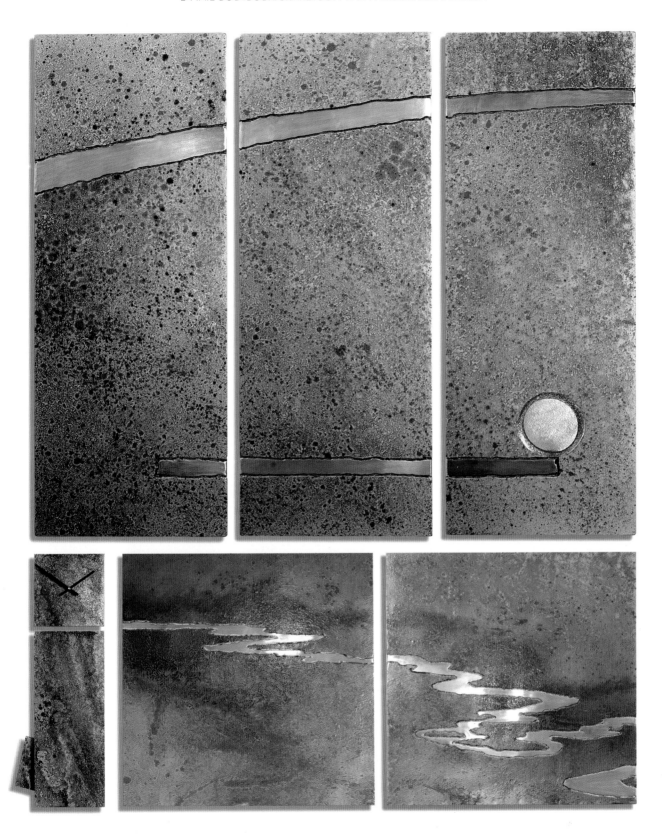

Top: *Lying Low*, 2006, dyed copper, bronze, and iron over aluminum, 29" x 36".  Bottom left: *Duet*, 2006, pendulum wall clock, dyed copper, bronze, and iron over aluminum, 24.5" x 7".  Bottom right: *Desert Passage*, 2007, dyed copper, bronze, and iron over aluminum, 24" x 50".

# JON MICHAEL ROUTE

PO BOX 378 ■ FREDERIC, WI 54837 ■ TEL 888-345-2602
E-MAIL JON@JONMICHAELROUTE.COM ■ WWW.JONMICHAELROUTE.COM

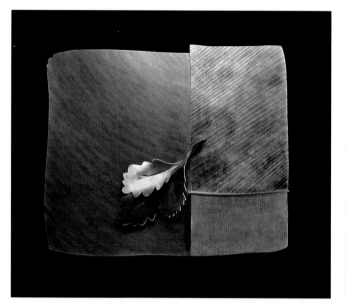 

Top left: *Oak Leaves IV*, 2007, pewter, copper, and brass, 20"H x 24.5"W x 2.25"D. Top right: *Lilac Landscape*, 2007, pewter, copper, and brass, 19"H x 14.5"W x 2.25"D. Bottom: *Bird and Wall*, 2006, pewter, copper, and brass, 22"H x 26"W x 2.75"D.

# JAMES T. RUSSELL

JAMES T. RUSSELL SCULPTURE ▦ 1930 LOMITA BOULEVARD ▦ LOMITA, CA 90717 ▦ TEL 310-326-0785
FAX 310-326-1470 ▦ E-MAIL JAMES@RUSSELLSCULPTURE.COM ▦ WWW.RUSSELLSCULPTURE.COM

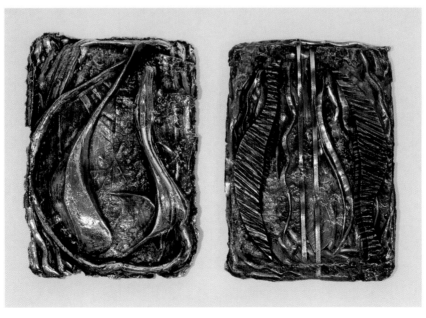

Top: *Relic 4*, 2007, cast stainless steel, 18" × 12".
Bottom: *Relic 3, Relic 1*, 2007, cast stainless steel, 12" × 9". Photographs: Satoshi Furukawa.

# JOHN E. STALLINGS

STALLINGS ART ■ 1020 WILLETT DRIVE ■ JOHNSTOWN, PA 15905
TEL 814-255-5013 ■ E-MAIL SCULPTURE@STALLINGSART.COM ■ WWW.STALLINGSART.COM

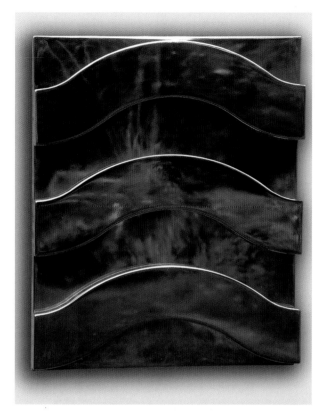

Top left: *Wave*, polished aluminum, 36" × 30".  Right: *The Sail*, polished aluminum, 7' × 1'.
Bottom left: *In and Out*, polished aluminum, 30" × 30".

# MURALS, TILES & WALL RELIEFS

# MARY LOU ALBERETTI

ALBERETTI STUDIOS ■ 16 POSSUM DRIVE ■ NEW FAIRFIELD, CT 06812 ■ TEL 203-746-1321
E-MAIL MLALBERETTI@SBCGLOBAL.NET ■ WWW.SOUTHERNCT.EDU/~ALBERETT/

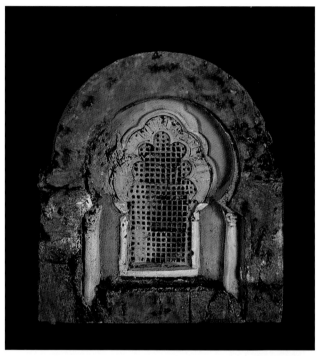

Top left: *Cuenca*, ceramic relief, 13" x 13" x 2". Top right: *Intrados*, ceramic relief, 15.5" x 14" x 2".
Bottom: *Chiarita*, ceramic relief, 18" x 25" x 2". Photographs: Bill Quinnell.

# ANNE OSHMAN MOSAICS

ANNE OSHMAN ■ 71 STONEBRIDGE ROAD ■ MONTCLAIR, NJ 07042
TEL 973-222-6937 ■ E-MAIL STUDIO@ANNEOSHMAN.COM ■ WWW.ANNEOSHMAN.COM

Left: *Miami Beach Mah Jong Club.* Photograph: Greg Leshe.
Right: *The Connoisseur,* 33" x 27.5". Photograph: Peter Jacobs.

# DOMSKY GLASS

BARBARA AND LARRY DOMSKY ■ 3720 WEST OQUENDO SUITE #104 ■ LAS VEGAS, NV 89118
TEL 702-616-2830 ■ E-MAIL DOMSKYGLASS@AOL.COM ■ WWW.DOMSKYGLASS.COM

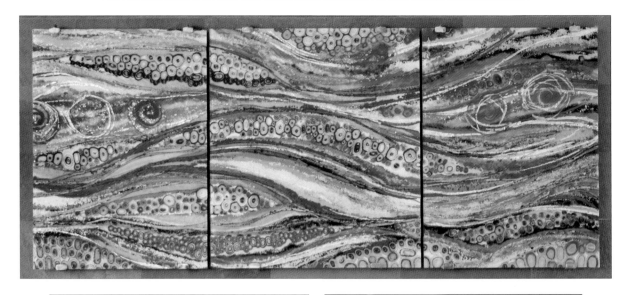

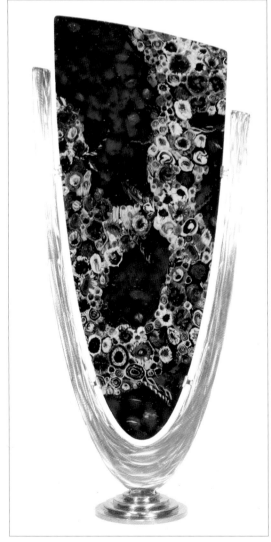

Top: *Tranquility*, private commission, hot-fusion glass painting, 48" x 102" x 1". Bottom left: *Deep Blue*, private commission, hot-fusion glass and steel sculpture, 5' x 23" x 1". Bottom right: *The Coral Reef*, hot-fusion glass painting, 84" x 42" x .5".

# KATHLEEN EGGERT

EGGERT GLASS ▪ 1918 EAST BEVERLY ROAD ▪ SHOREWOOD, WI 53211
TEL 414-962-0808 ▪ E-MAIL EGGERTGLASS@AOL.COM ▪ WWW.EGGERTGLASS.COM

Top: *Grapevines*, mural for backsplash, 2007, 12"H × 20"W.
Bottom: *Ferns and Leaves*, tile sampler, 16"H × 16"W.

# BONNIE FITZGERALD

MAVERICK MOSAICS ▨ 3401 HICKORY HILLS DRIVE ▨ OAKTON, VA 22124 ▨ TEL 703-716-4890
E-MAIL CONTACT@MAVERICKMOSAICS.COM ▨ WWW.MAVERICKMOSAICS.COM

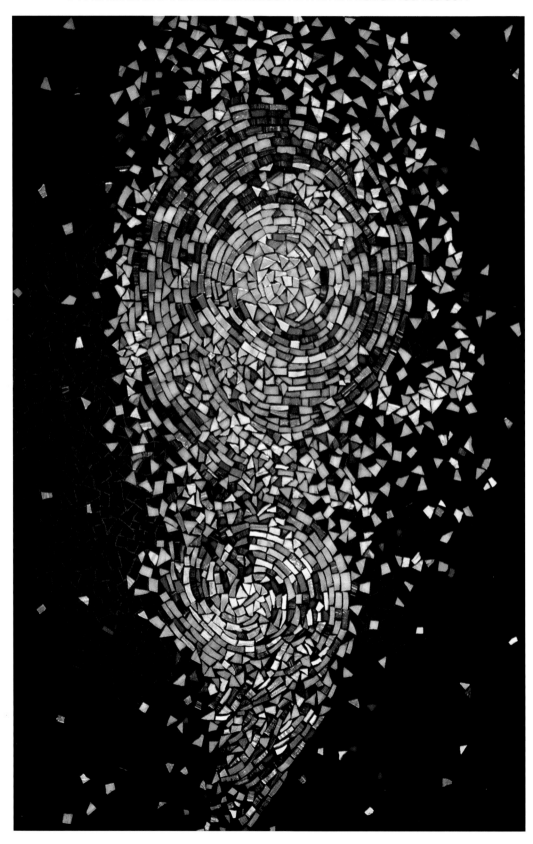

*Merging Galaxies*, 2007, private collection, hand-cut glass and gold mosaic, 42" x 32".

# GASCH DESIGN

MICHAEL GASCH ■ 1649 SUNFIELD STREET ■ MADISON, WI 53704 ■ TEL 608-469-7276
FAX 608-442-9831 ■ E-MAIL MIKEG@GASCHDESIGN.COM ■ WWW.GASCHDESIGN.COM

Top left: *Harvest*, 2006, Indian slate and copper, 30" × 42" × 1". Top right: *Harvest* (detail).
Bottom: *Wisconsin Morning*, 2005, Indian slate, Mankato limestone, and copper; 48" × 70" × 1". Photographs: Hymaphoto.com.

# ELISE GRAY

ELISE GRAY STUDIO ■ 1483 OGLETHORPE STREET ■ MACON, GA 31201
TEL 478-738-0438 ■ E-MAIL E_BGRAY@COX.NET ■ MEMBERS.COX.NET/ELISEGRAYART2

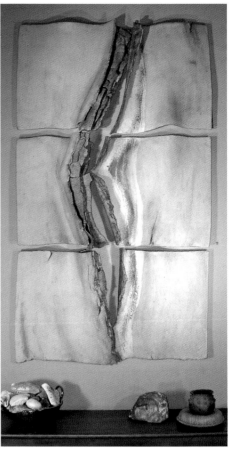

Left: *Gathering Storm*, 1995, ceramic, 72" × 45" × 9". Top right: *Mountain Stream I*, 2003, ceramic, 42" × 43" × 9".
Bottom right: *Formation: River Gorge*, 1983, Elise Gray Home, Macon, GA, ceramic, 67" × 41" × 6".

# JOAN ROTHCHILD HARDIN

HARDINTILES ■ 393 WEST BROADWAY #4 ■ NEW YORK, NY 10012 ■ TEL 212-966-9433
FAX 212-431-9196 ■ E-MAIL JOAN@HARDINTILES.COM ■ JRHARDIN@USA.NET ■ WWW.HARDINTILES.COM

*Harem Shower,* 2007, New York City, hand-painted art tiles among glass and ceramic commercial field tiles.  Photographs: Erik Lieber.

275

# RHONDA HEISLER

RHONDA HEISLER MOSAIC ART ▦ 8 STONE MOUNTAIN COURT ▦ SKILLMAN, NJ 08558 ▦ TEL 609-466-2231
FAX 609-466-9043 ▦ E-MAIL RJHEISLER@PATMEDIA.NET ▦ WWW.RHONDAHEISLERMOSAICART.COM

*Breakaway II*, a two-panel composition in hand-cut glass mosaic, each 54"H x 24"W.  Photographs: Ross Stout.

# IMAGO DEI, LLC

6817 FLINTLOCK ROAD SUITE A ▥ HOUSTON, TX 77040 ▥ TEL 713-466-9990
FAX 713-466-9998 ▥ E-MAIL INFO@IMAGODEIGALLERY.COM ▥ WWW.IMAGODEIGALLERY.COM

Left: *Sagrantino Di Montefalco*, 2007, acrylic on canvas, 36" x 48".
Right: *Northern Italia Trompe L'oeil*, 2005, acrylic on canvas, twelve panels: 4' x 12", one panel: 8' x 14'.

# JENSEN & MARINEAU CERAMICS

BARBARA JENSEN ■ MICK MARINEAU ■ 22017 NW BECK ROAD ■ PORTLAND, OR 97231 ■ TEL 503-621-3487
FAX 503-621-3297 ■ E-MAIL BJENSEN@JENSENANDMARINEAU.COM ■ WWW.JENSENANDMARINEAU.COM

Top: *Leaves & Vines*, glazed, carved earthenware mural, each tile: 6"; dragon inset tile: 7.5" × 9".
Bottom: *Vegetable Garden and Peonies*, kitchen wall and countertop, glazed, carved earthenware mural, each tile: 6".

# ELIZABETH MacDONALD

PO BOX 186 ■ BRIDGEWATER, CT 06752 ■ TEL 860-354-0594 ■ FAX 860-350-4052
E-MAIL EPMACD@EARTHLINK.NET ■ WWW.ELIZABETHMACDONALD.COM

*Color Study*, ceramic wallpiece, layered powdered pigments on textured stoneware, 36", limited edition.
Sculpture by Gerald Siciliano. Table by Neil Verplank. Photograph: Eric Ferguson.

# MITCH YUNG CERAMIC DESIGN

W. MITCH YUNG ■ 141 SUNSET DRIVE ■ HOLLISTER, MO 65672 ■ TEL 417-337-9227
FAX 417-336-0291 ■ E-MAIL MYUNG@CENTURYTEL.NET ■ WWW.MITCHYUNG.COM

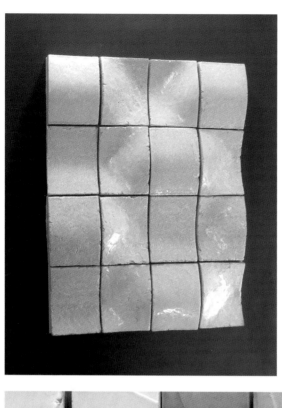

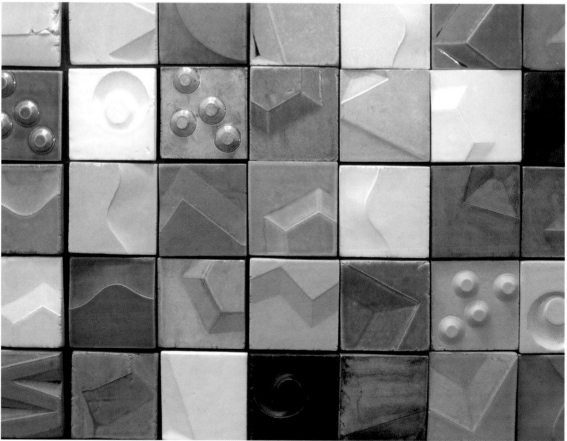

Top left: *Ice Ripple,* 2007, stoneware and glaze, 42" x 29" x 4".  Top right: *Landscape,* 2006, private residence, New York, NY,
stoneware and glaze, 40" x 60" x 4".  Photograph: Scott Mooney.  Bottom: *Geometric Tiles* (detail), 2007, stoneware and glaze, each tile: 6" x 6" x 1".

# SHAWN NEWTON

BIT BY BIT MOSAICS ▦ 101 SOUTH MAIN STREET ▦ WALLINGFORD, CT 06492
TEL 203-269-7332 ▦ FAX 203-269-7682 ▦ E-MAIL SNEWTONART@AOL.COM ▦ WWW.BITBYBITMOSAICS.COM

Left: *Verdure*, 2007, stained glass mosaic, 35" × 20". Top right: *Eve*, 2005, stained glass mosaic bas relief, 16" × 14".
Bottom right: *Adam*, 2006, stained glass mosaic bas relief, 16" × 14".

281

# DAVID STEINHARDT

STEINHARDT MURALS ■ 2230 22ND AVENUE ■ SAN FRANCISCO, CA 94116
TEL 415-566-9245 ■ E-MAIL DAVID@DSART.BIZ ■ WWW.DSART.BIZ

Top: *Dawn*, 2006, oil on canvas, ceiling mural, 12' × 18'.
Bottom: *Savannah*, 2006, acrylic on wood, exterior wall mural, 7' × 28'.

# T.S. POST

TOM AND SARA POST ▦ 604 BARBERA PLACE ▦ DAVIS, CA 95616
TEL/FAX 530-758-9365 ▦ E-MAIL TSPOST@OMSOFT.COM ▦ WWW.TSPOST.COM

Top: *View From My Window*, 2007, ceramic on Baltic birch, 24" x 24".
Bottom: *Dream House*, 2007, ceramic on Baltic birch, 24" x 24".

# GEORGIA WALLER

FIRE LIGHT RANCH ■ HIGHWAY 90 EAST ■ ALPINE, TX 79830 ■ TEL 432-837-3435
FAX 432-837-9448 ■ E-MAIL CLANGEL2@HUGHES.NET ■ WWW.GEORGIAWALLERGALLERY.COM

Top: *Monster Slayer*, 24.25"H × 24.5"W.
Bottom: *Fremont Warrior*, 21"H × 24"W.

# LIBBY WARE

LIBBY WARE STUDIOS ■ 2005 POTTERY LANE ■ PORT ORANGE, FL 32128
TEL 386-304-6102 ■ FAX 386-788-1641 ■ E-MAIL LIBBY@LIBBYWARE.COM ■ WWW.LIBBYWARE.COM

Top: *Argonaut*, Marriott Crystal Gateway Hotel, Crystal City, VA, fifty porcelain cubes, 60" x 120" x 6".
Bottom: *Winter in Berlin*, private collection, forty-nine porcelain cubes, 48" x 48" x 6". Photographs: Art Pierson.

# JUDITH WEBER

50 WEBSTER AVENUE ■ NEW ROCHELLE, NY 10801 ■ TEL/FAX 914-235-9027
E-MAIL JWSTUDIO@OPTONLINE.NET ■ WWW.JUDITHWEBER.COM

*Tile Fish*, 2001, Mamaroneck, NY, ceramic porcelain puzzle, 4' x 4'. Photograph: Jason Mandella.

# FIBER WALL ART

# Alex Anagnostou

"The client was looking for an avant-garde mural with a feel for the 1960s, when the Bohemian Embassy, in which these lofts and condos are located, was most active with artists happenings. The designer specified the dramatic black-and-white color scheme. The idea behind the piece was a population burst expressed with natural forms, which was inspired by the image of city lights as viewed from an airplane."

— Alex Anagnostou, artist

*Burst* ■ 2006 ■ Toronto, Canada ■ blown glass ■ 12'H x 16'W x 8"D ■ See more of Alex's work on page 124.

# SUSAN EILEEN BURNES

596 EARHART ROAD ■ ROGUE RIVER, OR 97537
TEL 541-582-8967 ■ E-MAIL SEBURNES@EARTHLINK.NET

*Darkness into Light*, 2004, hand-stitched fiber on painted canvas.  Photograph: Newcomb Photography.

# CALLING

CALLING PAPERWORKS ▮ 5203 COLEMAN RANCH ROAD ▮ CHICO, CA 95928 ▮ TEL 530-893-0882
TEL 530-354-4339 ▮ FAX 530-893-1319 ▮ E-MAIL CLING@SHOCKING.COM ▮ WWW.CAL-LINGPAPERWORKS.COM

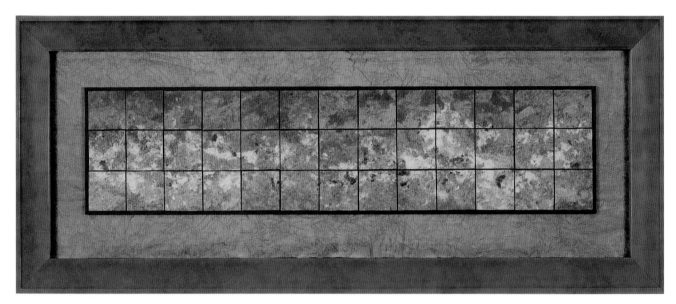

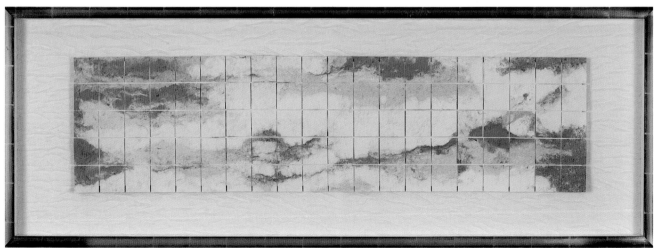

Top: *Meditation View*, handmade paper mounted on cotton and rayon, 18" x 48".
Bottom: *Late Afternoon*, handmade rag paper tiles mounted on silk, 15" x 49".  Photographs: Davin Schreindl.

# CALLING

CALLING PAPERWORKS ▪ 5203 COLEMAN RANCH ROAD ▪ CHICO, CA 95928 ▪ TEL 530-893-0882
TEL 530-354-4339 ▪ FAX 530-893-1319 ▪ E-MAIL CLING@SHOCKING.COM ▪ WWW.CAL-LINGPAPERWORKS.COM

 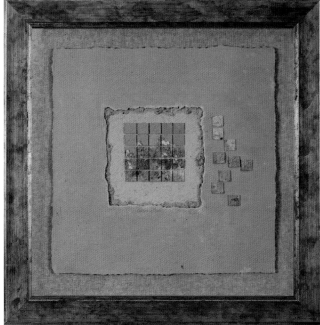

Top: *After the Rain*, handmade rag paper mounted on cotton and silk, 18" x 48". Photograph: Davin Schreindl.
Bottom left: *California Gold*, handmade rag paper tiles mounted on other rag papers and linen 28" x 29". Photograph: Davin Schreindl.
Bottom right: *Thursday*, handmade rag paper tiles mounted on other papers and linen, 28" x 29". Photograph: Paul Jeremias.

# MARILYN FORTH

BAYBERRY ART STUDIO ■ 7658 HAYLAGE CIRCLE ■ BALDWINSVILLE, NY 13027
TEL 315-638-3666 ■ E-MAIL MFORTH@TWCNY.RR.COM

292    Top: *Wild Flower Waltz*, painted batik, 45" × 45".  Bottom: *Celebration*, painted batik, 40" × 40".  Photographs: Anthony Potter.

# MARILYN FORTH

BAYBERRY ART STUDIO ■ 7658 HAYLAGE CIRCLE ■ BALDWINSVILLE, NY 13027
TEL 315-638-3666 ■ FAX 315-458-4828 ■ E-MAIL MFORTH@TWCNY.RR.COM

*Vineyard Dream*, painted batik, 58" x 37". Photograph: Anthony Potter.

# Libby Ware

*"I first saw Libby's work at an ACC show, and I was very excited about it. I hadn't seen anything like it before and it just said 'wow.' I told Libby I loved the boxes she used but that I wanted to 'think outside the box' by having her create a wave theme. Libby and her husband came and installed the piece, and it just speaks volumes. It was definitely made for the space."*

— Tom Jackson, ASID, Copenhagen Imports, Sarasota, FL

*Azure Sea* ■ 2007 ■ Sarasota, FL ■ ceramic with blue glaze ■ each cube: 6" x 6" x 2"-6" ■ See more of Libby's work on page 285.

Jack McCarty

# KAREN HENDERSON

19 KUHN ROAD ▥ LAYTON, NJ 07851 ▥ TEL 973-948-5801
E-MAIL KARENHENDERSONFIBER@YAHOO.COM ▥ WWW.KARENHENDERSONFIBER.COM

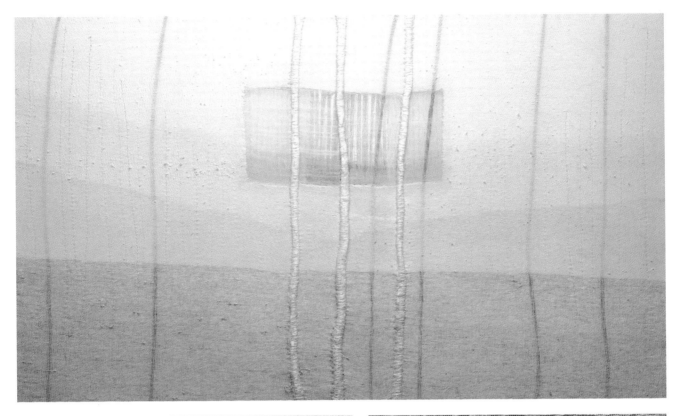

Top: *Accept*, 2007, hand-woven silk with mixed-media fiber, 30"H × 61"W. Photograph: John Sterling Ruth. Bottom left: *Comfort*, 2006, hand-woven linen with mixed-media fiber, 13"H × 12.5"W. Photograph: John Sterling Ruth. Bottom right: *Memory: Tinicum*, hand woven silk with mixed-media fiber, 20.5"H × 16.25"W. Photograph: D. James Dee.

# NATALIA MARGULIS

MAGIC THREADS ■ 117 CROWN COURT ■ LIVINGSTON, NJ 07039
TEL 973-992-8487 ■ E-MAIL NATALIAMARGULIS@YAHOO.COM ■ WWW.NATALIAMARGULIS.COM

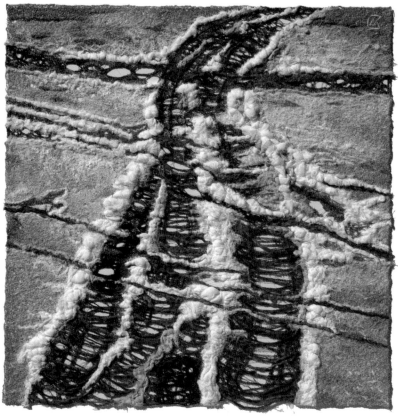

Top: *Hay Bales*, 2006, embroidery, 24" x 24", one of a kind.
Bottom: *Snow Track*, 2005, embroidery, 24" x 24", one of a kind.

# MARJORIE TOMCHUK

M. TOMCHUK FINE ART ▪ 44 HORTON LANE ▪ NEW CANAAN, CT 06840
TEL 203-972-0137 ▪ FAX 203-972-3182 ▪ E-MAIL MTOMCHUK@AOL.COM ▪ WWW.MTOMCHUK.COM

Top: *Approaching Storm*, 2006, unframed embossed multiple on handmade paper 26" x 36".
Bottom: *Midnight Sun*, 2007, unframed embossed multiple on handmade paper, 26" x 36".

# ALICE VAN LEUNEN

VAN LEUNEN STUDIOS ▥ 9025 SE TERRACE VIEW COURT ▥ AMITY, OR 97101
TEL 503-835-7717 ▥ FAX 503-835-7707 ▥ E-MAIL AVANLEUNEN@MSN.COM ▥ WWW.ALICEVANLEUNEN.COM

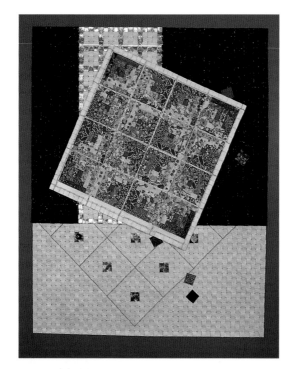 

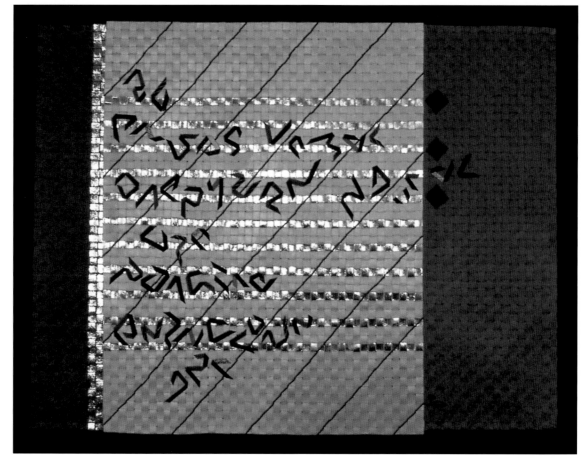

Top left: *Log Cabin IV: Heirloom,* 2007, woven paper with paint, metallic foil, stitchery, and collage, 40" x 32". Top right: *Delectable Mountains: The Silk Road,* 2007, woven paper with paint, stitchery, and collage, 27" x 23". Bottom: *The Calligraphy Lesson,* woven paper with paint, metallic foil, stitchery, and collage, 32" x 40".

# ART QUILTS

# APRIL CAVERHILL

CAVERHILL QUILTS ■ 3835 CUMBERLAND ROAD ■ VICTORIA, BC V8P 3J1 ■ CANADA
TEL 250-727-0870 ■ E-MAIL INFO@CAVERHILLQUILTS.COM ■ WWW.CAVERHILLQUILTS.COM

*Siddhartha's Son,* art quilt, painted and dyed on unprimed canvas, hand and machine stitched, 53.5" × 35.5".
Photograph: Ted Clarke, Image This Photography.

# HILARY GIFFORD

CUSTOM CLOTH ▦ 15 EAST MAIN STREET ▦ TRUMANSBURG, NY 14886 ▦ TEL 315-345-4946
FAX 607-387-3748 ▦ E-MAIL HILARY@CUSTOMCLOTH.COM ▦ WWW.CUSTOMCLOTH.COM

Left wall: *Yellow Fly,* hand-painted cotton quilt, 92" x 101". Right wall and inset: *Dragon,* hand-painted cotton quilt, 71" x 43".
On bed: *Orange Sunset,* hand-painted cotton quilt, 87" x 88". Cabinet of reclaimed materials by SteveWhittlesey.com.

# JOAN SCHULZE

SCHULZE STUDIO ■ 808 PIPER AVENUE ■ SUNNYVALE, CA 94087 ■ TEL 408-736-7833
TEL 415-642-8312 ■ FAX 408-736-7833 ■ E-MAIL JOAN@JOAN-OF-ARTS.COM ■ WWW.JOAN-OF-ARTS.COM

Top: *Ceylon III,* 2007, quilt, 20" × 24.5".
Bottom: *Poet's Place,* 2007, quilt, 20" × 24.5". Photographs: Sharon Risedorph.

# SHERRY SHINE

238 EPPIRT STREET ▦ EAST ORANGE, NJ 07018 ▦ TEL 973-674-9049
TEL 973-280-2617 ▦ E-MAIL SHINE_ART1@YAHOO.COM ▦ WWW.ARTBYSSHINE.COM

*Friendship*, 2007, hand-painted art quilt, 30" x 36".  Photograph: Bill Rogers, Digital Arts Imaging.

303

Interior design by Tony Raffa, see page 28. Photograph: Rex Spencer.

# RESOURCES

# ARTIST STATEMENTS

## ERIC ABRAHAM
Home Accents
Page 78

Art is magic and the artist is a magician! What else can be said about art? Most of my work is influenced by the seventeenth- and eighteenth-century Baroque and Rococo periods of art history, as well as most decorative art movements, "outsider-naïve-visionary" art, and, of course, my own personal nostalgia. I do enjoy looking at art in all its various forms and non-forms. I have always been in love with intricate and very busy art forms! More is more—less is less. My method of work is quite spontaneous, sometimes it leads me and sometimes I lead. Although I have both a B.F.A. (Kansas City Art Institute) and M.F.A. (University of Nebraska), I have chosen a more independent direction through the medium of high-fired porcelain. When the magic is explained, it is no longer magic. Being an art magician is an admirable occupation! More information at: www.ericabraham.net.

## MARY LOU ALBERETTI
Murals, Tiles & Wall Reliefs
Page 268

Throughout my career as a sculptor, I have lived, taught, and studied the architecture of Spain, Italy, France, and Ireland, looking for clues and insight from the fragments left behind. My creative impulse and curiosity have found expression in clay sculptural reliefs, most recently, a fusion of Moorish and classical, forms that are multi-fired with slips, stains, underglazes, and dry textural glazes. I apply color meticulously—by sponge, brush, or spray—to capture the light, textures, and colors of ancient walls, arches, and other architectural forms from history and my imagination. Through these multi-layered works, I seek to evoke the depth and mystery of the human experience.

GUILD SOURCEBOOKS: *Designer's 14, 15; Architectural & Interior Art 16, 17, 18, 19, 20, 21; Residential Art 4, 5*

## ALEX ANAGNOSTOU GLASS STUDIO
Sculpture
Pages 124, 288

I developed my own technique for creating intricate glass web structures within hollow glass vessels during several years of experimenting with blown glass techniques. Each unique *Filaments* sculpture is inspired by microscopic images and the underlying structures found in nature, as a metaphor for the strong and fragile connections found within and between us. The woven textiles of my grandmother in Greece were also a strong influence on my work. *Golden Spiral* is the newest of my sculptures. Commission pieces can be designed for the home, place of work, or as awards. Work is held in private collections in the United States, Canada, Australia, and Europe. To view more work, visit www.alexanagnostou.com.

EXHIBITIONS: *Collect,* 2008, London; Material Matters Contemporary Glass gallery, 2007, Toronto (solo show); SOFA, 2006, Chicago; West End Gallery, BC; Palette Contemporary, NM; Third Dimension Gallery, HI; Galerie Elena Lee, Montreal

AWARDS: Emerging Glass Artist Award, 2004, Glass Art Association of Canada; Mary Corcoran Award for Craft, 2004; Glass Award, 2005, Toronto Outdoor Art Exhibition; Two Glass Studio Residencies, 2003, Glass Art Society Scholarship

## MAUDE ANDRADE
Mixed & Other Media Wall Art
Page 242

I am enchanted, challenged, and seduced by paint and painting. The properties of the mixed media I work with encourage my creativity. I paint on board or deep wooden boxes, which add a sculptural element. Geometric graphics, art papers, and photos form my collages, which I work with in a series, revisiting and reconfiguring them until they morph into the next series. Dichotomies, such as simple/complex, ancient/modern, and order/chaos, fascinate me. When I paint the final layer of oil, I'm abstracting representational images, creating abstracted landscapes, or mapping an emotion. Through this mixed-media process, I want to convey a visual story that transforms an everyday image with new meaning. Recent group exhibits include *Originals*, 2005, Santa Fe Museum of Fine Arts, and *Miniatures* at the Albuquerque Museum. Sizes range from 4.5" × 4.5" × 2" to 30" × 36" × 3", and each box has a special surprise pattern/painting on the reverse.

## ANNE OSHMAN MOSAICS
Murals, Tiles & Wall Reliefs
Page 269

The art of mosaic is created by combining small pieces of tesserae to form a larger image. I use this ancient medium to capture twenty first century reflections of ourselves. Using 3/8" micro-mosaic tile, marble, and/or glass, these portraits express the relationship between people and their surroundings. Details that would otherwise go unnoticed are highlighted, yet the feeling of anonymity creates a sense of voyeurism for the viewer. The newest evolution of my work is shifting toward the sculptural: the objects themselves. They, too, have quirky elements which lend context and personality, conveying a story behind them. Although my work is typically representational, mosaics can be used to create decorative features such as patterns and borders. I welcome the collaborative process to create specific mosaic designs for residential and commercial sites.

COMMISSIONS: Crescent Parking Deck, Montclair, NJ; Thread Clothing Store, Montclair, NJ

EXHIBITIONS: Lana Santorelli Gallery, 2007, Southampton, NY; Saks Fifth Avenue, 2006, New York, NY; New Jersey Crafts Annual, 2005, Jersey City Museum

## SCOTT E. ARMSTRONG
Furniture
Page 34

My work is shaped by thirty-five years of artistic and creative living, learning, and working. Growing up in northern Wyoming nurtured my independent spirit and love of natural materials. Getting my B.F.A. from Kansas City Art Institute taught me to direct my creativity and showed me the value of the decorative arts and the beauty of modern design. Working eight years as a senior product designer in the furniture industry gave me an education in production and a respect for traditional forms and ornamentation. For the past fifteen years, I have been running my studio and drawing on this varied background to create graceful, animated, one-of-a-kind, limited-production, and commissioned pieces of fine cabinetry and furniture. I use solid woods for strength and figured veneers for their rare beauty and ecological benefits, then add a touch of inlay for fun.

## ART BY CARMEN
Mixed & Other Media Wall Art
Page 243

I began my unique composition of life, color, and art from the small country town just outside of Frankfurt, Germany, where I was born. With generations of fine art flowing through my veins, I was able to combine formal training with my innate talent and abilities. This sheer respect for my craft has enabled me to place my work in private homes, as well as business locations from North America to the British West Indies. "Transitional abstract," sometimes referred to as "three-dimensional wall furniture," is composed of a variety of color transitions. Each transition represents the essence of color and energy. Transitional art demands a great deal of time. My art takes one on an imaginary journey, and no two journeys are ever alike. Words fall short of explaining this rare technique. One must see the art, feel it, and touch it in order to truly experience the magic. My vision is to share my art with the global community so that people from all over may enjoy the same happiness and harmony that I feel from my heartfelt work.

## BARBARA JACOBS
## COLOR AND DESIGN
Floor Coverings
Pages 11, 87-88, 90

*Silk Road Weaves* emerges from my long-time love of textiles, combined with my passion for color and over twenty years as a colorist and architectural color consultant for clients nationwide in their homes and places of business. *Silk Road Weaves* is the second line of hand-knotted Tibetan rugs that I have designed. As I select the colors and materials that best bring each design to life, I often compose a single visual color field using multiple colored yarns or even a variety of fibers having unique visual and tactile qualities. In this way, I am able to apply the principles of "optical color mixing" to add visual and textural dimension and richness of color to the overall work. I hope you will enjoy using these rugs as much as I enjoy the inspiration and process of creating them.

COLLECTIONS: Private residence, Minneapolis, MN; Private residence, Medfield, MA; Private residence, Boston, MA; Borchers Law Group, Medway, MA

EXHIBITIONS: Zullo Gallery, Medfield, MA: numerous annual juried exhibitions 1990-2007

## SONYA LEE BARRINGTON
Home Accents
Page 79

Over the course of forty years, I created work that ranged in size from bed quilts to small pieced and appliquéd work that was matted and framed for presentation. During this time I also produced a line of hand-dyed cotton fabric for quilt makers. More recently, I have been working exclusively with wool. The patchwork is made from recycled garments. The 100% wool batting and the backing from Pendleton® are new materials. I use embroidery to embellish the hand-quilted throws and quilts, pillow tops, and small upholstered furniture pieces. This new direction is very exciting for me. Wool is a wonderful fiber to work with, and I like the concept of recycling to produce work that is both functional and attractive. Commissions accepted.

GUILD SOURCEBOOKS: *Residential Art 4, 5*

## BEL VETRO
Lighting
Pages 67-68

Bel Vetro is a blown glass lighting company. We design and create limited-edition and one-of-a-kind art glass lighting. Our unique, custom-made fixtures are influenced by classical Venetian techniques and contemporary design. We specialize in creating functional works of art in the form of pendants, chandeliers, and sconces for private homes and public spaces.

## JAN BILEK
Objects
Page 104

Inspired by nature, I hope to create work that is sensitively crafted and evokes a sense of natural wonder, harmony, and beautiful perfection. The decorative nature of my work reflects my background as an interior decorator and watercolor artist. Although I began making functional work, it became clear early on that my greatest fascination in ceramics is with the wheel-thrown porcelain vessel, in particular the bottle form. I continue to love the challenge of perfecting the bottle, inspired by the natural harmony and balance of forms in nature and challenged by the skills required to create the most delicate of tall, narrow necks. In order to create a union between form and surface, I utilize multiple layers of flowing glazes to express a sense of movement and dimension that is organic in nature. The fluidity of the glaze and translucent color flowing into color enhances the expression of the vessel form and inspires a body of work that explores the theme of nature and growth.

## BOYKIN PEARCE ASSOCIATES
Furniture
Pages 35, 72

"Sensitively Designed and Carefully Crafted." A simple phrase we use defining furniture created by Boykin Pearce Associates. It describes an intense drive for technical and design excellence. Our concepts are developed in CAD and built with loving care, melding historically proven techniques with the best of today's advancements. Our palette consists of the world's finest materials, including hardwoods carefully selected for grain pattern and color to yield furniture with beauty, balance, and strength. We're inspired by the quest for excellence and the endless possibilities of design and technique. The result is lovingly developed heirloom-quality furniture built to be passed on for generations. The work appears in numerous private, commercial, and liturgical collections. I teach, consult with design professionals, and serve on advisory boards at the Art Institute of Colorado and the Denver Art Museum. You are invited to see more at boykinpearce.com.

## BRADFORD WOODWORKING ■
## PAMELA HILL QUILTS
Furniture
Page 36

My furniture incorporates the new and the old. Raised on a farm in Pennsylvania, I learned that nothing should be wasted. While studying at the Rochester Institute of Technology, I developed this idea into my design aesthetic. Since 1980 I have given old lumber a new life, whether in a chest of drawers or an armoire: pitchforks become the backs of benches and chairs, and ax handles are the legs for stools. The blend of new wood, salvaged barn boards, ax handles, and pitchforks all combine to create the distinctive "Brad Smith look." I produce a small line of furniture, and a number of one-of-a-kind pieces on commission.    – Brad Smith

My quilts combine the history and tradition of the craft with my use of bold pattern and strong, clear color. Although frequently used as decorative wall pieces in public and private interior spaces, the quilts are designed and constructed to be durable for everyday use as bedcovers. I grew up in an Amish area of Illinois where there was a strong tradition of quiltmaking. I established my own studio in the California Gold Country in 1976. My work has been exhibited in major galleries and museums throughout the United States.    – Pamela Hill

## URSULA J. BRENNER
Paintings
Page 159

My paintings reflect a wide range of moods, from light and playful to deep and mysterious. I am influenced by old-world museums, music, and architecture. My art makes a strong, bold statement, yet it can be very ethereal as well. I want people who look at my art to be transported into another realm, to transcend the normal human experience. I like to focus on the fundamental nature of a scene—the values, colors, and shapes—using "notan" study, a Japanese method of examining lights and darks. My paintings are in private and corporate collections worldwide. I have worked with interior designers and art consultants, and accept commissions in a broad range of sizes. Prices range from $600 to $10,000.

## DONNA BRANCH
Sculpture
Page 125

My work is informed by patterns of color, form, and texture, which occur ordinarily in nature with such ease of simplicity, without artificiality, or constraint, that they heighten my sense of the mystery and spiritualism I continually find in the natural world around me. By exploring these elements, I continue to seek the graceful, yet powerful, nature of something that is much larger than me; something I cannot comprehend. My compositions explore color, light, texture, and depth using several traditional casting, lampworking, and carving techniques. Texture is imparted by use of *inchiso and battuto,* carving techniques achieved by use of a lathe and a diamond wheel. By exploring *battuto* I discovered ways to highlight elements such as color and light refraction. *Battuto* gives an unexpected visual and tactile characteristic to the glass and complements the simple forms I create. The depth produced by the "honey-combing" of the glass and manipulation of the carving directs the viewer's attention to areas of light, depth, color, or pattern. All of these convey my wonder in the smallest detail.

## JEANINE BRIGGS
Sculpture
Page 126

Seeing different things and seeing things differently, I begin transforming discarded materials into art. My imagination takes form through freestanding sculptures, wall sculptures, and paintings. Environmental sensibilities influence my constructive processes as well as my choice of materials. Just as nature inspires my work, I hope my work in some way serves nature by suggesting creative and conservational solutions to consumer practices. Appearing in galleries, museums, public spaces, trade shows, corporate collections, and government offices, my work has been exhibited extensively in California and most recently in New York City. Commissions of any scale welcome. Imagine the possibilities.

AWARDS: Artist in Residence, 2000, SF Recycling & Disposal, San Francisco, CA

PUBLICATIONS: *Show & Tell: The Art of Harmony,* 2007, Zimmer Children's Museum, Los Angeles, CA

GUILD SOURCEBOOKS: *Designer's 15; Architectural & Interior Art 16*

## CHRISTINE BRENNAN
Paintings
Pages 158, 372

Often dreamlike and enigmatic, my work features a host of symbolic and allegorical references, images drawn from the unconscious leading the viewer into richly lit narratives that evoke personal stories and associations. Never setting out to illustrate a specific theme or story, I create each image as I go, changing and shaping it along the way. I studied at the Rhode Island School of Design earning a B.F.A. in illustration in 1987 and have been exhibiting and selling my work through galleries and museums since then.

COLLECTIONS: City of Ventura CA, Municipal Art Collection, City Hall; Carnagie Art Museum, Oxnard, CA; Sir Anthony Hopkins, Malibu, CA; Drew Barrymore, Los Angeles, CA; Ventura County Museum of Art and History, Ventura, CA

EXHIBITIONS: *Figures and Forces,* 2007, Jan Baum Gallery, Los Angeles, CA; *Birds of a Feather,* 2005, HumanArts Gallery, Ojai, Ca; *The Imaginary World of Christine Brennan,* 2001, Utopia Design, Studio City, CA

AWARDS: Featured Artist, 2001, Focus on the Masters Program, Ventura, CA; Director's Choice "Master in our Midst" award, 1998, Carnagie Art Museum, Oxnard, CA

## DEBORAH A. BRUNS-THOMAS
Lighting
Page 69

I'm driven by color, light, transparency, and chance. The interactions between colors in a given environment become inspiration for my work. I am ever conscious of the color and light of my surroundings. One such inspiration came from a cup of tea. I was intrigued not only by the color of the tea, but also by the tea bag itself. The use of tea bags in my artwork evolved into the creation of lampshades and allows me the opportunity to explore the many elements of color and light. Taking an innocuous object and transforming it into something with greater presence intrigues me. Each lampshade is handmade from individual 3" x 5" tea bags dyed with acrylic paint, then glued together to create larger compositions. An acrylic polymer medium encases and preserves the sheets. I began BeeLine Studio for my functional, unique lampshades and lamp designs. More images of my work can be found at www.BeeLineStudio.net.

## BARBARA K. BUER
Prints
Pages 211, 356

As a signature member of both the nationally acclaimed American Watercolor Society and National Watercolor Society, I have had work featured in over fifteen major art publications, including *The Artists Magazine, Splash,* and five editions by North Light Books. I believe it is my dedication to the study of light and its effects, and a discriminating sense of composition, design, and a contemporary viewpoint, that have formed my artistic signature. In addition to working in watercolor, my large canvases are created using oils. All Buer fine art images are available in giclée form on canvas or paper. Each Buer giclée print is available sized to order, signed by me, and personalized, if requested. Since each individual print is a giclée original, my printer and I personally inspect each print and both sign an accompanying certificate of authenticity.

## FRAN BULL
Prints
Pages 212-213

*Rastros* is a Spanish word meaning traces, shavings, bits, shades. I chose this word to entitle the pieces because it comes very close to describing their essence: they are fleeting things; they are an honoring of mere gesture, recordings of brief moments in time. They are meant to invoke nature in all of its flux and flow. To fix the fleeting is one of the impossible dreams of art: to capture the light of a country afternoon, in paint; to fix the butterfly's flight on a pin; to fix the mood on a face in a photograph; and here, to fix the living hand's movement across the surface of a plate by making that movement visible. Through etching it becomes possible to print the image of the gesture as I have done here, onto gossamer, fibrous paper. Now gesture becomes thing, becomes image. These works are records of that process. To view more of my work, you can visit my website at www.franbull.com.

## MYRA BURG
Mixed & Other Media Wall Art
Pages 15, 241, 244-246, 252

Somewhere between tapestry and jewelry, *Quiet Oboes* and sculptural installations adorn spaces in a free-floating, peaceful way. Hand-wrapped fiber and burnished metals are combined to create inspired sculptural pieces that meet clients' needs and wants within the requirements of the space. The bigger the challenge, the more the fun. Collaborations are welcome.

COMMISSIONS: Western Asset, London, England; Boston Children's Hospital; *Japonaise,* Universal Studios, Japan; *Galactic Curve,* Universal Studios, Japan; *Quiet Oboes,* Caribé Hilton, Puerto Rico; Travelocity, Dallas, TX

EXHIBITIONS: American Craft Council; SOFA, Chicago; Los Angeles County Museum of Art, CA; Howard Hughes Center, Los Angeles, CA; Orange County Museum of Art, CA

GUILD SOURCEBOOKS: *Designer's 10, 13, 14, 15; Architect's 14, 15; Architectural & Interior Art 16, 17, 18, 19, 20, 21; Artful Home 1, 2, 3, 4, 5*

## MYRA BURG & LIZ CUMMINGS
Mixed & Other Media Wall Art
Page 246

At long last, we have done it! We are now celebrating our collective fifty years of artistic experience by producing a whole new art form that begins on the wall and blooms, becoming spatial elements as well. Liz, with twenty-five years of experience as an artist painting romantic architectural and scenic images, and Myra, moving from the practice of architecture to creating architectural wrapped wall elements, have joined efforts in their respective specialties. We are combining lustrous oils on canvas, creating two-dimensional color fields that provide an environment for sumptuous wrapped fiber. The planar canvases and dimensional cylinders work in tandem, engaging one another in this brand new and highly versatile mixed-media format. Somewhere between the image and the imagination, these combinations give new life to the act of placing color in a living space.

## SUSAN EILEEN BURNES
Fiber Wall Art
Page 289

My work is about the movement of colors and patterns, the repetitions of feeling that come through nature and life experiences. Using traditional techniques, I create original wall pieces of contemporary fiber art. I stitch by hand rows upon rows of fine wool, silk, cotton, and rayon threads onto even-weave fabric. As paint and pastel pigments are applied over the fiber, layers of color emerge and flow into each other. These simple geometric forms relate to each other as they evolve into rhythmic, textural patterns of light and shadow. Each element is then hand sewn onto painted and stretched canvas. Awards include: First Place, 2004 and 2003, AAUW Art Exhibition, Grants Pass Museum of Art; and First Place, 2001, Rocky Mount Art Center.

GUILD SOURCEBOOKS: *Architectural & Interior Art 19; Residential Art 4*

## BETTY BUTLER ■ ITALA LANGMAR
Paintings
Page 160

We are artists who work in a collaborative process we call Responsive Art, in which two artists observe and interpret the other's work, and then respond with a new piece of their own. We each bring our own strengths to the project: Butler employs a strong use of color and gesture, while Langmar uses a softer luminescent approach. The results are calming yet delightful pairs of paintings. These diptychs are from our series of abstractions based on the ephemeral patterns of clouds. The work will appeal to anyone who desires to enrich their environment with beauty, harmony, and the clear message of communication through the coordination of color and treatment. Our work appears in *American Art Collector, Juried Competition of New Work—Central States,* 2007. We have shown together in galleries, and our work hangs in public and private collections. See more of our work at www.responsiveart.com.

## CALLING
Fiber Wall Art
Pages 290-291

My artwork is a dialogue with the many voices that we call creativity/art. It comes from nature, people, and the cosmos at large. It is about color and light, and how it affects our perceptions and emotions. It is about transitions from one state of mind to another, from one day to another day, and from one part of life to another part of life. The conversations are private and universal, and reflect the mysteries and magic of nature and the interplay of the human spirit. Most often my work references earth and sky, calling attention to our physical environment for a moment in time. That moment may be inspiration, vision, silence, or reflection in our home, work place, or social space. My art is an expression of joy, a record of the journey, and my conversation with the viewer. The artwork you see is all handmade rag paper and has been a green art form for the past thirty years. Commission work is a specialty.

GUILD SOURCEBOOKS: *The Guild 1, 2, 3, 5; Architectural & Interior Art 21, 22; Residential Art 4, 5*

## CARLSON GLASSWORKS
Home Accents
Page 81

Carlson Glassworks is a collaborative effort between Kurt and Lynda Carlson. Our work together is a rare combination of mutual care and attention to an unusual multistep process. Kurt begins by creating an interior design of murrini and trapped air in glass, which is encased in the center of the hot sculpted head. The entire piece is shaped by manipulating the hot glass for two to three hours. This is a multistep process that Kurt has developed over the years. The piece is then cooled in a two-day annealing cycle. Once the piece has cooled, Lynda adds detailing to each head by drawing a design onto the glass. The piece is then taped and sandblasted. The designs are enhanced with hand-painted enamels and multi-fired to achieve the finished look. When finished, the original design is still visible inside the head. Looking into the clear area, the viewer is able to see the interior design, in addition to reflections of the outer design, giving the sculptural head depth, mystery, and intrigue.

## ANDREW CARSON
Sculpture
Page 127

My interest is not in metal itself, but in what it can become if assisted by the wind, water, or the environment. All the materials in my installations are intricately cut, forged, hammered, and patinated by hand. With bearings, balance, and color, I like to craft these sculptures not only to work within a chosen landscape, but to elaborate on its artistic energy. My large kinetic sculptures range from frenetic to serene. I graduated from the University of Washington in 1986. My sculptures can be found in public and private collections throughout the United States, with a wide range of high-profile clients among them. Smaller works range from $2,000 to $6,000. Larger works range from $7,000 to $60,000. Special commissions are welcomed.

## ALI CARTER
Furniture
Page 37

I believe that my role as an artist is to be of service; therefore, I do custom work and strive to be unbiased in my response to the parameters a client presents. I do not work in any particular style, but search for what is appropriate to a situation. Left to my own inclination, however, I work in the contemporary idiom. During the past twenty years, wood has been my primary material, with functional furniture being the usual format, although I have also built an entire octagonal school building. In recent years I have incorporated stone, metals, and glass as accents—or even primary components—of a piece. Also, the functional aspect has given way to a more sculptural perspective. I enjoy collaborating with others and sometimes rely entirely on their expertise with materials other than wood. Two grants from the New York State Council on the Arts attest to this. Natural and reclaimed materials are my preference. Please note that my e-mail address has changed from that published in the *Residential Art 5* book. It is now ancientcedar@yahoo.com.

GUILD SOURCEBOOKS: *Residential Art 5*

## APRIL CAVERHILL
Art Quilts
Page 300

For me, there is no greater pleasure than the process of creating my art quilts, which combine the tactile, welcoming feel of a quilt with the crisp, graphic quality of an illustration. Subject matter is varied, but all pieces tell a story and are designed to entice the observer's eye to linger. Working with intense, luminous colors, I dye and paint on pieces of unprimed canvas and other natural fibers, generally starting with one large background upon which I appliqué other hand-dyed layers. The texture of the fabric, combined with bold imagery, result in a gorgeous "quilted painting." My work is exuberant, reflecting a love of the sensual and the unexpected. I have completed commissions for a wide variety of international clientele. You are invited to view my portfolio at www.caverhillquilts.com.

GUILD SOURCEBOOKS: *Residential Art 5*

## CÉSAR
Fine Art Photography
Page 222

My travels around the world have given me the opportunity to capture many distinct and stunning landscapes and natural details. I see the subjects around me as beautiful living art. I translate that into my photography. By incorporating my graphic style into the natural components, I am able to enhance the images making them the perfect blend of color and light. My works immerse the viewer in a world that is the perfect blend of reality and make-believe. My prints are archival in quality, printed on art paper.

## KLARA CHAVARRIA
Paintings
Page 161

My work reflects a deep interest in humanity—our yearnings and a search for a true purpose in life. I want to make the invisible visible and the intangible tangible. In my work I want to capture experiences, relationships, deep emotions, and feelings, and how these influence our existence. I thrive on finding and expressing our human potential, what unites us and what we share in our world, cultures, and society. I want my paintings to be a vehicle that transfers you and your imagination to a deeper, more meaningful place. I work in a variety of mediums, using layers of color, gestures, strokes, and textures in my work. My paintings are in collections throughout the United States and abroad, including a public collection piece exhibited at the Museum of Science and Industry and at O'Hare International Airport, both in Chicago, Illinois. I have participated in and have had several exhibits nationally and internationally.

## CARRIE CRANE
Paintings
Page 162

My love of the landscape is a natural extension of my life growing up on a farm in Massachusetts and studying the natural sciences in college. I am inspired by the age and complexity of the world, the inter-relationship between elements in the landscape. Working from my imagination, I paint the essence of a view, not the details. Colors change, shapes are embellished, textures are brought in until each compositional element has individual character and the real world is left behind. I am pulled toward the surreal and imaginary and am less interested in representing the world as we actually see it. I find there is humor, wonder, and hopefulness in our world that is more likely to rise to the surface the less I try to paint what is obvious to the eye.

COMMISSIONS: Mayo Clinic, 2007, Rochester, MN

AWARDS: Jacob Knight Award for Painting, 2005

## KINGA CZERSKA
Paintings
Page 163

I am an artist, engineer, and designer. I see the world around me as an inexplicable amount of information and connections that my mind has to process. This world has an unbelievable amount of nuance and detail that interlace to create a whole. In turn, I thin-slice my surroundings as I seek to understand the structured environment around me, which is chaotic yet at the same time graceful, precise, elegant, and balanced. I do this by visually flattening the environment in front of me into one plane and analyzing its contents. As the world restructures by shifting and undulating, I strive to capture the moment of stability before another shift occurs. I try to understand how it all fits, what holds it together, and most importantly, how one part can affect all others. The size of my work varies from intimate to large-scale murals and has been shown throughout the U.S., as well as Europe and Mexico. My work is currently in multiple collections, including the Francis J. Greenburger Collection, NY; Immunex, Seattle, WA; Microsoft Corporation, Redmond, WA; Time Equities Inc., NY; and numerous private collections.

## DAVID J. LUNIN FURNITURE MAKER
Furniture
Page 38

I work in a small studio creating original, one-of-a-kind pieces of furniture in wood. My background in eighteenth-century American antiques has deeply influenced my work. When I first opened my shop, I made very strict reproductions of important antiques. More recently, I desired to make my own mark in the world of furniture design. I begin with traditional designs and give them a contemporary twist. What is never changed is the level of craftsmanship that was employed by colonial craftsmen. Hand-cut dovetails, as well as mortise-and-tenon joints, are used throughout. I also prefer the use of traditional finishing material, such as shellac and varnish.

## PETER DELLERT
Furniture
Pages 39, 60

I use lumber that is left live-edged, that is, with the natural curves, textures, and flaws found on the outside of the tree. I use the technique of book-matching—using sequentially cut boards from the same log, flipping the second board so that the faces are mirror images of each other. This gives the work an inherent symmetry. In the *Mariposa* series of cabinets, the pieces act as the abstracted wings of butterflies. In the *Canyon Series Dining Tables*, only the ends are joined, leaving an intentional negative space in the middle. This allows one to look through the table, a rare and wonderful treat. Legs are either sculpted and painted or turned and ebonized.

COMMISSIONS: Judie's Restaurant Bar Top, 2007, Amherst, MA; Conference table, 2002, Smith College Art Department, Northampton, MA

EXHIBITIONS: Sculpture New Hope, 2007, New Hope, PA; Contemporary Sculpture at Chesterwood, 2007, Chesterwood Museum, Stockbridge, MA; Exposed!, 2007, Helen Day Art Center, Stowe, VT

AWARDS: Best in Furniture, 2006, Craft Boston, Society of Arts and Crafts; Niche Award Mixed-Media Finalist, 2004, *Niche* Magazine

GUILD SOURCEBOOKS: Residential Art 1, 2

## DICKINSON DESIGNS
Lighting
Page 70

Simple yet bold is the look I strive for. I am fascinated by the enticing potential that comes from combining wood and ceramics, as well as by pattern and repetition. The result? Handcrafted lighting in timeless contemporary designs in a variety of colors and styles. Subtle variations in the color and texture of the glazes add to the one-of-a-kind beauty of every lamp. Wood components are hand-crafted from hardwood and either finished naturally or with paint. Custom-made shades of paper or parchment come in shapes and sizes to complete the fashion-forward designs. All of my lamps are assembled with UL-listed parts and range in size from small reading lamps to floor lamps.

EXHIBITIONS: The Sprinkler Factory Show, 2005, Worcester Artist Group, MA; Patterns of Worcester, 2004, ArtsWorcester, Worcester, MA; Da Yu Xiao Hu International Small Teapot Competition, 2004, Saddleback College, Mission Viejo, CA; Visions 2003, Krikorian Gallery, Worcester Center for Crafts, MA

AWARDS: Accepted into the Mentor Program, American Craft Council Baltimore Show, MD, 2006

PUBLICATIONS: *New England Home,* May/June 2007; *Niche,* Spring 2006

## LILLIANA S. DIDOVIC
Paintings
Page 164

My art is a reflection of my own journey in life. I was born in the former Yugoslavia. In 1992 I escaped the war in my homeland (Sarajevo, Bosnia) and was granted political asylum in the United States for my family and me. En route to our exile in America, we stopped in Philadelphia, where we found our new place in the sun. This city, where we made our new home and where my son's life has been saved so many times, has become a theme and inspiration for my paintings. My life, which has been full of surprises and is very difficult to describe in words, is visible in the colors I use for my art—brave, dynamic, and unpredictable. Done in acrylic on canvas or black drawing paper, my paintings show a celebration of life and existence. I am spreading that celebration all over the world, with my art included in private collections in Europe, Australia, and South America, and throughout the United States.

## MARGARET DOBBINS
Paintings
Page 165

My paintings are colorful abstracts of layers and shapes that suggest movement and light . . . this is my creative dance. My influences include many forms of art expression: music, movement, color, and nature. I always paint to music while exploring the relationships of color and shape. I use play and experimentation to drive my work. With over thirty years of painting experience as a professional artist, I find the journey is even more important than the destination. My work is found in numerous corporate and private collections throughout the United States and abroad.

COLLECTIONS: Chevron Corp., Littler Mendelson Law Offices, Chapelwood Methodist Church, Houston, TX; Weingarten Realty, Risk International, St. Martins Episcopal Church, Katy Hospital, Katy, TX

EXHIBITIONS: Individual exhibitions, 1550 Gallery, 2007, Kerrville, TX; Mossrock Studio, 2007, The Woodlands, TX; Daily Review Café, 2007, Houston, TX; Brazosport Center for the Arts, 2005, Clute, TX; Carl Jung Center, 2004, Houston, TX

## JOY DOHERTY
Fine Art Photography
Page 223

There is something magical that happens when we pause—and pay attention to—the world around us, to the mysterious play of light and form. This is nature's limitless palette. My photographic images and digital darkroom expose and explore this extraordinarily beautiful yet often unnoticed world. Selected images are processed onto unique and innovative substrates, such as hand-textured metal panels, archival gallery-wrapped giclée canvas, different density fabrics, plexi, and other plastics and resins. The resulting art has a fresh, contemporary look—perfect for adding color, mood, or intrigue to any environment. The versatility of the process and materials gives clients the freedom to choose the shape, size, and substrate style that suits their project's unique requirements. My art is displayed in private collections, corporate offices, healthcare facilities, spas, and residential high-rises.

GUILD SOURCEBOOKS *Architectural & Interior Art 21; Residential Art 5*

## DOMSKY GLASS
Murals, Tiles & Wall Reliefs
Page 270

As two professional artists, we came together sixteen years ago to share our vision in creating beautiful works of fine art glass. Over the years we have developed our own technique and style of glass working, crossing the boundaries of glass fusion, blending it with hot glass elements and metal. We have termed our developed process "hot fusion," and the results reveal a distinct quality of work known as "Domsky Glass." With hot-fusion glass we create both sculptures and glass paintings, panels of glass that are wall mounted. Our intent is always to intrigue the viewer with a unique work of art, displaying visual depth and beauty of design in every piece we create. Our glass is always one of a kind. We are accustomed to commissions, respecting the specific needs of our clients' unique residential or commercial environments.

COMMISSIONS: Nike, Cirque Du Soleil, Bellagio Hotel, Mandalay Bay Hotel, Wynn Hotel, City of Hope

COLLECTIONS: Germany, New Zealand, Australia, India, and throughout the United States

## SUZANNE DONAZETTI
Metal Wall Art
Page 260

About eighteen years ago, I began experimenting with coloring metal, which has been an interesting journey. I have developed a process of painting on copper with metallic leaf, inks, liquid acrylics, and powdered pigments. I wax the painted copper and weave it into abstract wall sculptures. The materials are durable, low maintenance, and easy to install. I enjoy working with copper and seeing the random complexities that result from weaving the paintings together. My vision is to create large-scale, site-specific art that will provide an experience of contemplation, healing, and mystery. My work is represented in galleries and public, corporate, and private spaces. I welcome commissions and enjoy working with architects, art consultants, and clients to create art to enhance an environment.

GUILD SOURCEBOOKS: *Designer's 9, 12, 13, 14, 15; Architectural & Interior Art 19; Residential Art 1*

## PATRICK W. DOYLE
Sculpture
Page 128

After my studies in San Diego, California, I began working with redwood burl and was led to Northern California for this unique resource in the 1970s. I gained a position managing Ford Burl Supply, a subsidiary of Korbel Winery, which was doing an extensive land-clearing operation in the heart of the redwoods. I spent over a decade processing, grading, and finishing thousands of tons of the high-grade virgin burlwood stumps, remainders of the old growth logged off in the 1860s. The very best of these exotic pieces I selected to personally finish into furniture, fountains, sculptures, and carvings for Korbel's finish department. I was also contracted by Korbel's clients to set up finish shops, machinery, and train personnel throughout the U.S. This in-depth experience with burlwood, along with my artistic studies, come together now to create my finest pieces. As I create a new piece now, I feel like I am transforming it from a lost, ancient, earthen nugget into a visual feast to be enjoyed again.

## PATRICIA DREHER
Floor Coverings
Pages 87, 89, 240

After obtaining my M.A. in classical painting and art history, I worked with textile design in Sweden as a Fulbright fellow and in England as an artist-in-residence. The floorcloth—a canvas painting made for the floor—embodies my love of combining the beautiful with the functional. My favorite challenge is to collaborate with a client, designer, or architect to create an installation that resonates with the larger concept for the space. My designs can harmonize or they can dominate, as the client chooses. My repertoire is broad and diverse, from classical antiquity, Asian themes, and ethnic designs, to modern abstracts and geometrics. I make wall-to-wall installations and rug-format pieces of any size or shape, using the very best materials. Floors I made twenty years ago retain their color clarity and remain fresh and beautiful. I sign all my pieces.

## DEBRA DRESLER
Mixed & Other Media Wall Art
Page 247

I treasure old books. Worn leather, beautiful paper, and vellum. As our messengers from the past, lovingly passed from hand to hand, mind to soul, books hold the memories of who we are. It's a shame then, to see some old, well-fingered, dog-eared and loved tomes discarded. Instead, I give them a new life in art by combining books, paper, text, and images into collage. There is depth and beauty in the craftsmanship, patina, and the marks of human hands in these antique volumes. Our primal senses can appreciate the old. When you see my collages, I hope you sense the richness and texture of another time. Allow the beauty of aged materials to tell their new story. Transformed, these materials are no longer what they were, but what they have become, over time, just like every one of us. There is beauty in experience and change. Visit www.DebraDresler.com to see more of my work.

## KATHLEEN EGGERT
Murals, Tiles & Wall Reliefs
Pages 267, 271

I create glass tiles for installation or to be mounted on board as art panels. Each tile is individually sand-blast-carved in low relief. Multiple layers of vitreous enamel fired onto the tiles create depth and richness of color. I have been developing techniques for enameling on glass for over twenty years. Examples of my early work in tableware are in the permanent collection of the Corning Museum of Glass, and my figurative sculptures have been widely collected. In addition to my own portfolio of designs inspired by the natural world, I welcome custom commissions. I can adapt my technique to any style of décor, often using a design element from another feature in the home as my starting point.

## ERIC EHLENBERGER
Sculpture
Page 129

I approach my sculptures as meditations of form and color. Using the vibrant colors and glow achieved by combining neon light with glass and brushed metal, I explore the emotional impact of luminous color and simple forms. My pieces range from the use of simple geometric forms in contemplative abstractions to a theme-based series of sculptures in which I explore a fantasy world of luminous flora and fauna, including the hanging neon and blown glass *Jellyfish* sculptures. In designing my work, I place importance on both practical installation and maintenance considerations, as well as the aesthetics.

## BRADLEY EHRSAM
Furniture
Page 40

My art is a product of my youth, when I spent time on the farm in Indiana with my grandmother, learning about and restoring antiques while watching my uncle work on his combines and tractors. This history blends with my other artistic disciplines, such as sculpture, motorcycle building, and painting, to influence my studio furniture. While I produce traditional pieces, I also study many styles of furniture making and add my own twist by blending the familiar and the unique to create an endless range of possibilities. I focus on details, fine finishes, and incorporating found objects in unique ways. I see my work as creative and experimental, yet functional.

## JOLINE EL-HAI
Lighting
Pages 3, 71

I fill my glass panels with a sense of movement, rich coloring, and bold, detailed imagery of a narrative quality. The drama of the natural world often informs my designs. My reductive glass painting technique gives depth and mystery with graininess reminiscent of mezzotints and old photographs. I incorporate glass fusing for complexity of color and texture. Internally illuminated, my glass panels range from large murals set into walls to small, intimate glowing sculpture for the table or shelf. I also design and fabricate naturally lit windows. I began creating leaded glass panels in 1975. Over the years I have expanded the scope of my work to include glass jewelry, fused glass wall sculpture, giclée prints of pastel drawings, and a nationally known and popular production line of decorative lights. My work has won awards and has been featured in group and solo shows in galleries and museums across the country.

GUILD SOURCEBOOKS: *Architectural & Interior Art 22*

## THE ELEPHANTWORKS STUDIO
Paintings
Page 166

I paint to bring something a bit finer to the viewers' day. I paint to bring images of light and color alive. I enjoy taking familiar shapes and animals to a new, abstracted place. I paint work that is engaging to children. I want children to enjoy my work, as I want my work to continue to hold an attraction to the adults that view my paintings. I think it is important to engage children in fine art. I am Sri Lankan-American and that component of my life is also a factor that impacts my artwork. I love the color, texture, and brilliance of Sri Lanka, and I pull those elements into my work as well. I have studied elephants for about ten years; I find them engaging as a subject matter. They have delightful personalities, rich texture of skin, and endless wrinkles that provide for incredible linear exploration. Please visit my website, www.elephantworksstudio.com, to see more of my work.

## BARRY ENTNER
Sculpture
Page 130

My sculptural glass represents an idealized continuum of otherworldly botanical and sentient life. I devise unique processes to attain this concept. The techniques employed range from hand and steamblowing to poured casting. The resulting work is alternately sleek, saturated with color, or roughly textured with characteristics of primitive forms. Exhibitions include the International Exhibition of Glass Kanazawa and the International Exposition of Sculptural Objects and Functional Art. Commissions include the Hale Koa Hotel, Honolulu, HI, and the Langham Place Hotel, Hong Kong.

GUILD SOURCEBOOKS: *Residential Art 4,5*

## NANCI ERSKINE
Paintings
Page 167

I am an oil painter, inspired by the transitory nature of flowers—their fragile translucence, the sensuous nature of the petals, or the forms they take when only the stems and leaves remain. I am intrigued by seductive colors and unique, evocative postures that create an emotional resonance. I see each painting as an intriguing fictional world. All my work is original, from intimate to large scale, on either canvas or rigid surfaces.

COMMISSIONS: Inquiries are welcome.

COLLECTIONS: American Century Investments, Denver, CO; Seattle Arts Commission, WA; Coe College, Cedar Rapids, IA; Mundt / MacGregor Law Firm, Seattle, WA; Safeco Insurance, Seattle, WA; University of Oregon, Eugene

EXHIBITIONS: Pierce College, 2007, 1997, Tacoma, WA; Francine Seders Gallery, 2005, 2003, 2000, 1997, 1993, 1990, Seattle, WA; Davis and Cline, 2005, Ashland, OR

AWARDS: Individual Artists Fellowships, 2002 and 1998, Colorado Council on the Arts

PUBLICATIONS: *New American Paintings,* Western Edition, #36 (2001) and #54 (2004)

## CONSTANTINE FEDORETS
Furniture
Page 41

I completed my classical art education in the Ukraine. For ten years I focused my work on painting in different media. Having always admired fine furniture makers and their art, I was inspired to study and build furniture. In my work I reflect classical styles and movements in a modern interpretation. When working with special commissions, I collaborate closely with the client in order to bring their vision and ideas to life. My work can be viewed on my website at www.constantinesinteriors.com. It is also shown at the annual Providence Fine Furnishings show in Rhode Island.

GUILD SOURCEBOOKS: *Residential Art 4, 5*

## ERIN McGEE FERRELL
Paintings
Page 168

Painting in plein air is what I do best—alone or surrounded by crowds. I sit in the flatbed of a pick-up, painting open fields and salt marshes and fighting against wind. I stand on a crowded street in Philadelphia and paint the bustling Italian bakery across the street. Painting is my passion; it is what I do. My work is done in two different mediums, but I treat both in the same way. I paint with my watercolors as I do my oils; straight out of the tubes. Intense color in the watercolors is achieved by this technique. I'm equally rewarded by both styles. I'm a Kentucky girl and bluegrass music, colorful quilts, and big skies with bright green rolling hills are in my blood. My childhood home was in an historic Victorian Louisville neighborhood and my paintings today continue to reflect my love of fanciful architectural details, color, and open landscape. My father and grandfather spent most of their lives in Nigeria, and my love of brilliant color, pattern, and tilt toward abstraction come from the West African sculptures and paintings that decorated my childhood home. I'm a prolific and fast painter and create detailed renderings of local scenes quickly. Big paper and big canvases are my loves.

## LINDSAY FEUER
Sculpture
Page 131

Suspended in the realm between fantasy and reality, my sculptures explore the organic processes of growth, replication, and locomotion. Deliberately ambiguous combinations of biological imagery reflect the perfect integration of form and function found in the natural world. Through an intuitive process, I allow these elements to respond to one another, creating "hybrid" forms with movement and fluidity. Porcelain is an ideal medium for my work because its white luminescence showcases rich surfaces and curvilinear components. The strength and responsiveness of this clay also enable me to achieve whimsical and delicate sculptural elements. Hidden building techniques allow my sculptures to exist in a space of seamless illusion where they appear "born" rather than "made." Inspired by the mysteries of nature, these pieces deliver an animated and fantastical view of our biological surroundings. I invite my audience to draw upon their experience and imagination, and to discover a unique reality for each piece.

## STEVE "SPIKE" FINCH
Objects
Pages 8, 105

Creating a vessel is about exploring the unknown. When I work with stone I'm intrigued by its antiquity—each piece millions of years old, with a rich, mysterious history behind each spectacular hue, striation, and vein. I feel like an archeologist, uncovering something never seen before. My signature style of artistry is uniting exotic materials from around the world, including alabaster, soapstone, copper, and wood. My creation style is organic. When beginning to turn each vessel, no decision is made on the final design; I allow the material to reveal its shape as I bring it to life. Each day I challenge myself, refining my materials and tools to create fresh, extraordinary, one-of-kind pieces that draw people to touch and explore their sensuous shapes. I invite you to visit my website to learn more about my work. Commissions welcome.

## BONNIE FITZGERALD
Murals, Tiles & Wall Reliefs
Page 272

My passion is to create custom mosaics with a particular focus on architectural enhancements to enrich spaces with a lovely blend of classic and contemporary design while honoring the craftsmanship and tradition of mosaics. Infused with texture and color, my mosaics complement the environments in which they reside. Using high-quality glass such as Italian or Mexican Smalti, vitreous tiles or stained glass, and in many instances blending these materials together in a design, my creations are one of a kind. Working under the name of Maverick Mosaics, my artwork ranges in size from small decorative pieces to large exterior and interior architectural installations. My works have been seen on HGTV and many are in private collections. Large-scale architectural commissions include projects for Whole Foods Market, Inc. (2007 and 2006) and Rockville Town Square (2006), Rockville, MD. I am an officer in the Society of American Mosaic Artists.

## KELLY FITZGERALD
Fine Art Photography
Pages 221, 224

For years I have been photographing the California Sierras and the Hawaiian Islands. I began this series of work largely out of a desire to preserve a beauty still largely unhampered by commercial development. I also recognize that progress is encroaching and it will not last. I wanted to reach beyond what the color photograph conveys, so I chose to document each series in black-and-white infrared film to convey the dreaminess and magical quality each place holds. My photographs have appeared in numerous exhibits in various art galleries around the world. My work has also won several awards, including The Golden Light Award. Limited-edition print prices range from $750 to $2,750. Prints are available as archival fiber base silver gelatin and chromogenic, Type C prints. Print sizes range from 11" x 14" to 30" x 40". Each print is scrupulously hand printed by a master printer.

GUILD SOURCEBOOKS: *Residential Art 1, 2, 4*

## MARILYN FORTH
Fiber Wall Art
Pages 292-293

The art I present to the world is large and unique. The painted dyes are modulated and layered. You can actually see the layers in some instances. White lines are a very important part of my work. Many of my pieces are based on natural forms taking on a human context. The pieces entitled *Singing Flowers* and *Wild Flower Waltz* are examples. As reference material for the art exhibited in this book, I walked back into a vineyard, lay down, and took a photo up through the vines. The art is called *Vineyard Dreams*. My prices range from $1,500 to $5,000, depending on size and complexity. Photos of completed commissions are sent to the client for final approval. I have exhibited in many national shows and created art for corporate and residential clients. I have also taught fiber art classes at Syracuse University. My pieces are light resistant and guaranteed.

GUILD SOURCEBOOKS: *Architect's 6; Designer's 6, 7, 8, 10, 11, 12, 13, 14; Architectural & Interior Art 16, 20; Residential Art 2, 5*

## JOANNE FOX
Paintings
Page 169

I am not a polite artist. I want my paintings to be confrontive, explosive, and a bit intimidating in the same way that meeting a very beautiful woman or a tall, powerful man can be. The oil paintings' large size, muscular composition, bold gestures, and sensual colors help to convey this presence. These abstracts are not for those who want a small window onto an untarnished world, but for those of us who wish to celebrate the power and beauty of paint and of the human spirit.

GUILD SOURCEBOOKS: *Residential Art 2*

## FRANCESCO
Paintings
Page 170

I found my passion in abstract art after studying at Akron University, the University of Tampa, independent study in Italy, and then moving with my family to Florida. My works are deeply emotional and visceral. I am inspired by daily events including emotions, environment, and music. I express my feelings through the use of bright colors and hidden objects. I paint in a small studio with little space and visual effect. The hand of an indescribable muse motivates my art. To promote the arts in my community, I work with The Group of Gala Corina, promoting young artists with differing artistic interests, while sharing a passion for finding beauty, harmony, truth and purity of expression in all forms of art.

EXHIBITIONS: May International Show, 2007, Museum of the Americas, Doral, FL; SOLO, 2007 Art Expo, New York, NY; Hoffman Porges Gallery, 2007, 2006, 1999, Ybor City, FL; Aspirations Winery, 2005–2007, St. Petersburg, FL; Esperanza! 2006, Gala Corina, Tampa, FL; *Buttons 4 Eyes*, One-man show, 2005, Park Art Gallery, New York, NY; Park-Art Gallery, 2005, New York, NY; *The Art of Kroslak & Francesco, Two Generations*, 2005, Hoffman; Porges Gallery, Ybor City, FL

### RONALD R. FRANKLIN
Objects
Page 106

A pot reflects the actions that create it. The effect of two types of reduction, kiln atmosphere and post firing, are essentially evident. Red/bronze glaze responds beautifully to kiln reduction. Its bright reds and greens reflect circulation. Patina and matte type glazes produce wonderful flashing effects by post firing. Copper, a key ingredient to both of these glazes, becomes mystical under such conditions. The touch of fire, temperature, atmosphere and circulation, are all beautifully recorded by copper's keen responsiveness. Through precise craftsmanship and the probity of the fire, the mystery of smoke, flash, and crackle communicate a beauty beyond the elements of a simple pot. My work has been shown in numerous galleries and museums. Exhibitions include the First World Ceramic Biennale 2001 International Competition, Ichon, South Korea, and the Cheongju International Craft Competition—both 2001 and 2003—in Cheongju, South Korea. I am honored to be in the permanent collection of the World Ceramic Center in Ichon, South Korea.

### JEFF FREEMAN
Furniture
Page 42

I was always intrigued by the techniques of welding aluminum and the not-so-simple task of designing contemporary furnishings. My work originally came from a personal desire to own furniture different from others. While renovating our home, I decided to fabricate tables, chairs, range hood, etc., from aluminum. I purchased some equipment and taught myself how to TIG weld. Friends and visitors to our home suggested showing some of my pieces and the sales started from there. Always experimenting with ideas evoked from music and song lyrics, my 660 CELCIUS furniture line is functional with a sculptural flair. Primarily constructed from ten-gauge aluminum, polished concrete, and recycled glass blocks, my furnishings are completely affordable, with prices ranging from $400 to $2,500. Some of my more popular works are replicated and constantly evolving. I invite the challenge of commissions.

### CHERI FREUND
Prints
Page 214

I think of my work as a unique communication between the art and the individual viewer. I create with a surrealistic and ethereal flare, intending to invoke inner feelings and emotions. Visible within my abstract work is a hint of realism, which provides the viewing audience with multiple interpretations. My inspiration comes from color, everyday objects, and most importantly, music. I approach each image as a challenge and strive to create something completely different from the previous image. Creating within the digital realm (with occasional blending of traditional art) takes my work in unexpected directions, allowing for unlimited possibilities. As any artist will tell you, it is "knowing" when the image is complete. As a diversified artist, I am able to create in a multitude of directions. My work has been commissioned by the publishing, software, and music industries. I was an exhibitor in the New York *Prevailing Human Spirit—911 Tribute* (hosted by the Society of Illustrators) and have been featured in *Photo Electronic Imaging* magazine. Additionally, my giclée prints have been shown internationally. To view additional samples of my work, please go to www.pixel-artist.com.

### GASCH DESIGN
Murals, Tiles & Wall Reliefs
Page 273

My name is Michael Gasch. As the owner of Gasch Design, I create a contemporary style of mosaic art using a variety of techniques and materials to accommodate many different projects and locations. I work in residential and commercial settings to create fine art that may be functional in nature or serve as an enhancement to the existing ambiance. As a trained carpenter and mason, I am licensed, insured, and have the capabilities to complete any type of related project, no matter what the size or technical requirements. By incorporating standard masonry practices and sound business principles with my art, I am able to create lasting works that are both unique and completed in a professional manner, no matter where the location. I absolutely love creating fine art. I am very passionate about what I do, and it shows in my finished works. Please feel free to take a look at my website, www.gaschdesign.com, to find out more about Gasch Design.

### JOE GEMIGNANI
Fine Art Photography
Page 225

I alter Polaroid photographs by hand using a technique applied directly to the film. Like an artist paints a canvas with a brush, I stroke the entire surface of the photograph's emulsion with my tools. The process creates an image that is more like a painting than a photograph. Because each image is created individually by hand, my work is characterized by a unique style. The subtle transformations I make on the film intensify the beauty of the simple, everyday images I capture on camera. The manual process frees me to produce a picture that more closely resembles what I see with my eyes and my heart.

### HILARY GIFFORD
Art Quilts
Page 301

My business name, Custom Cloth, represents a desire to create unique yet functional works of art with a variety of textiles and techniques. Since 1980 I have been working full time making wearable art, decorative fiber art for display, and functional fibers for the home. The majority of my work is one-of-a-kind art textiles, although I have enjoyed designing for production, designing and working in collaboration with other artists, and for scarf and fabric companies. Among a broad range of experiences, I have had my designs produced overseas, owned a wearable arts clothing boutique, and taught textiles at Syracuse University. I wholesale my scarf lines nationally and retail scarves, quilts, and art items through American Craft Council shows and my website, www.CustomCloth.com.

## KEVIN GILL
Furniture
Page 43

My furniture is designed to exude feelings of elegance and sensuality that exist in harmony with the surrounding environment. I believe in balancing my own creative expression with the desires of my customers and the settings in which my work will reside. Flexibility in design, attention to detail, and sensitivity to deadlines are of paramount importance when collaborating with clients on a project. My work has been displayed at the Philadelphia Furniture and Furnishings Show and has been depicted in *Woodshop News* as well as *The Free Press* and *The Free Press Online* serving midcoast Maine. The chess and backgammon table in this publication was commissioned by an architect and interior designer for a luxury waterfront home in Tenants Harbor, Maine. It was designed to compliment the *Sting Chair* by Gijs Papavoine.

## GLASSICS
Objects
Page 107

Using glass as a means of artistic expression is a practice as old as measured time, and I feel privileged it is my life's work to continue this ancient tradition. The artworks created in my studio are simply the latest effort, brought forth from a lifetime fascination with form, color, and texture. I am currently exploring various multimedia collaborations. Assisted by my talented husband, this has opened up many exciting new avenues of expression and creativity. My award-winning work can be seen at several shows across the western United States. This year also marks my twenty-second anniversary as an exhibitor at the world renowned Festival of Arts in Laguna Beach, California.

GUILD SOURCEBOOKS: *Residential Art 4, 5*

## NANCY GONG
Architectural Elements
Pages 14, 93-95

The energy and spirit of living things have always intrigued me. It continues to be at the very core of my art. I constantly strive to capture grace, movement, and dimension of life in a simple yet powerful style. Facets of nature by way of lyrical abstractions are the soul of my art. With a rich, personal style and an impressive command of my medium, I create sensitive, responsive, and enduring glass designs with quality craftsmanship for architectural installations and art collections. My work has been published in *Interiors and Sources, Contemporary Crafts for the Home, The Design Journal of Korea, Architect Design Collaborative, American Style* Magazine, *Stained Glass Magazine,* and previous Guild Sourcebooks.

COMMISSIONS: American Institute of Architects; Artwalk of Rochester Artistic Bus Shelter; Constellation Brands; Cornell University; Corning Tropel Corp.; Duke University; Oakhill Country Club; Port of Rochester; Sharon Vermont Vietnam Honorial; and private residences in IL, NC, NJ, NY, PA, SC, TX and Austria

EXHIBITIONS: SOFA Chicago, 2004; Crafts National 38/27, ArtForm International, 2003. To see more, please visit www.nancygong.com

## ELISE GRAY
Murals, Tiles & Wall Reliefs
Page 274

As a sculptor my work is an attempt to respond to the natural beauty of our earth. My forms are made of materials from the earth—clay, water, glazes, and oxides—and the resulting shapes speak of land formations, mountains, cliffs, sky, wind, and flowing water. The creative process starts with single large slabs of stoneware clay. These are stretched, folded, ripped, textured, and layered to the desired form. After bisque firing, selective staining, and glazing, each piece is high fired individually. Several individual layers are then cemented together and attached to backings for hanging to form the final design.

COMMISSIONS: Unitarian Church, 1994, White Plains, NY; GE Capital, 1992, Stamford, CT; Florida Percent for Art, 1988, Commission, Education Building; Florida Department of Education, 1988, Tallahassee

COLLECTIONS: Capital One, Stamford, CT; Museum of Arts and Sciences, Macon, GA; Carnival Cruise Line, Miami, FL; Morgan, Lewis & Bocius, Miami, FL; IBM Corporation, Williston, VT

AWARDS: Georgia Council for Arts, 1993-94, Individual Artist Grant; Pollock-Krasner Foundation Grant, 1990-91

## CAROL GREEN
Objects
Pages front cover, 10, 108-109

Like you, my heart catches in my throat when I encounter scenes of great natural beauty. It's a feeling that we've shared with our ancestors throughout the world and over the millennia. Artists have always created objects for utility, pleasure, and symbolic meaning. My goal is to combine the beauty of the natural world with objects that serve. The *Gourd Vessel* series is wheel thrown using mica-impregnated earthenware and is raku fired. The lids are copper and cast bronze and finished with a hot patina. The *Candle Branch* series is cast bronze and finished with a hot patina. Commissions include The Palace Hotel, Beijing, China; Allegany Power, Hagertown, PA; and Kaiser Permanente, Cleveland, OH. You can see more of my work at www.carolgreen.com.

## DON GREEN
Furniture
Pages 6, 44

It is my intention to make studio furniture that is sound in construction and simple in design. As with every artist, there is a desire to be original. As a result, I have cultivated my own methods of building that are exclusive to my work. Investing in the time to develop of my own techniques has made me a more resourceful and inventive artist. My intention is to make a clean, straightforward aesthetic statement with my furniture. My work is pared down to simple elements that are designed and executed well. Decoration has never been my thing. I am motivated to produce strong, honest work that is both functional and sound in construction. I am not trying the reinvent the wheel, but to develop my own language of form while, at the same time, honoring tradition.

## GREG ARCENEAUX CABINETMAKERS, INC.
Furniture
Page 45

I draw on Louisiana's unique Colonial heritage with its French, Spanish, Anglo, and Native American influences as inspiration for my designs. Using native woods I create furniture that brings beauty and utility to peoples' lives. By using time-honored traditional joinery, I have created pieces that have survived floods, fires, and hurricanes. With normal use this furniture should last generations, as the original Creole and Acadian antiques have lasted. This style was predominant throughout the Mississippi River Valley and its tributaries when Louisiana went from the Gulf of Mexico to Canada. So many people have Louisiana roots today without knowing it. Many of my clients want our pieces to blend with their antiques, so I offer a look of neglected elegance with or without distressing. The finish that I use is hand-rubbed oil and wax, as well as decorative painted gold leaf finishes. I am currently using trees felled by Hurricane Katrina milled at local saw mills, as well as sinker logs being pulled from the lakes, rivers, bayous, and salvaged material. I am striving to maintain our unique Louisiana heritage and culture through these traditions.

## CAROL GRIFFIN
Paintings
Page 171

I delight in exploring color, taking a limited palette and mixing the colors in various combinations to create my "plaid" paintings. The palette for my paintings is often based on the colors that occur naturally in marble or other natural stone. I find that nature, particularly stone, provides a superb source of inspiration for my work. A palette might also be inspired by a majestic mountain, the colors of a flower, or a dramatic sunset. I also love to choose colors that evoke memories of a special place visited as a way to remember the experience. I believe my work lends itself especially well to residential applications, as well as to hotel and corporate applications. Prices range from $500 to $5,000. My work has been exhibited in group shows in New York City and East Hampton, New York. Commissions are welcomed. To view my website, please visit http://web.mac.com/cgriffin6.

## JOAN ROTHCHILD HARDIN
Murals, Tiles & Wall Reliefs
Page 275

From my New York City studio, I work with designers, architects, and private clients to create custom hand-painted ceramic tiles for installations in kitchens, bathrooms, fireplaces, murals, and other projects where beauty and durability are the goal. Designs can be your own, mine, or something we develop collaboratively. HardinTiles have added liveliness and richness, sometimes whimsy, to residential and corporate settings. My tiles are known for their sophistication and depth. They often make people smile. With thirty years' experience in the studio, I have developed techniques for layering glazes on the tiles to create a look not usually seen in the medium. HardinTiles are featured in gallery and museum exhibitions, and books, and have been included in corporate and private collections worldwide. For a wider selection of my work, please visit www.HardinTiles.com.

GUILD SOURCEBOOKS: *Designer's 14, 15; Architectural & Interior Art 16, 17, 18, 19, 20; Residential Art 3, 4, 5*

## HARRINGTON SCULPTURE
Sculpture
Page 132

Dostoyevsky said "Beauty will save the world." This is both a profound and challenging statement to me. In order to understand and respect it, I am forced to search for the real meaning of beauty. I am obliged to go beyond the surface of my subject matter and challenge my own initial pre-conceptions. To find real meaning in beauty, you must embrace it in all forms, not just its canons of ideology. My work reflects these goals by focusing on the representation of the human form, with an emphasis on movement, sensuality, emotion, strength, and beauty. The product is the manifestation of my search for truth and beauty. To view more examples of my work, I invite you to visit my website at www.harringtonsculpture.com.

## MARY HATCH
Paintings
Page 172

I was surprised when brides began finding their way into my paintings and even more surprised when they refused to leave—always a sign that something needs to be said. *Bouquet Day* is part of what has now evolved into a series of paintings based on wedding photographs that friends and family have been kind enough to loan me. Not portraits, but charming evidence of the social change always revealed in our rituals. Today's brides have transformed themselves by their dress and their demeanor—not quite traditional, but still mindful of tradition. (Much like our world is being transformed by technology, requiring us to develop new social norms as we move toward an ambiguous future.) Please visit my website to see more of this ongoing series, as well as other paintings and prints and my resume. I'm always happy to answer questions and/or send a price list.

## JOHN HEIN
Furniture
Page 46

I design and build restrained hardwood furniture using interlocking hand-cut joints and wooden pegs. A traditional respect for nature combined with a contemporary structure result in rectilinear spare pieces of furniture in which the intrinsic quality of woods and their grains are allowed to stand out.

## RHONDA HEISLER
Murals, Tiles & Wall Reliefs
Page 276

My mosaic art is grounded in my fascination with the color, patterning, and textural properties of fine opaque and metallic stained glass. My technique is akin to painting in hand-cut art glass. I draw my inspiration from the material itself, and as I cut into the glass, I edit the sheet for the choicest bits, creating tesserae that vary in size and shape. In laying the tiles, I juxtapose surfaces that are matte, shiny, or iridescent; color that is solid, shaded, or streaky; textures that are smooth or irregular. In my abstract compositions, I sketch only minimally and work spontaneously and expressively, using modulated color progressions and variations in shape, scale, and texture to create visual metaphors for complex ideas. Commissioned mosaics may be abstract or representational, single- or multi-panel, to bring drama and dimension to any living space. I am an officer in the Society of American Mosaic Artists.

GUILD SOURCEBOOKS: *Architectural & Interior Art 21, 22; Residential Art 4, 5*

## HEMBROUGH GALLERY
Fine Art Photography
Page 226

It is the light that is special, and it is with us always, everywhere. I see it, am sensitive to it, and wait for it. Like the Mississippi River that I lived by and watched every day, I cannot stop it from moving, and I cannot see the end. I photograph the rocks as people. They have seen all, heard everything, and their stories are there. I have been following the stories for twenty-five years in the sacred places of Ireland, Nova Scotia, the American West, the Southwest, and elsewhere. I work with natural light and do not manipulate the scene, the subject matter, the exposure, or the printing process. I will always continue to use film. Through these images I show the remarkable in the mundane, the unfamiliar in the commonplace, as in my series called *Images from Another World*. My work has been exhibited in galleries spanning the country and is found in numerous private and corporate collections. Please visit www.hembroughgallery.com.

## KAREN HENDERSON
Fiber Wall Art
Pages 287, 295

I'm originally from Bucks County, PA, but now live in beautiful, rural northwest New Jersey. I learned to weave while studying textile design at Moore College of Art & Design in Philadelphia, PA. My work is landscape inspired, and I'm interested in the connections between place, self, emotion, and time. Seasons, atmospheres, and the time of day intrigue me. I try to recreate these natural occurrences, evoking emotions that I associate with them through the use of color, line, and texture. I use different dye techniques (batik, shibori, discharge), as well as sewing with my weavings and fabric pieces. I draw lines by stitching with thread. Dimension is added with tucks, layers, or other manipulations of fabric. Most of the techniques I choose to use are very contemplative, encouraging introspection; other processes are spontaneous and unpredictable. Works range in size from small, intimate pieces to those that are large and expansive. Commissions are welcome.

## STEPHEN HENNING
Paintings
Pages 173, 180

I enjoy quiet, natural surroundings that are far away from the noisy demands of everyday life. I strive to capture impressions of the fleeting beauty of such places that are uncluttered by man, whether it be a wilderness waterway illuminated by the morning light or an abandoned pasture bathed in the colors of evening. My primary artistic goal is to provide a pleasing, peaceful image that can be brought indoors, a sort of escape portal where one's mind is free to stretch and dance. I prefer to create large paintings that make a big impact and are easy to "step into." Once your eye has entered one of my paintings, you will be entertained by a wide spectrum of colors that are built up in many overlapping layers or intertwining brushstrokes, a playground of hue, value, and varying texture that gives a rich depth to a seemingly simple scene.

## HIGH BEAMS LTD.
Lighting
Page 73

Designers Trenny Robb and Bob Michaud began in 1980 with Victorian reproductions and restoration work. Now into the Arts and Crafts era and everything in between. Period lighting and design work of all types: wall sconces, ceiling lamps, desk lamps, standing lamps, table lamps, chandeliers, bathroom fixtures, lanterns, and outdoor lighting. Also, all of the lampshades are made with real leaves and petals, mica, fabric, parchment, and more. Interior lighting design consulting available for houses, restaurants, offices, hotels, camps, etc. Please browse our web galleries at www.highbeams.com, then contact us for your lighting needs.

COMMISSIONS: Foy's Beach Bar, Jost Van Dyke, British Virgin Islands; Y.M.C.A. Camp, Silver Bay, Lake George, NY; Landmark Project, 2003, St. Johnsbury Athenaeum, St. Johnsbury, VT

## ELIZABETH HOLMES
Fine Art Photography
Page 227

I have always been interested in the idea of community and how we define a sense of place. In my photographs I use landscapes and cityscapes to symbolize the connection I make to a sense of place and time. Using black-and-white infrared film and interpretive hand coloring, I isolate my subjects as the main characters of my images. I work with infrared film to create soft, grainy images that convey a sense of timelessness. Rich black shadows heighten the mood. In some photographs I hand color specific areas to emphasize certain elements, and in others I color the whole image with oils and pencils to add an impressionistic quality. Using this process I'm able to enhance the emotional content of the image while retaining the realistic quality. My work has been exhibited in numerous galleries and art centers, and is held in private and corporate collections, including Pfizer and Latham & Watkins.

## HUBBARDTON FORGE
Lighting
Pages 5, 74, 351

Thirty-three years ago Hubbardton Forge® was founded as a two-person craft studio located in an old barn in Hubbardton, Vermont. At that time, products were one of a kind, sold at craft fairs throughout New England. Though we have outgrown the barn, our products are still hand-forged by skilled craftsmen. Our designs are truly timeless—simple, classic, elegant, original—form and function inseparable in every piece. By blending time-honored blacksmithing techniques with environmentally friendly technology, Hubbardton Forge creates wrought-iron lighting and home accessories that sell through retail showrooms throughout North America. Visit us at www.vtforge.com. You can also find a selection of Hubbardton Forge products in The Artful Home catalog from The Guild, and at their web site, www.artfulhome.com.

## BRIAN A. HUBEL
Furniture
Pages 47, back cover

I have been woodworking for more than fifteen years and started my business, Hubel Handcrafted (Hubelhi.com) in 1998. I am passionate about designing and crafting each piece to perfection. Each piece should stand on its own, graceful yet strong, something you never tire of viewing. I run the one-man shop where each idea and creation takes place. Every aspect of design, wood selection, and crafting is carefully thought out in order to create a piece that is visually appealing, functional, and will stand the test of time.

EXHIBITIONS: Masters in the Art of Furniture, 2006, Shidoni Gallery, Santa Fe, NM; Fabric, Furniture and Furnishings, 2006, Steamboat Springs, CO; Collector's Event, 2003-2006, Shidoni Gallery, Santa Fe, NM; Denver International Airport, 2005, CO; Colorado Springs Pioneers Museum, 2002-2004, Colorado Springs, CO

AWARDS: Design Portfolio, 2007, Custom Woodworking Business; Quilts and Fine Woodworking Exhibition, 2004, Colorado Springs; Pioneers Museum

PUBLICATIONS: *Custom Woodworking Business*, 2007; *Woodworker West*, 2005; *Colorado Springs Gazette Telegraph*, 2004

## HUCK FISHER METALWORKERS
Home Accents
Page 82

We combine finely detailed traditional artistic blacksmithing with contemporary design. Our motto, "Attention to detail adds strength to design," is apparent in all of our work, which includes large static and kinetic sculptures, whimsical garden sculptures and weathervanes, heirloom home furnishings and lighting, and exterior and interior railings and gates.

COMMISSIONS: Bronze and stained glass grand entrance chandelier, Government of Canada; Large forged and fabricated aluminum hand-painted signage for McKelvie's Restaurant, Halifax, Nova Scotia

COLLECTIONS: Design of hand-forged wrought iron and copper perimeter fencing and central gateway for the sculpture court of the Art Gallery of Nova Scotia; Design and creation of forty-four hand-painted aluminum fish that hang from light standards throughout the seaport of Lunenburg, Nova Scotia, a UNESCO World Heritage Site

GUILD SOURCEBOOKS: *Architectural & Interior Art 20, 21*

## JOEL HUNNICUTT
Objects
Pages 103, 110

Pottery. No, definitely glass. Oh my, it's wood. That is the reaction I am looking for. I work to create vessels out of the organic medium of wood that have the elegance and luminosity of glass. Using the technique of segmented turning, I am able to achieve shapes and designs that are usually associated with the ancient pottery forms of Greece, China, and Egypt. The use of classic forms and vibrant colors create a delight for the senses. Segmented turning utilizes the technique of cutting boards into precisely measured small pieces, then gluing the pieces together into circles that create the forms that will be turned on a lathe to the final design. Toners and dyes are added to lacquer during the finishing process to give the vessel the appearance of blown glass or thrown pottery. To fully appreciate the work, it needs to be touched and handled. This allows you to have an understanding of the technique and the texture of wood that gives it a blown glass feel. Each piece is a unique creation, as there may be subtle differences in shape and color.

AWARDS: Niche Award Finalist, 2007, 2006

GUILD SOURCEBOOKS: *Residential Art 5*

## DOUGLAS HYSLOP
Paintings
Page 174

My artistic strong suit has always been drawing, particularly the human figure. Handling the human figure well usually requires a certain amount of articulation. And when I paint the human figure, I try to include the articulation of the pencil's line, as well as the emotion of the brush stroke and pigment. A number of years ago, I was taken by the Comedy of Art, and have clung to it ever since. The Comedy deals with the happenings of old and well-worn characters, including Harlequin, Columbine, and Pierrot. To depict them necessitates inclusion of narrative elements. In my paintings, I try to raise the narrative element to a level commensurate with the formal composition. I think I have been so taken by the Comedy because it seems to refuse to let go of humanistic values. As a friend of mine said, "You make paintings for people who read."

GUILD SOURCEBOOKS: *Residential Art 5*

## KAREN IGLEHART
Paintings
Page 175

My paintings reside in an ambiguous space between landscape and abstraction. Impressions of places are expressed through reference to landscape, without depicting specific details. Impressions of mood, weather, atmosphere, and space are expressed through the use of line, color, placement, and scale. I want the viewer to find his/her own space in my paintings and to experience it without definition or explanation. I work in oil . . . on canvas, paper, or birch panel. Recently, I have been including graphite markings. I work in layers of color, letting each dry before continuing to the next. An important part of this process is observing what is happening on the canvas, being aware of when to leave a mark or area alone, and how to respond to the painting as it evolves. I have been a professional artist for twenty-five years, have shown in many national juried and invitational shows and galleries throughout the U.S. I have work in the collections of Dr. Hauschka Skin Care, Inc., Sakyong Mipham Rinpoche, Shambhala Int'l., and other private collections.

## IMAGO DEI, LLC
Murals, Tiles & Wall Reliefs
Page 277

We are a creative arts firm in Houston, Texas, with clients and projects spanning the globe. Imago Dei, founded by husband-and-wife artists Jeremy and Jamie Wells, has grown into a team of international artists who share a passion for collaborative creativity and a vision for excellence and integrity in all matters of business. Our showroom and studio are made available to our clients throughout the creation of their artwork. Our creative works are visible through an accomplished portfolio of fine art, custom murals, decorative wall treatments, and public art. We value each client ranging from individual collectors, galleries, and design professionals to corporate, hospitality, and city art committees. Current projects include a large-scale installation for the Chevron Art Collection that features over 2,500 square feet of abstract fine art suspended by a custom-designed metal sculpture. Recent commissions include: Breast and Bone Hospital, Dr. Nikko Cosmetic Surgery Center, Christus St. Elizabeth Hospital, and the private residence of ASID designer Carolyn Durrett.

GUILD SOURCEBOOKS: *Residential Art 5*

## IPSO FACTO PRODUCTIONS
Objects
Page 111

New product development is the driving force behind Ipso Facto. We plan to continue refining elegant designs and putting a new twist on functional forms. The *Form Study* groupings are a modern study of line, shape, and color. The result is simple style and graceful symmetry. The forms are designed with careful consideration of the negative spaces between, and grouping the forms reveals this interesting relationship. All forms are made by hand without the use of molds, and each form is unique due to the process. Represented by galleries internationally, Ipso Facto meets the demands of the designer glass market with quick turnaround times and commission opportunities.

## JL SULLIVAN PHOTOGRAPHY
Fine Art Photography
Page 228

I revel in color and in the inspiration of our beautiful world. The colors beneath the surface of the seas are some of the most brilliant, the life so beautiful and fragile. I search for the same rich colors and patterns above the seas as below, seeking the essence and intrigue of flora, landscape, and architectural details, preferring the use of a macro lens and ambient light when possible. I appreciate the drama of rich color against inky blackness and extend the drama into my signature archival framing—white-core black matte combined with the clean lines of a simple black frame. All fine art prints are available in image sizes from 5" x 7" to 18" x 24" with studio standard framing or to requested specifications.

EXHIBITIONS: Solo exhibition, *Close-Up: An Alternate View*, 2007, Hollingsworth Gallery, Brevard, NC; *A Sense of Place Exhibition*, 2007, Transylvania Community Arts Council, Brevard, NC; Fine Arts and Crafts Showcase, 2006, Transylvania Community Arts Council, Brevard, NC; *Faces and Facets Photography Competition and Exhibition*, 2003, Panama City, FL; *Faces and Facets Photography Competition and Exhibition*, 2002, best of category award [underwater], *Legs*, Panama City, FL

## ADAM JAHIEL
Fine Art Photography
Pages 13, 229

I like to look, and I like to share what I see. But I like to do that sharing wordlessly. Over the years some of my peers have accused me of being mostly interested in the "fringe" people. Maybe so. But I like to think I am drawn to those who seem to exist outside of time in forgotten corners and cultures. They seem somehow more in touch with, or part of, the human condition. I try and document people, places, and life in an honest, straightforward, respectful, and intimate way. And preserve it forever. I work in black and white because it allows me to boil elements down to their very essence—shape, lines, and light. Light can be indescribably beautiful and fascinating. I love to watch it completely transform something. The same scene can go from being unremarkable, to extraordinary, and back to unremarkable in a heartbeat. Even after all these years of working, the ability to freeze a moment in time and preserve it forever, although mostly science, to me is really like magic. More detail available at www.adamjahiel.com.

## DORI JALAZO
Sculpture
Page 133

I make art to create meaning in my life and to give to the larger family of humankind. I have always been a painter. I started working with clay to fulfill a spiritual need, to create pieces that sing with joy. I have created commissioned life-story sculptures, which speak so much more eloquently than portraits. My work reflects the journey of our lives through rocky terrain to sweet sunshine, art that speaks to your heart and soul. The work is in public and private collections throughout the world, including the collections of Bernie Siegel, Dr. Ruth, and Henry Winkler.

## JAMES T. RUSSELL SCULPTURE
Sculpture / Metal Wall Art
Pages 9, 134, 265

The concept of my sculpture is based on the juxtaposition of contrasting contours. Opposites attract opposites. I use highly polished stainless steel because it is alive with reflective energy. Through this medium I transform my inner emotion into permanent form. I have edition sculptures that range from $5,000 to $50,000. Monumental sculptures start at $60,000.

COMMISSIONS: Coast Aluminum and Architectural, 2003, Santa Fe Springs, CA; Astra Zeneca Pharmaceuticals, 2002, Wilmington, DE; Chico Municipal Airport, 2001, Chico, CA

COLLECTIONS: Four Seasons Hotel, Hong Kong; City of Cerritos, CA; Bellagio Hotel, Las Vegas, NV; Motorola Corporation, Beijing, China; Riverside Art Museum, Riverside, CA; A.T. Kearney Inc., Chicago, IL

EXHIBITIONS: *Impact*, 2004, Tadu Contemporary Art, Santa Fe, NM; *Miniatures*, 2004, Albuquerque Museum of Art, NM

PUBLICATIONS: *Santa Fe Reporter*, Oct. 2004; *Leaders* magazine, Sept. 2004

GUILD SOURCEBOOKS: *Architect's 7, 8, 12, 14; Architectural & Interior Art 16, 17, 18, 19, 20, 21; Residential Art 1, 3, 5*

## CAROLINE JASPER
Paintings
Page 176

Using the language of color, my paintings focus on light and its intrinsic meaning. Colors express my feelings during an exact moment when the light, enriching an otherwise ordinary subject, caught my attention. I prefer the rich colors of early mornings or late afternoons, when the sun is low and shadows long. Each work starts on a red-hot canvas, the axis for impact dynamics. At close range subjects lose identity. Brushstrokes, denoting abstract color blocks, juxtapose bits of unpainted red ground, generating optical/psychological effects.

COMMISSIONS: The City of Bel Air, MD; The Community College of Baltimore County, MD; Harford Community College, Bel Air, MD; Philip Insurance Co, Bel Air, MD, The Ritz-Carlton, Orlando, FL

COLLECTIONS: The Circuit Court of Harford County, MD; Cisco Systems, Denver, CO; The Comus Inn at Sugarloaf Mountain, Dickerson, MD; Duncan Financial, Carlsbad, CA; HK Holbein, Inc., Williston, VT; Kilpatrick Stockton LLP, Washington, DC; McGraw Hill Publishers, Columbus, OH, and New York, NY

GUILD SOURCEBOOKS: *Designer's 15, Architectural & Interior Art 16, 22*

## NICOLETTE JELEN
Paintings
Page 177

What inspires me is the way light travels through veils of color, enhancing one while the others stand by. Like mists, they are all part of each other. My work reflects this balance, starting with one dark red and layering transparent and opaque veils of color that build upon each other to form the final image. When I paint, I think about the travels of light and time.

## JENSEN & MARINEAU CERAMICS
Murals, Tiles & Wall Reliefs
Page 278

Partners in life and work for more than thirty years and working from our studio in Oregon's Tualatin mountains, we handcraft ceramic tiles that we think of as functional art for everyday living. From carved earthenware to incised black engobe to slip-trailed blue and white tiles, we offer a variety of styles suitable for the most intimate to the most public spaces. Images vary in mood and theme, and include shore and water life, animals, plants, and people in the places and activities they love. Jensen and Marineau installations create spaces so beautiful that they become central to the life of a home. We are happy to work with clients and designers to create a custom design. Visit us at www.jensenandmarineau.com to tour our handmade home and studio, visit a gallery of finished installations, and browse our catalog to see our complete tile line, from classic to contemporary.

## JERRY MADER PHOTOGRAPHIC IMAGERY
Fine Art Photography
Page 230

I have been in love with the photographic process since the day in my childhood when my father loaned me his Vest Pocket Kodak and, after many failures, I at last made a picture. Since then, my love affair with the photograph has taken me to wonderful places. Now, after thirty-five years in the profession, I have added historic processes to my palette: large-format platinum/palladium and carbon tissue contact prints. I will continue to make silver gelatin prints but plan to convert that process into the entirely handmade print as well. Each of these processes allows me to expand the traditional context of the photographic print, particularly the limitations of the rectangular boundary. My most recent efforts in this area have been photographs printed on kiln-formed glass, specifically, carbon emulsion transfers. I find this fusion of image and sculpture especially exciting.

## JOEL ANDERSON PHOTOGRAPHY
Fine Art Photography
Page 231

My photography is about telling the story of a place. I want to go beyond quick details and show the full personality, whether the subject is an old farm building or a remote Irish island. I'm drawn to strong lines and a sense of mystery and depth. Favorite subjects are out-of-the-way places and those struggling in the noise of modern life. I use large-format film cameras and print in a traditional wet darkroom.

EXHIBITIONS: *Art of the State*, 2007, State Museum, Harrisburg, PA; *Images 2006*, Robeson Gallery, State College, PA; Solo Exhibition, 1999, Lexington Art Gallery, Lexington, VA; *Yosemite Renaissance*, 1998, Yosemite Museum Gallery, CA; *The Natural World*, 1994, Carnegie Museum of Natural History, Pittsburg, PA

AWARDS: Best in Show, 2007, Arts Alive, Ocean City, MD; Best in Show, photography, 2005, Ann Arbor State Street Art Fair; Grand Prize, 1994, Natural World International Competition, Carnegie Museum, Pittsburg, PA

## JOHN CHILES GLASS
Objects
Page 113

Many of the traditional glassblowing techniques that are practiced today have been passed from generation to generation for thousands of years. Along the way craftsmen have left something of themselves in what they have made. The desire to master my craft, make a living doing what I love to do, and to leave something of myself in the work is what compels me to return again and again to the studio. The process of designing glass is essentially the attempt to best realize the medium's potential within its technical constraints. Trying to coax the material into new forms gives rise to technical solutions and inspires new design ideas. I get a lot of satisfaction out of this process and find designing both product lines and one-of-a-kind pieces to be equally challenging and rewarding in their respective ways. When I first started making the pieces that have evolved into my current work, I was preoccupied primarily with making simple and elegant classical forms. Over time I began to elaborate on these forms by adding colorful shapes to their exteriors. With the addition of external elements, the pieces began to take on more character-like attributes. These expressions of character have become more emotional in nature as they have found their way to the insides of the vessels.

## BARRY WOODS JOHNSTON
Sculpture
Page 135

My job is to visualize and then breathe life into inert clay, bronze, or stone. I strive to grasp the heart of what makes life worthwhile. My sculptures, often light and lively in sentiment, are generally upbeat. I seek to compliment an architectural setting while adding levity, movement, and humanity. Clothing is rendered in faithful detail, but with flowing movement and compositional unity. My degree in architecture gives me a regard for aesthetics and the ability to integrate art into its architectural setting. I view public commissions as an opportunity to capture the vision of the community. Many pieces symbolically incorporate a macro expression extracted from a micro observation in nature. When creating a sculpture, I look for an abstract form that symbolically embodies the overall vision, and then integrate that abstraction into a realistic statement. My subjects show a rich array of symbolism and are derived from mythology, religion, literature, psychology, and the contemporary dilemma.

## K4 GLASSART
Mixed & Other Media Wall Art
Page 248

Alicia and Beatriz, both architects by training and glass designers, began working in glass in Venezuela in 1983; now we continue our work in Asheville, NC. We develop art for the wall and sculptures using architectural-influenced designs, techniques, and materials to bring out the desired optic effects, forms, textures, and a wide array of structures and colors. We include in the mixed-media line travertine, copper, gold leaf, copper/gold wire, and glass.

COMMISSIONS: Sibel kitchen panels, 2004, Boston, MA; Juan Pablo II Cathedral, 1991, Caracas, Venezuela; Standing panels, Lineas Azules, 1990, Caracas, Venezuela

COLLECTIONS: The White House, 2004, Washington, DC; King Hussein of Jordan, 2002, Jordan; Arnold Shwarzenegger, 2000, CA; Bolivar Hall, 1995, London, England; Glass Museum, permanent collection of Modern International Glass Art, 1991, Ebeltoft, Denmark

AWARDS: Niche Winner, 1999, Philadelphia, PA; Toni Hall Award, 1998, Washington, DC; National Award of Fine Arts XXII, 1995, Valencia, Venezuela

## KATHY BARNARD STUDIO
Architectural Elements
Pages 96-97

Kathy Barnard Studio designs and fabricates sculptural carved art glass, stained glass windows, deep-carved glass panels, and murals. My site-specific commissioned work is found in commercial, religious, and private environments throughout the country. A love of nature, a commitment to the client's vision, and a distinctive sense of design and detail are incorporated to produce representational and abstract installations in glass and granite.

COMMISSIONS: Adventist Hospitals, 2002–2007, Boulder, Littleton, and Denver, CO; St. Mary's Hospital, 2006, Langhorne, PA; Mormon Temple, 2005, Apia, Samoa; Diocese of Wichita, Bishop's residence, 2003, KS; Stillwater National Bank & Trust, 2000, Tulsa, OK; RLDS Temple and World Headquarters, 1992, Independence, MO; Jewish Community Center and Federation Headquarters, 1988, Overland Park, KS; Midland Theatre, 1987, Kansas City, MO; and many private homes throughout the United States

AWARDS: AIA Allied Arts and Craftsmanship Award, 1990

GUILD SOURCEBOOKS: *The Guild 3, 4, 5; Architect's 9, 10, 13; Architectural & Interior Art 16, 22*

## HOLLY KATZ
Paintings
Page 178

I have always been fascinated by abstract expressionism. Its rejection of the formalities of representation in favor of spontaneity, freedom, and expression is what has inspired me since I started working as a painter over thirty years ago. The physical act of painting plays a major role in my work. I apply multiple layers of paint to create a highly textured, dynamic surface made up of bold, vibrant colors. I try not to overthink my choice of colors, but rely on intuition and emotion. I want the viewer to experience my paintings without feeling confined to the boundaries of the canvas or limited by any objective realism. Traveling is also an important inspirational source for me. I keep a visual diary of what I see and feel. I have had numerous one-person and group shows, and my paintings are in collections throughout the United States.

## KIM ELLEN KAUFFMAN
Fine Art Photography
Page 232

*Harmony* is a limited-edition photo collage created from multiple scans of original objects. It is from my body of work titled *Collaborations* which utilizes a cameraless, filmless imaging technique. Cameraless images are as old as photography itself, begun with Henry Fox Talbot's photogenic drawings of plants (ca.1830s) and Anna Atkin's cameraless studies of algae (1843). Today's tools have facilitated a new direction in this tradition. *Collaborations*, and its companion, *Florilegium*, number one hundred images and growing. Through *Collaborations* I share the beauty of the forms nature repeats across all living things and how we humans have mimicked these designs in numerous ways. See synecdochestudio.com for my vita, additional information, and to view the collections.

COLLECTIONS: Duke Integrative Medicine, Durham, NC; Kresge Art Museum, East Lansing, MI; Umstead Hotel, Cary, NC; North Ottawa Community Hospital, Grand Haven, MI; BGSU Firelands, Huron, OH; Northwestern Mutual Life Insurance, Milwaukee, WI; American Board of Emergency Medicine, East Lansing, MI

GUILD SOURCEBOOKS: *Architectural & Interior Art 22; Residential Art 5*

## RAY KELSO
Furniture
Page 48

I do not feel bound by the confines of the straight line or by any of the other conventions of classical furniture design. In fact, many walks in the woods have taught me that a straight line and a flat plane are not natural occurrences, but are man-made devices created to provide a sense of simplicity and order in our lives. I believe that furniture, perhaps even more than the structures in which we place it, is such an intimate part of our lives that it needs to manifest the natural and playful world of which we are a part. I attempt to do just that in each piece that I create. Like a walk in the woods, I stray from the straight line and the sharp corner. And like trees that provide raw material and much of the inspiration for my work, my furniture begs to be touched. I attempt to instill a sense of playfulness in each piece, all the while being conscious of the fact that it must function as intended. If my work raises the spirit and brings a smile to the face, then I have been successful.

GUILD SOURCEBOOKS: *Residential Art 5*

## ANNE KESSLER
Paintings
Page 179

I have a passion for landscapes that bring light and color into a room. I believe people need landscapes as a reminder of where the stillness of the earth meets the human eye. Something in our nature needs to experience the ancient outer ease of the world to remember who we are. Water surfaces are my specialty, also florals in clear, bright color. My larger architectural paintings often read well as abstracts. Commissions are welcome. I grew up in Cambridge, Massachusetts, and attended Radcliffe College. I currently live on the wild north coast of California. I have shown my work in galleries in San Francisco, Scottsdale, New York City, Paris, and Zurich. When Masako Owada was married to Prince Naruhito, the Crown Prince of Japan, one of my paintings was presented to the royal couple as a wedding present and hangs in the private collection of the Japanese royal household.

## JOHN KINGSLEY
Furniture
Page 49

My work represents an experience of the world in which I live and intends to capture a simple pleasure or thing of beauty through color, texture, and form. I am a furniture maker and artist who makes my home in the Finger Lakes region of upstate New York. I am inspired by a wide range of influences from the playfulness of my children's drawings to the endless rows of produce that stretch over the land. I develop my work by bringing together ideas and images. I playfully combine hand-carved textures and lines with colors created with natural pigments and milk paint. Careful sanding of the painted surfaces reveals both the complex dynamic patterns and the beauty of the wood on which it's created.

## DAN KLEIN
Furniture
Page 50

It has been more than thirty years that I've worked with wood in one form or another. I worked first as a carpenter, home builder, creator of school and children's play structures, then as a custom cabinetmaker, and architectural mill worker, acquiring furniture commissions along the way. In this long odyssey, furniture making is reaping the benefits of these past experiences as I now focus exclusively on furniture. My furniture has appeared in the *Boston Globe Magazine* and *Fine Woodworking Magazine*. I am challenged by the myriad of opportunities offered by working with solid wood slabs, as well as figured and exotic veneers. I can work with you to craft a commissioned piece that incorporates your ideas and desires and brings my knowledge of materials and resources together to make furniture that's both pleasing and unique. Alternately, there maybe a design in my portfolio that grabs your attention and could be a stunning addition to your home.

## BARBARA KOBYLINSKA
Sculpture
Page 136

Through my creation in clay, I feel and express my deep admiration for nature's wonders: organic, rich forms and abundant colors. I graduated from the Academy of Fine Arts in Warsaw, Poland, and received a master's degree in graphic design and later a degree in costume and stage design as a graduate student. I am a member of the International Sculpture Center and the Tri State Sculptors Educational Association. For a number of years, I have worked at the Logan Clay Products Company, mastering the techniques of transforming large pipes into birds and flowers. The heavy clay pipes are cut, altered, and reshaped by pounding them from the inside and out with wooden tools often as big as baseball bats. To construct different forms, two or more pipes are assembled together or stacked on top of each other. After an exciting process of creating the clay birds and flowers, the sculptures stay in the pipe factory for several weeks to dry until they are ready to be fired in gigantic beehive kilns. When the sculptures are fired, they look like terracotta, are very strong and solid, and can withstand all weather conditions. The sculptures are painted with oil stains and then sealed to protect the vibrant colors from the damaging effects of sun and rain.

## KRAMER SCULPTURES INC.
Sculpture
Page 137

I am a sculptor. I heat and hand forge metal until it gives form to expressions of human energy as it engages and relates. Heated metal is extremely forgiving; that's why I choose it as a medium. Through it I explore the forces that draw us together and that separate us from ourselves and each other. Having experienced both great tragedy and joy in my own life, I want my art to sustain relevant and meaningful encounters. I was born in Hamilton, Ontario, Canada in 1969. Through my world-renowned artist father, Richard Kramer, I learned blacksmithing techniques by osmosis; at home, art and metal were part of daily life. In 1995, when I completed a degree in fine arts at McMaster University and a Masters degree in Renaissance and Reformation history, I committed my artistic future to metal and joined my father at the forge. My influences include movements as diverse as Rayism and Impressionism. For me, the forging process is the seeking of form in balance that supports its own meaning. My sculptures have a home in numerous corporate and private collections, and can be found in the many galleries around the world that carry Kramer Sculptures.

## KROSLAK
Paintings
Page 181

I am a self-taught artist. I draw on my difficult and joyous life experiences to create what is in my heart and soul. I did not begin my life's passion until I was almost fifty years old. I have spent the ensuing years catching up on my art and expanding my abilities. My unique background has led to my using bold, controlled colors and forms. I want the viewer to achieve a sense of being the final creator of each piece of art. I want my work to stimulate and excite the minds of the viewers beyond what they see into what they feel. I believe that art is the soul of humanity and the community of man. The success of a business community is measured by the culture its members surround themselves with.

EXHIBITIONS: May International Show, 2007, Museum of the Americas, Doral, FL; SOLO, Art Expo, 2007, New York, NY; Gallery Street, 2006–2007, Atlanta, GA; Hoffman Porges Gallery, 1999, 2006, 2007, Ybor City, FL; Aspirations Winery, 2005–2007, St. Petersburg, FL; Esperanza!, 2006, Gala Corina, Tampa, FL; Park-Art Gallery, 2005, New York, NY; *The Art of Kroslak & Francesco, Two Generations*, 2005, Hoffman Porges Gallery, Ybor City, FL

AWARDS: Honorary Mention, 2007, Museum of the Americas

## MELODY LANE
Objects
Page 114

My art encompasses clay and glass. The clay is smoke-fired to evoke an ancient stone-like finish. The glass allows the light to create its own fire, changing as the light of the day changes. This is a combination of earth and fire that resonates with references to other cultures and civilizations. My aim is to bring the motifs of ancient cultures into a contemporary form, connecting the past and the present. In 2004 I was awarded an Artist Fellowship Grant from the Connecticut Commission on the Arts. In 2006 I was invited to participate in the Art in Embassies Program for the South African Embassy. My work is shown in galleries throughout the country, and I have exhibited at the Smithsonian Craft show, the Paradise City shows, and the American Craft Council trade shows, among others. To see other work, please visit my website at www.melodylanestudio.com. Prices range from $20 to $2,500.

GUILD SOURCEBOOKS *Residential Art 4, 5*

## THOMAS F. LEDERER
Furniture
Page 51

Lederer Studio was formed in the summer of 1978 to provide fine furniture, wood carving, and sculpture to select individuals. We are committed to delivering the absolute highest quality product to every client. Our approach is timeless. Our designs are a synthesis of enduring traditional designs including Shaker, Arts and Crafts, Art Nouveau, and Art Deco with an emphasis on simplicity and subtle, elegant lines. With a philosophy of structure, fine select materials, elegant lines, fine carving, and beautiful finishes, Tom Lederer designs each piece with patience, care, and an artistic approach after providing extensive design consultation to determine how each piece should be constructed to meet the goals of each client. We believe in using the best hand-selected materials, construction, and hardware. All furniture is constructed using domestic and exotic hardwoods and veneers, while executing traditional fine joinery techniques to include mortise and tenon, miter spline, etc. All carving and sculpture is hand carved in original designs.

## MARLENE LENKER
Paintings
Page 182

My work reflects my response to nature and time. My paintings express my love for landscape, light, and mood. I am governed by my intuition and instinct, capturing a moment felt. I work with acrylic, mixed media, and collage on canvas, paper, and board. Commissions are welcomed. Collections include: Arthur Young; Oppenheimer Fund; Lever Bros.; PepsiCo; Kidder Peabody; Warner-Lambert; Merrill Lynch; Horcht; Pfizer; Hoffman-Laroche; and Johnson & Johnson. Publications include: *Bridging Time and Space*, 1999; *Who's Who in America; American Artists; Women Artists; World Women; International Art;* and *The Art of Layering: Making Connections*. My work has been featured in previous Guild sourcebooks. The Winn Devon Art Group, international art publishers, publish my work as limited editions and open-end editions.

GUILD SOURCEBOOKS: *Designer's 10, 11, 12, 13, 14, 15; Residential 1, 2, 3, 4, 5*

## WILLIAM LESLIE
Lighting
Page 75

When I began working with paper, wood, and light, I called my pieces "lanterns." As my creativity and skills developed, I began to focus more on the sculptural aspect rather than the functional, and to create pieces that stand alone as works of art with the light on or off. My work reflects a fascination with how nature moves on graceful paths or organizes itself in flowing patterns. Why human consciousness contemplates this with joy is a delicious mystery to me. My task is to express and illuminate in ever more novel ways the swirl of texture in marble or wood grain, the evolving folds in flowers or seashells, the fluid patterns left on sea-swept sand. I strive to create beautiful forms that will invite people out of their mental busyness to see the timelessness in passing time. Human life, too, is a whirling dance of patterns within patterns.

## MARK LEVIN
Furniture
Page 53

During my adolescence I found the Sears catalog of materialism for its time: Hugh Hefner's *Playboy* magazine. I became a born again materialist by the time I discovered the centerfold. As hypnotized as I was by the women, I was equally fascinated by the ads featuring cars, stereos, beautiful clothes, and other wonderful things. Though I grew up in a middle-class Jewish family, my parents were anomalies for the demographic. They were non-materialist bordering on immaterialist. Eventually I realized it worked better being a materialist if you had truckloads of money, which I didn't, but I could still make very beautiful and expensive things, yet to be defined. I then came across the Italian design magazine *Abitare*, in which was a group photo of several architects, woodworkers, and other designers. They were all in beautiful suits. I made up my mind if I was to be an artist that is how I'd always present myself so I'd never be mistaken for one of those artist mutts. So here I am, post-Hefner and in love with anything Italian, making beautiful furniture for incredible clients. Life is good now, but would be better in a Brioni suit.

GUILD SOURCEBOOKS: *The Guild: 2; Residential Art: 1, 2, 3, 4, 5*

## LINDA LEVITON
Mixed & Other Media Wall Art
Page 249

The *Patterns of Nature Series* combines etched metal and curved wood frames that flow into one another to create undulating wall sculptures. Selecting from a palette of copper or brass, thirty-nine different patterns, six patina colors, and three different curves, I create unique work for each customer. Floating curves and ribbons are two different shapes in the series. Ribbons are thin curved forms on black wood frames, and floating curves suspend in front of the wall.

COMMISSIONS: Wells Fargo, Des Moines, IA, The Hartford Insurance Company, Hartford, CT; Abbott Northwestern Hospital, Minneapolis, MN; Shades of Green, Walt Disney World, Orlando, FL; Symantec Corp., New York, NY; Ross Heart Hospital, Columbus, OH; Kaiser Permanente, Pasadena, CA; Northwestern Mutual, Milwaukee, WI; Nestle/Ralston, St. Louis, MO; State of Ohio, Columbus; Med Central Hospital, Mansfield, OH; Akron/Summit County Public Library, Akron, OH; St. Vincent's Hospital, Indianapolis, IN; Northwest Airlines, Detroit, MI

EXHIBITIONS: SOFA, 2007, Chicago

PUBLICATIONS: *Color on Metal,* 2001

## ELISSA LIEBERMAN
Mixed & Other Media Wall Art
Page 250

I intend to illuminate the experience of being human through love, loss, growth, and desire for creation. In terms of the narrative style of my work, the depictions of events are loosely told through imagery from mythology and literature, as well as references to pop culture. I use a symbolic language to represent certain themes. Images act as metaphors for stages of life and growth. I travel through life stages and layers of consciousness, as do my multiple figures. I am influenced by Western art, but most recently, the handling of materials in Eastern art has been influencing my work. I paint out of my imagination with loose marks and no corrections as I confess to the viewer my errors and moments of decision making. The act of painting itself and the process of creation mimics my existential concerns. As the art and the artist are in the process of becoming, the paintings transcend the depiction of an event; rather, the process of painting *is* the event. My paintings stand testament to this process.

## MICHELLE LINDBLOM
Paintings
Page 183

At first glance my work is primarily about color, movement, and texture. You will often see abstracted figures and/or landscapes upon further examination. The figures represent autobiographical information and frequently serve as a metaphor for the diverse confrontations, dialogues, muses, and revelations I have had and will continue to have with the world around me. When viewing the work, my ultimate goal is to have the public venture into the pieces and extend their understanding by pursuing their own sensual experience. I work in small and large formats and primarily in acrylics on canvas and paper, as well as monotypes with the use of my printmaking press. My work is all original and has been exhibited across the country and in previous Guild Sourcebooks. You can view more work at www.mick-art.com. Prices range from $650-$2,500.

GUILD SOURCEBOOKS: *Architectural & Interior Art 18; Residential Art 2, 3*

## LISA KESLER STUDIO
Paintings
Page 184

My contemporary acrylic paintings and mixed-media works are a comment on the serenity and tranquility of the rural environment where I live. After earning a bachelor of fine arts degree from the University of Illinois in 1982, I lived in Phoenix, Arizona, for eleven years and then Seattle, Washington, for thirteen years, before moving back to the farm that used to belong to my grandparents in central Illinois. My work plays tribute to the patterns I find in the rural imagery around me. I continually experiment with materials and techniques. This act of experimentation is one of the things that inspires me most as an artist. My work can be found in private and corporate collections throughout the country.

GUILD SOURCEBOOKS: *Residential Art 5*

## CATHY LOCKE
Paintings
Page 185

My paintings are driven by light, and specifically, how light affects a subject matter. For this reason I tend to paint a broad range of subjects, from people to cityscapes. I am more interested in capturing a feeling than staying with one subject matter. Whether it's the early morning light on city rooftops or the way the light hits a glass vase, I am searching for a special moment. I describe light in my paintings through a strong color and value theme, building layers to create depth. Though I primarily work in pastels and oils, I have used every type of medium at one point in time. As an artist I believe it is important to always explore new ways of translating that special feeling that turns a canvas into poetry.

## ROB LORENSON
Sculpture
Pages 80, 138

My studio produces works in stainless steel, painted aluminum, and bronze. The scale ranges from small tabletop works to pieces over sixteen feet high. The methodology behind my work is to create a compositionally rich interplay of modernist elements that are exceptionally crafted to remove the hand of the artist. The purpose of this is to further emphasize the compositional qualities of the work. I also intend to make the work look manufactured, as though it was itself an industrial product, like the industrial forms that originally influenced it. Works have been placed in over seventy-five collections in residential, corporate, municipal, and educational settings. My scope of services includes design, fabrication, transportation, and installation of all works that I produce. The wholesale price range of my residential works is from $1,000 to $50,000. Recent residential projects have been completed in Boca Raton, FL; Belmont, MA; New York, NY; and Fayetteville, NC. Call for a printed catalog.

## SHANNY LOTT
Paintings
Pages 186, 210

I am interested in the shapes that are formed by cast shadows and reflected light. The variations are intriguing to me. Each painting is a jigsaw puzzle of colors and shapes that come together to represent the whole, and although the final result is a representational painting, its components are tiny abstractions that could stand alone as paintings themselves. The big picture comes together when the fragments are joined. I explore this reconstruction of the whole in subject matter that ranges from figures to landscapes. The process that I use reintegrates the soul. Commissions are welcomed.

## ELIZABETH MacDONALD
Murals, Tiles & Wall Reliefs
Page 279

I produce tile paintings that suggest the patina of age. Layering color onto thin, textured stoneware achieves a surface that combines the subtlety of nature with the formality of a grid. These compositions are suitable for either in- or outdoors and take the form of freestanding columns, wall panels, or architectural installations. Attached to .25" luan with silicone, the tiles (often 3.5" square) weigh approximately 1.75 pounds per square foot, are durable, and require minimum maintenance. I enjoy working with the requirements of clients and can produce small- or large-scale work. In 1999 I was presented with the Governor's Award for Visual Art. During the last twenty years, my commissions have included private installations, as well as the following: Dartmouth-Hitchcock Hospital, Lebanon, NH; Conrad Hotel, Hong Kong; Mayo Clinic Chapel, Scottsdale, AZ; and Nobu Restaurant, New York, NY.

## MEREDITH MacLEOD
Prints
Pages 209, 215

With my passion for printmaking and the skills of a glass tile maker, I find myself working back and forth between two media. When creating my prints, I use nontoxic paints and hand-carved rubber stamps to build layers of shapes and color, simulating a textile or wallpaper monoprint. Using the same stamps, I fuse high-fire enamel paint to the surface of glass to create a tile for wall or architectural application. Things that influence me are varied: living in the country, illustrations from the 1950s, bird books, gauche paintings of old textile patterns, 30s fabrics and color. I love the work of Japanese woodblock artist Shiko Munakata and the photographs of Karl Blossfeldt, as well as the work created from the Wiener Werkstatte Workshop. My goal is to evoke an interest in something old that recasts itself as new. Please visit my website for more information: www.meredithmacleodartist.com.

## SUSAN MADACSI
Objects
Page 115

Although steel is usually first thought of as an industrial material, I like to draw attention to our connection with it on a human level. I do this by creating objects that reveal the organic nature of the medium. By using traditional blacksmithing techniques in my work, I am transferring this Old World craft to a modern one and placing it in a more contemporary context. This work showcases the clay-like qualities of steel when it is forged at temperatures of up to 2,400 degrees. Large, heavy bars of steel are forged under a power hammer, cut, re-assembled into forms, painted, and then acid etched to achieve the colorful patinas.

COMMISSIONS: Ralph Lauren, DC; Baker Knapp and Tubbs, IL; Holmes Regional Medical Center, FL; Mohegan Sun Casino, CT; Saint Alphonsus Hospital, ID; Hygienic Art Gardens and Theater, CT

AWARDS: Second place, 2006, Katherine Forest Craft Foundation, CT; Connecticut Artist Fellowship Award in Craft, 2004; Emerging Artist Award, Philadelphia Furniture and Furnishings Show, 2004

PUBLICATIONS: *Blacksmithing: Inside and Out*; *Ironwork: Dynamic Details*, 2006; *Teapots: Makers and Collectors*, 2005; *Stylish Screens*, 2004

## JIM MALKOWSKI
Sculpture
Page 139

I draw my inspiration from natural forms and the human figure. Along with compelling form comes texture and color that can only be expressed by the forces of nature on the medium itself. The unique properties of the specific metal, such as the rust of iron, the patina of bronze, and the strata of stone, are exposed for their richness and for our appreciation of these natural elements. The sculptures are one of a kind, not editions. I received my B.F.A. in sculpture from the University of Wisconsin.

## JEAN MANDEBERG
Metal Wall Art
Page 261

I shape colorful printed tin and other thin gauge sheet metal over wood forms such as bowls, blocks, and boards. I gather metal during what has become a very social activity, finding materials at local restaurants and markets, as well as during international travel. All over the world, printed tin communicates, seduces, and preserves valuable contents. I rescue and recycle beautiful found tin, lay it out like fabric, emboss it, shape it, and reassemble it. My work is obsessive and carefully crafted; it explores the irregularity inherent in the process of reusing and remaking. The layers of tin and tacks simultaneously reveal and conceal an accumulation of information. For the past twenty-five years I have been an artist, a faculty member at The Evergreen State College in Olympia, Washington, and a community arts advocate. My work has been exhibited widely and is part of numerous private and public collections.

## JUDY MANDOLF
Fine Art Photography
Page 233

Although eclectic in subject and palette, my work tends to be peaceful and uncluttered, perhaps to offset an often chaotic world. (Someone once wrote, "Every doctor should prescribe take two Mandolfs in the morning.") Most images are photo based. They are then computer manipulated, printed on watercolor paper, mounted on wood panel, and coated with acrylic gel. Some are combined with encaustic (hot wax) painting and collage. I strive to produce art that doesn't look "digital."

EXHIBITIONS: Sony International Fine Art, 2006; Adobe Digital Imaging, 2004–2006; MacWorld Digital Art, 2003 and 2001; Seybold Digital Art, 2002

PUBLICATIONS: *Design Graphics Portfolio*, 2006, 2005; *Going Digital*, 2005; *Advance Guide to Digital Photography*, 2005; *Photography* (college textbook), 2002; *Secrets of Award Winning Digital Photographers*, 2002; numerous digital photography and fine art magazines in the U.S. and China

## NATALIA MARGULIS
Fiber Wall Art
Page 296

My goal is to reflect the beauty of our world and to share my love of nature with people. Hand and machine embroidery correspond perfectly to represent an endless variety of environments because they allow me to recreate nature not just in terms of color, but in all its manifestation of shape and texture. A complete list of exhibitions, publications, and awards is available on my website, www.nataliamargulis.com. Prices range from $500 to $15,000.

EXHIBITIONS: Craft Boston, 2006, MA; American Crafts Council, Baltimore, St. Paul, Atlanta, Chicago, Springfield, Sarasota, and Charlotte; Washington Crafts Show, Washington, DC; Crafts at the Castle, Boston, MA; Philadelphia Museum of Art Craft Show, PA; Diamond Celebrity, The World Quilt, 1998, Tokyo, Japan; The Fiber Artist Exhibition Macramé and Embroidery, 1992, St.-Petersburg, Russia

AWARDS: Best of 2D, 2006, Port Clinton Art Festival, Highland Park, IL; Best of Show, 2006, 2004, Art Fair on the Square, Madison, WI

PUBLICATIONS: *Sunshine Artist* magazine, Jan. 2007; *Exploring Textile Arts,* 2005; *American Art Collector,* edition 3, 2004; *The Crafts Report* magazine, May 2004

## SUSAN McGEHEE
Metal Wall Art
Page 262

Instead of fiber, I weave with wire and metals. I continue to employ the traditional tools, techniques, and patterns from my work in fiber. Weaving metals allows me to form a piece into a dimensional shape that will retain its form and undulating vitality. I weave primarily with anodized aluminum wire because it has the advantage of being lightweight, retaining its vibrant color and shine. Viewers will assume a piece is fiber; they are astonished when they discover it is actually woven metal. The *Kimonos* are cut and shaped from bronze or stainless steel screen, then adorned with scraps of wire left over from my weavings, electronic surplus bits, and other pieces I collect. I take pleasure in using the last part of twentieth-century surplus to create pieces that have the feel of earlier centuries.

GUILD SOURCEBOOKS: *Designer's 12,13,14,15; Architectural & Interior Art 16,17,18,19, 20, 21; Residential Art 1, 3, 4, 5*

## BILL MASTERPOOL
Architectural Elements
Page 98

My intention when creating a new piece is not to make furniture in the usual sense of the word but to create complex sculptural pieces that are of such interest and personality that they inspire awe. Stylistically, my interests are varied and range from modern industrial, contemporary, and simple geometric ornamentation (such as the fireplace and candelabra featured in this publication) to the intricate organic designs featured on The Guild's retail website, www.artfulhome.com. Recent exhibitions and honors include the Ernest Wiemann Top Job Gold Award, Forged Furniture, 2005, National Ornamental and Miscellaneous Metals Association; Western Design Conferences, 2007, Jackson, WY; 2006, 2004 (Hon. Mention, Best Artist, Metal) Cody, WY; and 2005, Santa Fe, NM.

## RICK MELBY
Lighting
Page 76

I have been designing and fabricating works in glass for over thirty years. Initially working with leaded glass, I now specialize in unique lighting and light sculpture, creating work for the wall, table, floor, and ceiling. Architectural glasswork includes windows, entryways, room dividers, and wall reliefs. Blown, kiln-formed, and etched glass, as well as wood, stone, and metal, are used. One-of-a-kind pieces and limited editions are available. I emphasize original design and quality craftsmanship, seeking to satisfy the aesthetic and functional requirements of each commission. Designs have contemporary/minimalist leanings, though I am fluent in many styles. I collaborate with other artists, architects, and interior designers to create and deliver objects that harmonize with the desires of the client. Working either in the private or public sector, I am able to offer the discerning customer a visually stimulating alternative in all phases of handcrafted glasswork.

## JENNIFER C. McCURDY
Objects
Page 117

I work with high fire translucent porcelain because it has a smooth, stony surface, and it can convey the qualities of light and shadow that I wish to express. After I throw my vessel on the potter's wheel, I alter the form to set up a movement of soft shadow. When the porcelain is leather hard, I carve patterns to add energy and counterpoint. I fire my work to cone 10, where the porcelain becomes non-porous and extremely hard. I received a B.F.A. degree from Michigan State University and have been working as a potter ever since. I currently maintain my studio in Vineyard Haven, Massachusetts. My porcelain is priced from $150 to $1,800.

GUILD SOURCEBOOKS: *Residential Art 3, 4, 5, 6*

## PETER W. MICHEL
Sculpture
Page 140

My work represents a stand for the possibility that art is for the expression of joy, aliveness, love, and relationship. Through color, humor, the play of ideas, and the effects of light and space, the viewer is invited to access his own spirit of playfulness and relatedness. From small tabletop and wall pieces to monumental outdoor public art, my work is refined with the aid of computer software and produced with computer-controlled water jet or laser-cutting methods.

COLLECTIONS: Oakton Sculpture Park, Des Plaines, IL; Wandell Sculpture Garden, Urbana, IL

EXHIBITIONS: Art in Public Places—Stamford Downtown, 2006; Sculpture Internationale, Atlanta, 2002; Pier Walk, 2000, 1999, Chicago; Chesterwood Museum, 1994, Stockbridge MA

PUBLICATIONS: *Fall in Love with Your Community Workbook,* 2007; *Educational Psychology,* 8th Edition, 2002

GUILD SOURCEBOOKS: *Architectural & Interior Art 16, 20, 22*

## BARRY MIDDLETON
Mixed & Other Media Wall Art
Page 251

My work expresses the beauties of wood in the form of wall sculptures and home furnishings. It has been influenced by a million pieces of this world, from Frank Lloyd Wright to the Japanese ikebana, to the colors in our fabrics. I have mixed colors in the textiles industry and in corporate art. The finish on the woods enhances their natural colors, textures, and grain. My shop is not highly automated. It is my patient and creative relationship with the wood that enables intriguing results. Scores of custom wall pieces and tables have been commissioned to residences and businesses all over the country since 1995.

AWARDS: N.E.W.A., 2004, Saratoga Springs, NY; Sono Arts, 2006, Norwalk, CT; Stockade Arts, 2006, Schenectady, NY; Armonk Outdoor Art Show, 2005, Armonk, NY

PUBLICATIONS: *Better Homes and Gardens Wood Magazine*, Dec. 2003

## MILLEA FURNISHINGS
Furniture
Pages 32, 54-55

Simply stated, my furniture is a vehicle for three-dimensional paintings that appeal to your sense of vision, touch, and functionality. Using traditional compound miter joinery, the furniture is built from Baltic birch and enhanced with leather upholstery, nickel or wood hardware, or vellum shades. The surfaces are painted with acrylic and finished in lacquer. I offer a full range of home furnishings, from cabinets, tables, and lighting to accent pieces such as mirrors, pillows, and ottomans. They are painted in four basic design groups: *Treatment, Introspect, Fifteen* and *One-of-a-Kind*. Each has its own character, but complements the others in color palette and spirit. The intent of my furniture is to provide energy and movement to an environment. Each piece is its own canvas of bold, abstract designs enhancing the structure itself. The furniture is sleek and unencumbered; it is the marriage to the painted acrylic surface design that is the focus.

GUILD SOURCEBOOKS: *Residential Art 2, 3*

## ELISE MILLS
Paintings
Page 187

I received a B.F.A., with honors, from Parsons School of Design, New York. In addition to attending the school in New York, I studied in Los Angeles and Paris with the Parsons School. My education continued at the Art Students League, The National Academy of Design, NYC, and the Silvermine School of Art in New Canaan, Connecticut. The Noroton Gallery in Darien, Connecticut, and the Rockwell Gallery Westport, Connecticut, currently represent me. Although I have received numerous awards, I derive the most satisfaction from seeing the pleasure others receive when viewing my landscapes. I gained invaluable experience from my prior career as an illustrator, which set a solid foundation for the way I portray expression and emotion. My oil and pastel paintings present a sense of place that evokes the viewer's memories based on past or present experiences and emotions. The gesture, brushwork, and calligraphy of my marks all echo the creative flows and rhythms found in nature. My work is in the spirit of Georgia O'Keefe: "Nobody sees a flower really; it is so small. We haven't time, and to see takes time—like to have a friend."

## LEE MILTIER
Sculpture
Page 141

Glassblowing as an art form is unique in its demand for physical skill and presence of mind. My purpose is to connect my experience as a glassblower with my talent as a natural healer. For me, the act of blowing glass has become my meditative, creative, and spiritual practice. Overtly, I am making pieces that are technically and aesthetically pushing my limits. The deeper result is that I channel into these *Energy Bottles* not my own limited energy, but universal energy—call it chi, prana, magic, whatever! Life sized, these are bottles with separate stoppers that mate delightfully, perfectly. In person, they have a presence that invites both eyes and fingers. This initial visceral attraction soon gives way to an intellectual appreciation and then the casual acceptance—a relationship, if you will. Relationships are a big part of making and collecting art. I enjoy the relationships I have with galleries that represent my work, and appreciate the collectors they work with. I'm choosing to market my work through The Guild as well, because some people prefer to work directly with the artist. If you like what I'm doing, and have a particular space in your life or home that you want to commission work for, please contact me at your earliest convenience. Thank you!

## BONNIE MINCU
Paintings
Page 188

I had built a career in business for more than twenty years when my life and passion changed dramatically in the course of a day. While on vacation in Istanbul, I happened upon an artisan studio. I remained there for hours, enthralled, and left Turkey with an inexplicable desire to create visual art. Upon returning home to New York, I immersed myself in oil painting, craving the flow of texture and color. I originally related most to the style of the early California Impressionists. I've since evolved to using soft geometric shapes and distinct forms. I begin each painting by determining the mood I want to convey through color. I create my scenes based on a flow of simple shapes, values, and patterns, infusing my work with vividness and luminosity. Attracted to timeless themes of landscapes and villages, I recreate the real world as it may appear in memories or dreams.

## MITCH YUNG CERAMIC DESIGN
Murals, Tiles & Wall Reliefs
Page 280

The work featured in this book explores texture, form, and color. I strive to overcome the flat, lifeless aspects of oxidation and electric kiln firing by layering stains, slips, and glazes. My sculptures are compositions of hand-built tiles that form contiguous drawings or fields of glazed colors. Sgraffito decoration, inspired by old masters' drawings, and vintage and contemporary photography, embellish many of my sculptures and functional work. Sculptures can be installed outdoors under protected areas, such as a patio. Custom imagery or commissions are welcome. I have been a professional studio artist for fifteen years. I earned a B.F.A. from Kansas State University in 1989 and an M.F.A. from Arizona State University in 1991. My work is shown in various galleries and exhibitions. For more information please visit www.mitchyung.com.

GUILD SOURCEBOOKS: *Residential Art 5*

### MORAG
Home Accents
Page 83

About twenty-five years ago, I left my home in Australia with a one-way ticket in my hand. My goal was to see the world. For the next several years, I walked the beautiful beaches of Thailand, struggled through the crowded cities of India, and slept in the jungles of Uganda. My travels opened my eyes to the sights, sounds, smells, and textures of our planet's diverse cultures. But the most important thing I learned was this: I love color. The more vibrant, the better. My work is really an expression of my love of color, glass, and texture. I have been creating one-of-a-kind glass sculptures for more than ten years. Each piece is designed to fit a particular space. Every one of my sculptures is the result of an intuitive blending of craftsmanship, creativity, and color.

GUILD SOURCEBOOKS: *Residential Art 5*

### AMY J. MUSIA
Sculpture
Page 142

For over thirty years, I have worked with private and public art committees, architects, engineers, and designers to create a multitude of successful commissions for private and corporate clients. Noted as a versatile designer/craftsman in many mediums and styles, I have focused on contemporary columns and capitals for the last four years. They are commissioned as a unique focal piece or as an anthology. Working closely with clients, pieces are created to reflect their vision. At times, corporate philosophies are interpreted into exclusive pieces of fine art. Using traditional woodworking techniques, each site-specific piece, indoors or outdoors, is hand carved and constructed in my Evansville studio. Pieces are finished in white with 24K, silver, and/or copper gilded embellishments. Other mediums available.

COMMISSIONS: Evansville, IN: Vectren, Evansville-Vanderburgh Public Library, Old National Bank, VNA Hospice

COLLECTIONS: City of Evansville, IN; City of Tochigi, Japan

GUILD SOURCEBOOKS: *Architectural & Interior Art 22*

### JILL MUSSER
Paintings
Page 189

My painting method is the opposite of how students are usually taught to paint in oil, starting thinly with the darkest dark. I begin by painting into a thick layer of white paint. For subject matter, I use the most colorful produce I can find or interesting plants in interesting pots. I use lots of pure color, very little mixing, and minimal brush strokes. I find I can achieve an exciting, glowing effect through the white paint. These fruits, vegetables, plants, and pottery want to be larger than life, filling large canvases. Toward the middle of my painting process, when I begin the edges of the subject, the paint is so thick, I actually feel like I am sculpting or carving while painting at the same time. I prefer painting from life, à la prima style, painting into wet paint, usually finishing the piece in one or two sessions. This approach allows me to maintain the same energy and mood throughout the painting process. Prices for original paintings range from $500 to $4,000. Please visit www.jillmusser.com.

### MARLIES MERK NAJAKA
Prints
Page 216

My objective when beginning a new painting is to create an atmosphere of heightened reality through the use of color and light. I hope to draw the viewer into the painting to enhance their perception of color. I am a signature member of the American Watercolor Society and the National Watercolor Society. I've won numerous awards; my paintings are included in private collections nationwide, as well as in corporate collections. My work can be seen and purchased on my website: watercolor-paintings.com. I work with architects and art consultants and can accommodate custom sizes for my giclée prints.

GUILD SOURCEBOOKS: *Designer's 14, 15; Architectural & Interior Art 16, 17; Residential Art 2*

### SHAWN NEWTON
Murals, Tiles & Wall Reliefs
Page 281

There is something challenging and somewhat miraculous about seeing random piles of richly colored glass evolve, through thoughtful assembly and creative cutting, into a coherent work of art. I use stained or vitreous glass, smalti, and tile to create mosaic images for hanging art, bathroom and kitchen installations, furniture applications, garden art, and signage for commercial or residential use. Member of the Society of American Mosaic Artists.

COLLECTIONS: Mapei Headquarters, Milan, Italy

EXHIBITIONS: Mapei Invitational, 2007, Mapei International Booth, Surfaces & Coverings Tradeshows; *Peace by Piece* Juried Exhibition, 2007, The Atelier, Miami, FL; National Juried Art Exhibition, 2006, Serenity Place Art Gallery, Big Bear Lake, CA; Society of American Mosaic Artists (SAMA) International Juried Exhibitions, 2002-2006; The Pieces of Our Lives Juried Exhibition, 2005, Higgins Art Gallery, Cape Cod, MA

AWARDS: Best In Show, Mosaic Category, 2006, National Juried Art Exhibition, Serenity Place Art Gallery; Juror's Choice Award, 2006, SAMA International Juried Exhibition; Members' Choice Award 2005, SAMA International Juried Exhibition

### OLD ELLICOTT FORGE, LTD.
Home Accents
Page 84

All my work is of my own design and made completely by me. My inspirations are drawn from my love of and fascination with metalwork I've seen over fifteen years of worldwide commercial sailing. My muse has an unlisted number, but she will, on occasion, call me with specifics. She is very plain spoken and has little use for arcane and esoteric language. The work is done in traditional and modern blacksmithing techniques to achieve an efficient balance between time and craftsmanship. This involves the use of various hammers, chisels, and a coal or gas forge to heat the steel till it is malleable. It is then worked over an anvil to stamp, draw out, upset, and fuller and finally, it submits to the shape I want. I assemble those elements together using rivets, collars, or mortise-and-tenon joinery. The work is then polished and sometimes a patina is added along with brass, bronze, or copper accents. The pieces are mostly for interior use, but they can be painted or powder coated for exterior use.

## OUT OF THE MAINSTREAM DESIGNS
Floor Coverings
Page 91

My textiles are contemporary, handwoven tapestries, rugs, and wall pieces, individually designed with sensitivity to architectural context, embellishment, and hand-finishing techniques. Each adds warmth, vitality, and a colorful focal point, and facilitates the expression of the client's taste and personality. I have been designing and weaving for more than twenty-eight years and continue to work in traditional and non-traditional fiber techniques. Research in historic textiles, twentieth-century graphic design, and architecture continue to influence my work. The densely interwoven cultural and human histories of my family members and their spontaneous, thoughtful, and happy natures help shape, direct, and inspire my creative process. Currently, my projects involve deconstructing the woven cloth when removed from the loom in an effort to design a surface that changes in texture and line. Prices and samples available through the studio.

## PJ BOYLAN PHOTOGRAPHY
Fine Art Photography
Page 234

God's creation and humanity's contributions fascinate me. I am drawn to unusual patterns and textures, and the way these are affected by natural light. I enjoy portraying natural and manmade features so that they appear almost abstract. Hopefully, the viewer is drawn into the image and challenged to use imagination to discover the subject or to create his/her own story. After capturing images with film or digitally, I make prints from my computer using archival paper and ink, choosing paper appropriate for each image. Larger sizes are printed at a custom lab. Most of my work contains little digital manipulation. All mounting and matting materials are conservation quality. I sign, limit, and number all images. I began entering competitions and juried exhibits in 2002. Since then I have earned more than forty awards with my photographs. I accept photographic assignments, which may also include travel writing.

## NINA PALADINO AND MICHAEL K. HANSEN
Objects
Page 118

Paladinohansen Art Glass Studio is made up of two glass artists who have been working together for thirty years. Nina Paladino and Michael K. Hansen work as a team to create magnificent freeform bowls and other masterpieces. We use the glass to express and reflect the beauty and power of nature. Many of our pieces are thought to be images of the ocean, sunsets, ponds, and even galaxies. The two refer to the glass as a canvas on which they paint with colored glass. We have developed our own technique of weaving around each other, building and creating until we achieve our vision. We focus on quality, not quantity, and we make each piece with care and consideration of color and design.

GUILD SOURCEBOOKS: *The Guild: 4, 5; Architect's: 6; Designer's: 6, 7, 8, 9, 14, 15*

## ANNIE PASIKOV
Sculpture
Page 143

After teaching art for twenty years (including eleven at a residential school for troubled teens), I responded to a health crisis by giving wings to my passion for creating. I began to do art instead of just assisting others with theirs. After a lifelong interest, I taught myself to sculpt in stone. My gracefully flowing forms emerge through a direct stone carving approach. I listen to the whisper of intuition that seems to guide me as I consider my design: a unique dance between art sense and sixth sense. My sculptures can be seen at Boulder Community Foothills Hospital, CO; Matrix Center, Boulder, CO; Whole Health Associates, Houston, TX; and in Lotte Hotel, Seoul, "Korea's leading hotel."

## PATTI MOLLICA FINE ART STUDIO
Prints
Page 217

I believe that a truly great painting is not about the "subject matter," but the way an artist communicates beauty, sensitivity, and integrity in whatever is depicted. Flowers, gardens, and sunsets are no more worthy as painting subjects than a bustling city street corner or a close-up of some old fire escapes. A painter's job is to point out the hidden beauty in all subjects and scenes, most especially the ones that are not commonly thought of in an artistic light. The heart of my artistic interest is the urban environment, its architecture and moods. My artwork has been acquired in numerous public collections, including Mellon Bank USA, Sociéte Generale, and Sheraton Hotels. I am currently published by the New York Graphic Society's ArtBeats division. A number of pieces have recently been printed as fine art posters and distributed through high-end retail chains nationally. Other publishing venues and commissions include Marcel Shurman, Hallmark greeting cards, Penguin Press, McGraw Hill books, magazine covers, and annual reports for Fortune 500 companies. Coveted by both decorators and private collectors, my work is known for its bravura brushwork and fearless use of color. All commissions, large or small, are welcome.

## PAULUS FINE FURNITURE
Furniture
Page 56

The purpose of life is the expansion of happiness. That is exactly the driving force behind the designs and creativity in the furniture that I craft. And it is the very reason why people are attracted to my furniture. Although I work within the four walls of my studio, my mind enjoys traveling beyond the limitations of traditional designs. This is where the creative ideas start, capturing that first glimpse and all the possibilities for its development. Ideas are translated to sketches, full-size drawings, and models. I would like to design for you that piece of furniture that will enhance the quality of life in your environment.

COMMISSIONS New Britain Museum of American Art, CT; Hakata Restaurant, New York, NY; Holt, Wexler & Farnam, LLP, New Haven, CT; Closebend, Inc., Tulsa, OK

AWARDS: Niche Award Finalist, 2007, Philadelphia Buyers Market; Juror's Award, 2006, *Lines into Shapes* Exhibition, Estes Park, CO; Niche Award Winner, 2006, 2005, Philadelphia Buyers Market; Judges Choice Award, 2004, Bethesda Fine Arts Festival, MD; Excellence Award, 2003, Mighty Midwest Biennial Exhibition, New Visions Gallery, Marshfield, WI; Best of Show, 2003, Will's Creek Survey Exhibition, Allegany Arts Council, Cumberland, MD

## JEFF PENDER
Sculpture
Page 144

Mystery is the enigmatic quality or character of something not understood. It stands as the launching pad for the imagination and is the reason why we desire to discover . . . things . . . about the world around us. As a child I explored the woods behind my house, searching under everything, looking for the unknown, the strange, the weird, not knowing what I would find. A multitude of energetic butterflies would fill my stomach each time I took on a new adventure in those woods. Searching for the unknown offers us the opportunity to explore and probe for new knowledge and insights. This mysterious void weaves its way from past to future and back again, stopping just for a moment, just long enough for the burning desire for discovery to latch hold. This cycle repeats. The ritual continues. Mystery moves. Discovery waits. My work seeks both to convey a sense of mystery and to invite discovery.

## BINH PHO
Sculpture
Page 145

I work primary on thin-walled vessels created on the lathe, then finished with airbrush and piercing technique. Through my work, life experiences are transformed—difficulties and struggles become works of art presented in a unique aesthetic language with traditional Asian iconography and contemporary painting on vessel forms.

COLLECTIONS: The White House Collection, Washington, DC; The Renwick Gallery, Smithsonian of American Art; Museum of Art and Design, New York, NY; University of Michigan Museum of Art, Ann Arbor, MI; Long Beach Museum of Art, Long Beach, CA

EXHIBITIONS: *River of Destiny*, 2006-2007, Solo exhibition, Long Beach Museum of Art, Long Beach, CA; *Presence of the Absence*, 2006, Special Exhibit from Collectors of Wood Art, SOFA, Chicago, IL

PUBLICATIONS: *River of Destiny—Life and Works of Binh Pho*, 2006; *The World* and *I* magazine, 2003; *Craft Art International* magazine, 2003

GUILD SOURCEBOOKS: *Designer's 15; Architectural & Interior Art 16, 17, 18, 19; Residential Art 1, 2, 3, 4*

## MICHAEL PLATT
Furniture
Page 57

I design and build contemporary furniture in a small studio in Boulder, Colorado. All of my furniture is designed to display simple, clean lines while exuding a playful elegance. Using a wide variety of construction techniques, I personally hand craft each piece of furniture from the most beautiful woods available. Most of my work is privately commissioned, so it reflects the freshness and originality that develops as my design tastes become infused with the desires of my customers. Prices range from $3,000 for the smaller pieces to $50,000 for my large-scale fitted cabinetry. Lead time for a custom-designed piece of furniture is currently between four and six months.

## SRI PRABHA
Paintings
Page 190

I strive to make soothing yet passionate and evocative works that radiate. My abstract paintings explore inner and outer worlds. Pure elemental forces of nature—fire, water, earth, air—inspire my outer world view. I experience these phenomena while hiking, kayaking, and traveling, and they flow through me onto my paintings. My inner world view comes from time spent meditating. And the Indian mantras I listen to while painting facilitates the bridging of my inner and outer worlds. I use acrylics, gold leaf, oils, film, digital still, video cameras, and scanners. I welcome commissions and love to work with other creative professionals.

## RACHAEL WALLER PHOTOGRAPHY
Fine Art Photography
Page 235

Horses are an amazing source of strength, endurance, and passion. They will give us so much based on trust. My work relies on this trust, whether I am with a herd or a single horse. Many of my subjects are rescued horses who are given a second chance at life and can therefore be very unpredictable. To be a part of this blooming process as I witness their becoming whole again is a visual treasure that articulates volumes. My work enables me to sculpt available light while watching the unfolding dance of the equine.

COMMISSIONS: The Santa Barbara Historical Preservation Society, 2006, CA; The Santa Barbara Native Arts Guild, 2000-2007; The Georgia Waller Gallery, 2000-2007, Alpine, TX

EXHIBITIONS: *Equine Dream Art Show*, 2007, The Horse Expo of the Western States, Sacramento, CA; The Santa Barbara Native Art Guild, 1999-2007, Cabrillo Pavilion Arts Center, CA; The Mint at California Institute of The Arts, 1999, Valencia, CA

AWARDS: Winner, 2007, Horse Expo; Winner, 2007, International Equine Photographers Network; Artist Of The Year, 2000, The Santa Barbara Native Arts Guild

## RAKU VESSELS
Objects
Page 119

Over the years my work has been transformed. Initially, my science background led me to believe that all in nature could be broken down into the simplest of components. Pottery, broken down, was a combination of earth and fire, nothing more. My work tried to convey that basic idea, using simple shapes, applying few colors. However, I soon realized that nothing man touches can remain simple. Even the most minimal of pieces invoked profound involved statements, which often overshadowed the original idea of the piece. Recently, I have begun to focus my attention on this strange aspect of man. I have stretched and twisted the idea of the vessel, hoping to invoke a search for the simple line of a familiar form. Colors have become complicated, so subtleties become a rare find.

## RAVEN LUNATIC STUDIOS
Mixed & Other Media Wall Art
Page 253

I have recently rediscovered an appreciation for whimsy and lightheartedness in art after a long period of darkness. The crows have been my spirit guides on this journey, providing inspiration in their dual roles as archetypal tricksters and repositories of primal wisdom. Their intelligence and playfulness offer a deep wellspring of raw material for the creative mind. I work in a realist/surrealist style and particularly enjoy doing Celtic and crow- or raven-themed art, though by no means do I limit myself to these themes. I like to use humor when appropriate, and value thoughtfulness and imagination in art. A successful piece, in terms of strong concept as well as skillful execution, is one of my greatest joys in life. Commissions are most welcome.

EXHIBITIONS: Finalist, Art of Inspiration Competition, 2007, The Guild; Pacific Northwest Ballet Nutcracker March, 2006 and 2005, Seattle, WA; Seattle Erotic Art Festival, 2004, Consolidated Works, WA

## RENEE DINAUER SCULPTURE
Mixed & Other Media Wall Art
Page 254

I create unique, sweeping freeform wall sculpture formed of steam-bent white ash. This process involves steaming previously milled, sanded strips, then hand shaping and glue clamping into integrated, freeform, or representational designs. Some are previously dyed in various color schemes, or painted before clear finishing. I have a life-long interest in constructivism as sculpture. My greatest interest involves the study of surfaces, especially those alluding to a four-dimensional topological extrapolation. My career really began during undergraduate studies at UCLA, when I would exhibit my work on the weekends. I have received numerous awards, including Best of Show and First Place, Sculpture at Beverly Hills, CA, and Portland, OR. My works reside in numerous residential collections, as well as corporate and public sites, including The Hyatt Regency Hotel, Deerfield, IL; Beverly Hills, CA, City Hall; Texas Tech University; and recent commissions for Macy's at locations in New York, Washington, DC, and Orlando, FL.

## SCOTT CAMPBELL REUMAN
Architectural Elements
Pages 52, 99

Curves are the connecting element in my work—flowing lines from water, wind, sky. Our natural world is lusciously curvaceous; our human-made world often square, sharp, hard. I continue to explore new materials and techniques to keep work and mind fresh, new, flowing. I make furniture, sculpture, fountains, and home accessories in stone, metal, wood, and synthetics. For over thirty years, my work has sold worldwide as Official Artist for the Environmental Protection Agency, Absolut Vodka races, Grand Marnier events, Vail World Cup, Michelin Golf, John Denver Ski Classic, Copper Mountain/American Express events, Red Zinger Bicycle Races, Women of the Rockies races, and the Memphis in May Triathlon. Visuals Unlimited and The Image Bank represented me. The State of Colorado commissioned my sculpture for the Department of Public Health and Environment.

GUILD SOURCEBOOKS: *Artful Home 2, 3, 4, 5*

## DIANA REUTER-TWINING
Sculpture
Page 146

As an architect I am fascinated by the plasticity of space. Sculpture, like architecture, has to work from all angles, with the added variable of light and time. A sculpture in broad daylight can be transformed into a silhouette at night. I work primarily in bronze, which I find to be a transforming medium. It is permanent, and with the artistic application of patinas, can simulate many beautiful materials. The focus of my art is the natural world. In designating a sculpture's appropriateness to an interior or exterior installation, I insist on looking at its scale relative to its surroundings. I enjoy working on commissions. My work ranges in price from $500 to $25,000.

GUILD SOURCEBOOKS: *Residential Art 4,5*

## STEVEN RHUDE
Paintings
Page 191

For sixteen years I've continued to explore my passion for themes that evoke the ethos of coastal communities in Atlantic Canada. Although my subjects are regional in scope, I confess to a quest for a grain of the bigger picture in the small, the universal in the local. Primary colors, humor, and familiar objects provide a critical frame of reference for my vision of a contemporary community. Commissions welcomed.

COLLECTIONS: My work is in numerous private and corporate collections. Here are a few examples: Marriot Hotel, Halifax, NS, Canada; Beacon Securities, Halifax, NS, Canada; City of Moncton, NB; Camrian Chemicals, ON; Canadian High Commissioner to New Zealand

EXHIBITIONS: I show annually at Argyle Fine Art, Halifax, NS, Canada

AWARDS: Elizabeth Greenshields Foundation, 1982, provided a year of study in Florence, Italy

PUBLICATIONS: *Turnrow, Monroe at Louisiana*, 2007, 2003; *Studio Rally Book*, 1999; *Antigonish Review*, Antigonish, Nova Scotia

## RICHARD HALL FINE ART
Paintings
Pages 8, 192

I am inspired by nature's settings, from serene sunrises and sunsets to the ominous strength of storms and dark clouds. I incorporate the lessons I've learned in my years of painting while weaving new ideas into my latest creations. My paintings bring a balance of space and light, giving a sense of tranquility that goes beyond a literal translation of the landscape. The oil paints are applied in thin layers, alternating colored washes and tinted glazes, which result in subtle changes in tone and depth. Each layer must dry between applications, and painting sixty or more layers is not uncommon. The paint particles suspended in the glazes catch the light and reflect it back to the viewer, creating a luminescent finish and translucent quality. My work has been published and collected internationally for almost thirty years. Original paintings and giclées are available. Custom commissions welcome. Visit www.richardhallfineart.com.

## DAVID RICHARDSON
Furniture
Page 58

After graduating from RISD in 1973, I landed in a wonderful old Boston area cabinet shop as an apprentice. For twelve years I restored the finest antiques for the North Shore carriage trade by day and painted at night. In 1986 I opened my own shop and continued with restoration and custom-made furniture for New England clients, slowly turning my creative energy from painting to studio furniture. Wendel Castle and Tommy Simpson showed my generation that a furniture maker could be inspired by Picasso and Richard Serra, as well as by Wharton Esherick and Jacques-Emile Ruhlman. I aspire to make furniture as elegant and well crafted as Rhulman's, and I just keep my eyes open for inspiration by whatever I might see. This is the definition of artistry to me. My goal is to connect with the past and, at the same time, to explore my own moment in history and nature.

GUILD SOURCEBOOKS: *Residential Art 4,5*

## BOB RICKARD
Metal Wall Art
Pages 259, 263

I am fortunate to work in a mountain studio surrounded by the natural beauty of Taos, New Mexico. This lends my work a certain quiet and calmness. I use industrial tools to challenge the immutable properties of metal. First I carve my designs into aluminum with a hand-held plasma cutter. Then I coat the aluminum with other metals, typically copper, bronze, and iron. Each of these metals reacts differently to the chemical patinas and dyes with which I finish the pieces. My work reflects my love of geometry, movement, and color. The Internet makes it easy to work with clients anywhere in the world, however I also enjoy having clients visit my studio to collaborate on the design and execution of my large pieces. This gives them a direct involvement with the creation of their work, and the rich culture of Taos provides a wonderful background for their visit.

## BETTE RIDGEWAY
Mixed & Other Media Wall Art
Page 255

In my work on metals, I explore the relationship between the smooth, slick surface and the layering of translucent flows of paint, which reveal a kind of mythic, subterranean history. Similar to ceramic glazing, the alternating of layers of color with resin suggests biomorphic form as well as the natural processes of accumulation and erosion. In my thirty plus years of painting and teaching, I have never felt so rewarded for taking risks. The panels are impervious to moisture; therefore they are perfect for spas and cruise ships! Using a series of panels in multiple sizes, the artwork can be designed to fill any space! I enjoy working with clients to transform their spaces, both commercial and residential. My website, ridgewaystudio.com, provides information on galleries, instruction, and upcoming exhibitions.

GUILD SOURCEBOOKS: *Residential Art 4, 5*

## ROB HARE, FURNITURE MAKER
Furniture
Pages 59, 345

Applying to Art School in 1967 I was asked why I wanted to study sculpture. I replied, "Because I love making things." People choose to work with me because they respond to my designs and use of materials. Creating pieces for my clients offers new challenges and a chance to grow. Existing designs become individual when together we decide the best height for a table, size a bookcase for a room, or pick a wood to set a mood. Entirely new pieces develop when existing designs may not fit or new solutions occur while reworking old problems. The interaction of function, sculpture, and a patina of use will result in an object to be cherished for generations. Since receiving my M.F.A. in sculpture in 1974, I have worked in many forms: sculpting, teaching, welding, contracting, cabinetmaking, historic renovation, architectural design, and furniture making. I have shown widely and my work has been featured in many publications. After forty years of making things, I still love what I do and look forward to sharing that joy with you. A selection of my work can be viewed at www.robhare-furnituremaker.com.

## CRAIG ROBB
Mixed & Other Media Wall Art
Page 256

My sculptures are viewed as a form of abstract imagery utilizing content-laden objects. Many of my ideas stem from a fascination with how things are connected, both literally and figuratively. Originally, I worked with the box format as the basis for these sculptures but have expanded outward from those original constraints. I utilize space to create an intimate setting that is filled with objects I have made and found. The use of space is very important to this work. I am interested in how objects function within a given space, i.e., how they occupy it and the relationships created with the other objects in that space. These objects contain an inherent meaning or symbolism, and yet they also hold an individualized meaning for different viewers.

## ROBBIE STUDIO
Home Accents
Page 85

Inspiration for my art is gleaned from a rich variety of sources, from the natural world to human creations; from the past, present, or contemplated future; from my own thoughts; or from ideas conveyed to me by others. Progression is often from just a glimpse of something that comes to my attention, provoking my imagination and developing into a full-fledged dream, through to creation of visual form. The *Candelabra Dream* is forged from steel and inspired by a pair of Elizabethan wrought iron candelabra. I had to learn the ancient art of blacksmithing to bring this object to reality; however, I also work in other materials.

## ROBERT MANN ORIGINALS

Furniture

Page 61

The grandfather clock is an American icon, but its design is stuck in the past. So I decided to take on the challenge of redesigning the grandfather clock so it would compliment today's decor trends. The designs I came up with are so unique I have U.S. patents for them. I make each clock from exotic hardwoods, which I meticulously sculpt into sensuous curves and flowing lines. I use an arduous laminating process to form the curved portions that surround the bent glass side windows. I then apply fifteen coats of hand-rubbed finish, which are polished to a dazzling sheen. I have over forty years' experience in the woodworking business and have spent the last twenty-nine years designing and patenting my clocks. I continue to accept other new furniture and cabinet projects. All pricing is negotiable. Articles featuring my work have appeared in the *Arizona Daily Star* newspaper, *Tucson Citizen* newspaper, *Custom Woodworking Business* magazine, and *Alumnus Magazine* of the University of Arizona.

## KEN ROBY

Architectural Elements

Page 100

My assistants and I create a variety of custom metalwork in forged iron, copper, bronze, and other metals. Projects and installations range from fire screens, furniture, lamps, and sculptural pieces to railings, gates, balconies, and other significant architectural works. I enjoy the process of figuring out how to make things work visually and functionally perhaps as much as I enjoy making them. My personal interest is largely in the art of the blacksmith. Most work continues to be done by hand in the forge and is signed and dated; however, plenty of current technology and machinery can be used in conjunction with traditional forging and joinery to accomplish the goals of any given project. Fortunately, my shop is well equipped for the wide variety of metalwork and installation work needed in bringing various works to fruition.

## KIM RODY

Paintings

Page 193

I have always been connected to the sea. I think the creatures that live near and below the ocean, with their intricate detail and vibrant coloring, are fascinating and compelling. Using acrylics, I work on large (up to 100") canvases and have established markets for my paintings and giclées in South Florida and the Bahamas in hotel lobbies, restaurants, primary residences, and second homes. My work is appealing to clients looking for a dramatic, bright, colorful, and tropical feel. My website, www.fishartista.com, showcases hundreds of images categorized by subject. In addition to original art, images are also available as limited editions on heavyweight watercolor paper, open editions on canvas, or posters.

GUILD SOURCEBOOKS: *Residential Art 5*

## LEITH A. ROHR

Fine Art Photography

Page 236

I received a B.F.A. from Art Center College in Los Angeles in advertising and illustration photography. While I was there, I attended my first photography exhibit. It happened to be an Ansel Adams exhibit of large black-and-white photographs. A rush of emotion overtook me and I felt like crying. I had never seen photography that beautiful. I worked in commercial and advertising photography for many years, but my real work was honing my craft in nature photography. Being alone and photographing in an outdoor environment is what I love most in life. Photographing designs with extraordinary light from the natural world can transport me to the most profound spiritual connection. When those magical moments happen, something is conveyed in the photographic image that translates to the viewer the feelings of what I saw and felt. I have used all formats of cameras and printed my own work in black-and-white and color. I now work in the digital realm. I still use film, but scan the negatives and transparencies into Photoshop on my Mac. This technology has brought me to a new level of creativity.

GUILD SOURCEBOOKS: *Residential Art 5*

## URSULA ROMA

Paintings

Page 194

A variation on the traditional family tree, this painting represents each family member, either as their favorite bird or one that captures their spirit. I enjoy illustrating light-hearted interpretations of the connection between animals and people as a way to portray the playfulness often present in that relationship. I use animals, trees, and faces as my subject matter and explore color and texturizing methods as I paint. When not painting, I can be found searching for materials and inspirational supplies to create mixed-media sculptures. As a salvager I see potential in all kinds of discarded shapes and misfit objects, often finding myself bringing them home to realize their destiny in future artwork. Items collected from junkyards, flea markets, and factories hold the potential to be transformed into figures, lamps, and wall compositions. This recycled work—as well as my paintings—can be viewed at www.ursularoma.com. Commissions encouraged. Call for prices.

## JON MICHAEL ROUTE

Metal Wall Art

Pages 9, 264

I seek to strike my own balance between art for art's sake and preserving time-honored techniques and craftsmanship, and I try to bring my twenty-five plus years of experience and love of metalworking to each and every piece. Combining metal's ageless appeal with vibrant patinas gives these fabricated wall pieces a very current design presence. They work equally well against wallboard, brick, or stone masonry. Three-dimensional elements are set on layered landscapes or patchwork fields of rich surface textures, patterns, and colors. Finely crafted from copper, brass, bronze, and pewter, these sculptural wall pieces can be custom made with varying themes, from natural to architectural, and to your size requirements up to about thirty-six inches. They are built on a framework that lifts them off the wall and allows them to be easily hung. Please refer to my website www.jonmichaelroute.com for resume and complementary work. Commissions and site-specific projects welcomed.

## LOIS S. SATTLER
Sculpture
Page 147

I have had a lifelong love for art. I spent many years studying painting, drawing, and sculpture, which eventually led me to my unusual style of hand-built ceramics. All of my work is one of a kind and can be special ordered to size and color for the client. My work, strongly influenced by my love of nature, can be seen in museums and galleries in the United States and other countries.

## TED SCHAAL
Sculpture
Page 148

I am exploring minimalist nonfunctional vessels in my latest bronze sculptures. My goal is to find pure geometric forms that challenge me as an artist. A departure from the purely ornate, these new designs incorporate a coarse corrugated texture to achieve their primitive aesthetic. I am moving in a more scultural direction in an effort to do interesting objects for the home. These pieces can be placed indoors or outdoors to enhance any environment. I hope that you will enjoy looking at them as much as I enjoy creating them.

## CAROLYN SCHLAM
Paintings
Page 195

I am a painter, mixed-media, and glass artist. I have explored many genres in painting, including what I call "visionary landscape" and abstract color field painting. These days I have brought all my studies in light, color, and the architecture of forms to bear on a figurative body of work, examples of which are illustrated here. My drawings in ink and crayon capture the fleeting moment, life distilled in a turn of head and a stance. The paintings are more complex and tell stories, or capture a mood—they are prose poems. Both aim for a feeling of intense, exuberant presence. My work in all media can be viewed on my website or at many fine galleries and juried shows. I accept commissions in all media for exhibition or publication. My work has been produced in limited editions, and I welcome further opportunities as well as illustration assignments.

## GEORGE SCHROEDER
Sculpture
Page 149

Founded in 1992, my studio has designed and produced an interesting variety of sculptures, furniture, lighting, and architectural metalwork. My primary service is to design, engineer, and produce these items in-house to ensure the highest level of quality. For more information and images of my work, please visit my website at www.schroederart.com.

## JOAN SCHULZE
Art Quilts
Page 302

Erasures, fragments, and layering are at the heart of my quilts and collages. Influenced by illuminated manuscripts, I use complex marks, drawings, images, and textures created by erasures and peeling while exploring a wide range of themes—gardens, abstractions based on nature, and the city/urban environment. My aesthetics reflect a fast-paced and complex world where beauty is in the details.

COLLECTIONS Adobe Systems, Inc., San Jose, CA; New York City, Museum of Arts & Design; Oakland Museum of California; Renwick/Smithsonian American Art Museum, Washington, DC

EXHIBITIONS International Fiber Exhibition, 2006, Suzhou University Art Museum, PR China; International Fiber Exhibition Invitational, 2006, Tsinghua University Art Museum, Beijing; QUILTS—Joan Schulze, 2005, Festival of Quilts, National Exhibition Centre, UK; International Fiber Exhibition, Shanghai Invitational, 2004; Six Continents of Quilts, The American Craft Museum, New York City

PUBLICATIONS: The Masters: Art Quilts, 2007; QUILTS—Joan Schulze, 2005

GUILD SOURCEBOOKS: The Guild 3, 4, 5; Designer's 8, 9, 10, 12, 13; Architectural & Interior Art 17, 20

## SHARI CORNISH CREATIVE
Floor Coverings
Page 92

As a surface designer, I have been producing my rugs and painted felts since 1995. My influences come from vintage fabrics, quilts, game boards, and contemporary graphic arts. My website, www.sharicornish.com, includes my resume and biography, along with my portfolio and pricing information. My painted felts are the first step in the process of creating the bold motifs that are my signature. It is the process of layering colors and shapes—both freehand and using stencils—that I love most. The felts are painted with textile pigments on synthetic industrial felt. They can be used on the floor, wall, or tabletop. I work closely with my clients to customize the rich color and lush texture of their rugs. My hand-crafted rugs are made one at a time in the U.S. by working in collaboration with production artisans using 100% New Zealand wool, which is prized for its durability and softness.

**SHERRY SHINE**
Art Quilts
Pages 299, 303

As an artist I usually start my process with a simple piece of whole cloth cotton. I sketch my idea directly onto the fabric, and then I start the process of adding color to bring the work to life. *Friendship* was created in this manner, along with the use of acrylics. The quilting adds dimension and movement to the piece through the use of thread. My work is in public and private collections and I have participated in group and solo exhibitions. To see more of my work, please visit my web site at www.artbysshine.com.

**YVETTE SIKORSKY**
Paintings
Page 196

After years of experimentation, I came upon a technique of sensuous abstraction that explores color and form. The images strike the viewer visually to reveal a true sense of design. The use of luminous colors plays across the spectrum while balancing a complex tension in design. I received an honorable mention and bronze medal from the City of Paris, France, my native country, and an Award of Excellence from Manhattan Art International. From 1985 to 2006, I showed my work in Paris, New York, Colorado, California, and The Schacknow Museum of Fine Arts in Florida. My work may currently be viewed in the World Fine Art Gallery in New York City. Sizes begin at 18" x 24". Prices range from $500 to $8,000. Work on commission, large or small, is welcome! I have also designed textiles for upholstery.

GUILD SOURCEBOOKS: *Residential Art 2, 3, 4, 5*

**PHILIP SIMS**
Furniture
Page 62

I design and fabricate custom furniture and fixtures for architects, interior designers, and private clients. Most of my commissions result from a client's need to solve a specific design issue: a difficult space, a desire for a functional but sculptural solution, or an idea for a piece that doesn't exist. For me, the collaborative design process is as important and enjoyable as the fabrication of something new. I always draw my ideas in 3D CAD and render them so the client can see the proposed design from different points of view prior to the start of fabrication. When called for I also do a full-scale mock-up so we can see the piece in its environment. In addition to furniture, I also design and fabricate architectural elements such as cantilevered staircases, cable railing systems, garden gates, and even tree houses. Each new project brings fresh design and fabrication challenges, and that is what keeps the journey interesting.

**JUNO SKY**
Mixed & Other Media Wall Art
Page 257

An understanding of the interpretive possibilities of a variety of materials has enabled me to create unique mixed-media works that are more fully infused with context and passion. My work offers a sense of drama, a humanizing force in efficient contemporary environments. Thick textures, intense or subtle colors, gold, copper, and silver leaf, oil and acrylic glazes are inter-layered. A painterly abstract dialogue and a sculptural quality results in work that can contrast or echo the visual features of a site. I have experience working with architects and designers on large, site-specific projects. My work is included in private and corporate collections throughout the U.S., Europe, and Asia. Prices range from $400-$75,000. Visit www.JunoSkyStudio.com for many current works.

COLLECTIONS: VISA, The U.S. Customs House, The Four Seasons, Hyatt Hotels, Honda Peace Collection, Eli Lilly, Hercules Offshore, Gulf Power, SAS Institute, Key Energy, Thermos Corp., US Gypsum, Battelle Institute

GUILD SOURCEBOOKS: *The Guild 3; Architectural & Interior Art 18; Residential Art 1*

**SELENE SMERLING**
Paintings
Page 197

In my paintings I try to bring things alive. My recent work is a series of antique timepieces painted in oil on watercolor paper. I like to think of them as not simply paintings of clocks, but paintings, that happen to be of clocks. I believe it is my responsibility as an artist to find the unexpected, the beautiful, and the rhythms of human spirit, even in a pocket watch or a chair. These objects that people can take for granted, when looked at closely, reveal powerful and interesting aspects. For the past ten years, I have sold paintings to private and corporate clients and have exhibited in the New York area. Prices provided upon request. Commissions accepted. Prints are also available.

**SARAH SOLIE**
Paintings
Page 198

Growing up in a farm community surrounded by a lush environment has been my biggest influence. In 2001 I first noticed a sharp decline in barns and farm buildings and began painting them. Elements of the natural world have been incorporated into many of the paintings. Most of the artwork is painted with acrylics on textured boards. I graduated from the Art Institute of Chicago with a bachelor's of fine art and Georgia's Savannah College of Art and Design with a master's of fine arts in 1997.

COMMISSIONS: *Tractor for Sale*, 2005, painting and poster for film, Wisconsin; *Barns and Farms*, 2003, painting and poster for juried exhibition, Kewaunee, WI

COLLECTIONS: St Claire's Hospital, 2005, Weston WI; Organic Valley Food Co-op, 2005, La Farge, WI; Jane La Chapelle McCarty Memorial Fund, 2004, Wisconsin

## DANIEL SROKA
Fine Art Photography
Page 237

I create abstract, dream-like images out of the simple elements of nature, such as fallen leaves, sticks, and seeds. I find most of my subjects as I walk through my suburban neighborhood, collecting things that have fallen to the ground before they are swept up for compost. Usually ignored, I find that these natural objects are rich in complexity and subtlety. As I explore each object I discover its unique character and personality, which I let guide the images I create. I feel much like a sculptor, who lets the flaws and veins of a stone guide his chisel. The resulting photographs are two-dimensional "sculptures" of light, form, and texture that possess a mysterious intimacy. I hope they give us the chance to think about how we relate to the natural world that we live in every day. To see more of my artwork, visit www.danielsroka.com.

## JOHN E. STALLINGS
Metal Wall Art
Page 266

My work is about the search for the infinite. For the past several years, I've concentrated my efforts on creating modern, minimalist sculpture with a timeless quality—clean lines and surfaces blended to create constant movement and balance within the occupied space. Infused with this concept of continuous motion, the designs neither begin nor end. ". . . Powerful in their reflection of surroundings and in their sublime and clean geometric volumes." Mariana Bego, Ezair Gallery, NYC. ". . . The polished surfaces of many of his sculptures blur the borders of matter and its surrounding environment. The viewer is left wondering which aspect is visual and which is physical. Thus each piece, at once autonomous and boundless, has a dialectical relationship with its setting. It is in this way that Mr. Stallings' minimalist approach to abstraction continuously proves itself to be among the most engaging and effective sculpture available today." Ruthie Tucker, Amsterdam Whitney Gallery, NYC. More of John's work can be seen at his website www.stallingsart.com.

## STEPHANIE STANLEY
Paintings
Page 199

I seek to represent a spiritual experience, so I invoke the power of color and texture in all my work. A true "color field" painter (like Rothko and Noland), I am concerned with exploring the effect of pure color on canvas. Being the daughter of artists, I was compelled to express myself at an early age. Inspired by my dreams, meditations, and experiences, my collection is filled with variant textures and vibrant colors. I think that while abstract impressionism is non-representational with regard to form, my work nevertheless represents very real and specific ideas. My work is created with oil or acrylic on canvas in varying dimensions, and all edges of the canvas are painted. A sample of my work can be viewed at www.StephanieStanley.com.

## STANTON GLASS STUDIO, LLC
Architectural Elements
Page 101

For more than twenty-five years, Stanton Glass Studio has been creating distinctive, one-of-a-kind architectural stained glass pieces for a broad range of clients, including churches, hotels, resorts, restaurants, and homeowners. Working in a centuries-old craft, our talented staff has produced masterpieces in glass, ranging from large church windows to many decorative elements at the landmark Driskill Hotel in Austin, TX. In the residential realm, our company handcrafts unique, custom-stained beveled glass elements—from doors, windows, domes, and ceilings to stunning light fixtures. Everything is custom tailored to the client. Our craftsmen also specialize in the preservation, restoration, and repair of historic stained glass windows. Recent restoration projects include The Guadalupe Cathedral in Dallas, TX; St. Patrick's in Ft. Worth, TX; and St. David's in Austin, TX. Our craftsmen practice the latest conservation and restoration techniques used in the preservation of historic stained glass. Working from our facility in Waco, Texas, we collaborate with other highly skilled and gifted blacksmiths and craftsmen to produce hand-forged ironwork to frame our windows, suspend light fixtures and domes, and set off our decorative glasswork.

## DAVID STEINHARDT
Murals, Tiles & Wall Reliefs
Page 282

Mural clients all have a unique, personal vision buried somewhere within them. I most enjoy working on murals that originate from the client's inspiration, and adapting my style to suit the best expression of his or her idea. Unusual requests are the most interesting. Thirty plus years of experience allow me to paint in a variety of styles and, when needed, on a variety of problem surfaces. I like the intimacy of direct dealings with the client and relatively small-scale works as much as large corporate and public murals. You will see different styles—classical realism, modernism, photo-realism, and abstraction—within my body of work. The qualities that unify my work are: creation of atmospheric space (depth); use of subtle color variations to create a fascinating visual surface; and great attention to finish, which lends each piece an unmistakable air of quality.

## JANE STERRETT
Prints
Page 218

My work combines photographic imagery with painterly effects to produce a unique and vibrant personal style strong in color and tactile values. My art has been commissioned by corporate and editorial clients. I have received numerous awards. Trained as a fine artist, I earned a B.F.A. from Rhode Island School of Design and an M.F.A. in painting from Yale, and studied with Oskar Kokoshka in Salzburg. I am currently on the faculty of Pratt Institute in New York City. Additional images can be seen at www.janesterrett.com.

COMMISSIONS: Atlanticare Regional Medical Center, 2007, Atlantic City, NJ; Phelps County Regional Medical Center, 2007, St. Louis, MO; Washington offices of NASDAQ, 2006, NASD University, Rockville, MD; St. John's Unity Hospital, 2006, St. Louis, MO; St. Joseph Hospital, 2004, Bloomington, IL; MBNA/Bank One, 2002, Wilmington, DE; Children's Hospital, 2001, Montefiore Medical Center, Bronx, NY; Opus One Restaurant, 1998, Naples, FL; Chase Metrotech Cafeteria, 1998, Brooklyn, NY

GUILD SOURCEBOOKS: *Designer's 14, 15; Architectural & Interior Art 16, 17, 20, 21*

## STEVEN WHYTE SCULPTURE STUDIOS
Sculpture
Pages 116, 150

Celebrated for my work's expressiveness, authenticity, and effectiveness, I am an accomplished figurative sculptor with a growing reputation for public works of varying scale. A noted portrait sculptor, I am former vice president of the prestigious London-based Society of Portrait Sculptors. During my career I have completed dozens of portrait commissions and nine public monuments, including the soon-to-be-unveiled multi-million dollar *National Tribute to Bob Hope and Our Nation's Military*. I have established a reputation for authenticity and professionalism, and I regard public commissions as a responsibility to the past and future legacies of the communities involved. I am experienced in collaborating with civic organizations and local governments, and at ease working within budget and schedule parameters. I also appreciate the creative challenges and rewards of site-specific installations; I work frequently with architects, designers and developers. With my in-house studio team, I provide my clients and collectors with the highest-quality fine art bronze to suit the needs of communities, homes, offices, congregations, collections, and public spaces.

## CHARLES STRAIN
Sculpture
Page 151

I draw my imagery from nature and from life experience. The human figure and human emotions are the basis of most of my compositions. Happiness, sadness, a moment in time, a familiar experience, a celebration—these events and emotions serve as catalysts for my sculptures. My dedication to mastering the lost wax method of casting bronze and a "labor of love" approach to art making serve to transform each bronze into a timeless statement. My sculpture can be installed indoors or outdoors. I enjoy working with clients who have the creative vision to transform outdoor spaces into works of art. I accept commissions in a broad range of sizes and can install sculpture on freestanding bases, or in fountains or ponds. Size range from 6" to 120".

GUILD SOURCEBOOKS: *Architectural & Interior Art 20, 22; Residential Art 3, 4, 5*

## KRISTINE SULLIVAN
Paintings
Pages 200, 220

As the daughter of a British diplomat with London as my home base, I have lived and traveled extensively abroad in such locales as Madrid, Milan, and Rome. A scholarship to dance at La Scala in Milan placed me amid the vast Italian art culture. After attending boarding schools in the U.K., I received a full scholarship to the prestigious Hammersmith College of Art and Architecture in London, and following my studies there, immigrated to the U.S. and founded KJS Art Association in Connecticut, where I teach adult artists pen-and-ink, pastel, gouache, and acrylic techniques. My vivid, shimmering, luminescent Expressionist paintings have graced numerous one-woman and group shows in galleries and museums throughout the country, including Fairleigh Dickinson University; New Jersey Institute of Technology; Madison Avenue's John O'Rourke Gallery; Pen and Brush Gallery, Greenwich Village, NY; The Springfield Quadrangle Fine Arts Museum, Springfield, MA; and East End Gallery in Nantucket. Currently concentrating my efforts on a very active in-home gallery in Granville, MA, my work can be viewed online on either my personal website, www.kjsfinearts.com or my online portfolio, www.kjsfinearts.com/Portfolio/.

## TRINITY SULLIVAN
Fine Art Photography
Page 238

My travels through the United States, Europe, and the Middle East have shaped how I visually see and interpret the world. I find beauty everywhere I look, whether it is the ancient city of Rome, a flower, or a junkyard. Presenting a place, an idea, or an object in a different way than how another sees it is the inspiration for my work. Everyone's vision is unique, like a kaleidoscope. It changes by the slightest movement, which can alter your perspective. I utilize a variety of photographic techniques ranging from early cameraless methods to the modern day of digital. My work is available on archival fine art paper, canvases, and metal to achieve the desired look of the space. Please visit www.trinitysullivan.com to view my complete bodies of work.

## T.S. POST
Murals, Tiles & Wall Reliefs
Page 283

We integrate painting, printmaking, and ceramic techniques in our wall works, resulting in compelling works of art. Cut and glazed clay shapes form the ground for layered brushwork, etching, and a tracery of delicate grout lines. The resulting patterns and abstract imagery become a vehicle for exploring and transiting edges and boundaries. Recent commissions include installations in hotels, offices, and hospitals, as well placement in private homes. Our wall pieces are among the twenty ceramic works featured in the online exhibit *Craft in America*, the May 2007 PBS documentary and have recently been reviewed in *Clay Times* and *Ceramics Monthly*. Additional wall works may be seen in the 2007 edition of *The Guild Sourcebook of Residential Art* and on our website www.tspost.com.

GUILD SOURCEBOOKS: *Residential Art 4,5*

## TAYLOR BACKES ■ TIBITU
Objects
Page 120

Simple, elegant forms combined with beautiful and, at times, complex colors and patterns describe the *Boat* series, our newest body of work. We pride ourselves on versatility and the ability to adapt sizes and colors to our client's fantasies. The images seen in this publication are a taste of what comes out of our studio. Taylor Backes specializes in corporate, sculptural, architectural, and private commissions. Our work is included in museums, galleries, and private collections internationally. Our glass studio and gallery are open to the public.

## CHARLES TODD
Furniture
Page 63

Long before I first tried to build a piece of furniture, I was an admirer of antiques. Old furniture, especially the kind that didn't look mass-produced, fascinated me. A tree was cut down more than a century ago and fashioned with hand tools into a graceful object that is still useful and beautiful. Most of what I build is "made to order." Yet whether I am building my own design or using a customer's pattern, I always try to build both with a respect for the tradition of woodworking and with an effort to let the wood speak.

## MARJORIE TOMCHUK
Fiber Wall Art
Page 297

Handmade paper has an extraordinary capacity for deep embossing, and this has been the primary medium of my artistic expression for twenty-six years. As paper sheets are created, a rich textural surface and exaggerated deckle edges become important. Embossing is created on an etching press from a master plate, and color is then added by hand with an airbrush. Recently, I've used my own archival digital photographs, collaging them over the embossing. My art can be found in thirty museums and educational institutions. About 200 major corporations include my art in their collections (please refer to website). A book entitled *M. Tomchuk Graphic Work* was published in 1998. An award-winning video was created for Connecticut Public Television in 2000. My work includes editions of prints, monoprints, cast paper, and large format (40" x 60") paintings. Commissions are accepted. Website: www.MTomchuk.com.

GUILD SOURCEBOOKS: *The Guild 5; Architect's 6; Designer's 6, 7, 8, 9; Architectural & Interior Art 17; Residential Art 5*

## GWEN PEINE TOOMALATAI
Paintings
Page 201

The rich textures and vibrant colors in my paintings transcend any style, yet possess an appealing classic quality. My paintings are a reflection of my own journey in life. It is a process of transformation, a method of adding and subtracting color, allowing paint residues to remain, and removing paint and marks that interfere. My process of painting and the use of panels are traced back to the origins of oil painting. I admire the light that illuminates from the paintings of early painters such as Rembrandt, Jan Van Eyck, and others. It is light that reflects through pure pigments, allowing my paintings to glow and illuminate, creating masterpieces that inspire to seek renewal along the path to a promised eternal home.

## STEPHANIE TORAL
Paintings
Page 202

I am amazed and inspired by nature. From a sprawling landscape from a hilltop in Tuscany to an acorn fallen from a tree in my backyard, I express myself through my impression of the natural world. Through the use of pattern, text, and graphic elements, I seek to give insight into how I have been touched by my subject matter. I discovered my love of art at an early age, spending much of my life sketching, drawing, and painting. I was immediately drawn to watercolor. The fluid spontaneity of watercolors is always fresh and fascinating for me. I love putting the brush to paper, not entirely certain where the flowing paint will lead my imagination.

## DARREL TRACY
Sculpture
Page 152

My artistic inspiration comes from the forests of the Pacific Northwest, where I played as a child and later worked in Alaska's Tongass National Forest with degrees in forest sciences and landscape architecture. I further explored the forested waterways as a ship's captain. I taught myself to paint with watercolors and eventually discovered three-dimensional art in the ceramic art studios of Montgomery College in Maryland. The first tree house sculptures were born there. Like the trees in the forest, each sculpture stands as a one-of-a-kind individual. My work expresses the relationship between nature and man, portrayed as tree and house. They are reminders of mankind's universal connection with nature. The house of man is supported by the tree. They are, in fact, cut from the same fabric.

## RACHEL TRIBBLE
Paintings
Page 203

My work is a reflection of nature. To explore the dimensions humans cannot see or experience regularly and make them visual to us. Color also reaches through the dimensions; and the human experience of color is individual on many levels. We experience color in our daily lives in a routine, but in dreams colors are often expressed in ways that do not exist in waking life. My expression of color is an attempt to reach into nature, explore the hidden realms, and share the beauty and serenity of the unseen natural world.

## JANE TROUP
Paintings
Page 204

I have painted since childhood and sometimes feel that painting is my first language and English my second. Nature is my source and inspiration. My style is slightly stylized and on the edge of surrealism. I create mostly landscapes that convey a certain energy, balance, and mystery to convey to the viewer the sense of the awe I feel for this amazing experience on earth. I approach the painting like a sculptor or set designer, visualizing every form in three dimensions before painting.

COLLECTIONS: Springfield Art Museum, Springfield, MO; Federal Deposit Insurance Corporation, Washington, DC; The Pickwick Hotel, Birmingham, AL; Blue Cross & Blue Shield, Philadelphia, PA; Reliance Standard Insurance Company, Philadelphia, PA

EXHIBITIONS: Katie Gingrass Gallery, Milwaukee, WI, 2006-2007; MOAK, Springfield Art Museum, Springfield, MO, 2002–2004; William Havu Gallery, Denver, CO, 2000-2003; Edgewood Orchard Galleries, Door County, WI, 2001–2003

## TUNSTULL
Paintings
Page 205

My current body of work consists of colorful landscapes and beach scenes, but, with a more abstracted version of these images than in the past. Water fascinates me, with its reflection and movement, and sunsets with their shifting displays of vividly hued light. My new paintings distill the world I see to the essence of its basic coloration. By reducing scenes to color dabs of light and shadow, I am able to recreate the feeling of a setting without an actual depiction through line. Part of this impact is directly evoking the feeling of the place, a sense of calm or the shimmer of water, as well as a series of abstract sensations that range from the size of the brush strokes to each painting's distinctive color palette. My hope is that the viewer will feel like they are standing in the painting's setting, a sort of transporting of the individual's soul to that location, through sensation.

## MIA TYSON
Objects
Page 121

Free of expectations, aiming to express a gaiety in movement and a fleshy tension in the surface. These elements allow the outer structure to reveal its intent of female spirituality, producing a continuity of form and outline. I am intrigued that birth celebrates but wounds, and death wounds but celebrates. Excitement is my reward when viewing my finished work, for it has been a laborious task, much like a pregnancy. Intimacy evolves between me and the piece, followed by the anguish of the unknown versus the known. In every piece I discover yet another facet of who I am, such as my struggle with issues of self worth in relation to what society imposes on me, perhaps disempowering my womanly intuitions. My work keeps me alive and growing in body and spirit. I hold a B.F.A. in fine arts from Winthrop University and attended the Penland School of Crafts from 1995-1997. I have owned Gallery Mia Tyson since 2000.

## UNITED ARTWORKS
Architectural Elements
Page 102

At United Artworks we take sculpture to the next level using digital tools to achieve a decidedly non-technical effect, producing (among other things) brass hardware, carved wooden panels and furniture, and cast wall ornaments that draw on nature for their inspiration. In-house 3-D scanning technology allows us to capture fine details from the animal, mineral, and vegetable realms and incorporate them into compositions that can assume various functional and decorative roles, or stand alone as art objects. Our computerized carving machines make it possible to transpose the intricate detail of natural objects to a wide range of materials, from metals and ceramics to wood and plastics. We are always looking for problems to solve and the opportunity to explore new possibilities—if you aren't satisfied with what's available elsewhere and want to do something really special, please let us know.

GUILD SOURCEBOOKS: *Architect's 8*

## ALICE VAN LEUNEN
Fiber Wall Art
Page 298

My artworks explore pattern, texture, and reflection. My approach is light-hearted. Many of the artworks make musical or literary allusions and feature calligraphic marks and symbols. Works range in size from small, intimate pieces to major architectural installations. Commissions are welcome. Commissions include the Mulia Bank Complex, Djakarta, Indonesia; National High Magnetic Field Laboratory, Tallahassee, FL (with Walter Gordinier); Fairview Auditorium, OK; Kaiser Permanente, San Diego, CA; Kodiak Auditorium, Kodiak Island, AK; and Playboy Towers, Chicago, IL. My works are in collections at Atlantic County Office Building, Atlantic City, NJ; General Motors, New York, NY; Seattle City Light, WA; and Calvin Klein Cosmetics, Wayne, NJ. I received the Oregon Individual Artist Fellowship in 1993.

GUILD SOURCEBOOKS: *The Guild 1, 4, 5; Architect's 6, 7, 11, 12, 13; Designer's 6, 9, 10; Architectural & Interior Art 16, 17, 20, 21; Residential Art 1, 2, 4, 5*

## DARRIN VANDEN BOSCH
Furniture
Page 64

Elements that enhance the clean lines of my designs include styles ranging from Shaker and Mission to Art Deco and Art Nouveau. Constructed from domestic and/or exotic woods, the finished pieces can be either contemporary or traditional in style. The premium wood in my inventory is waiting to show me what to create with it. I call this process "empirical design." In a sense the wood speaks to me! I get the satisfaction of my belief that working with wood is one of the most natural things man can do. My pieces are in homes from California to Connecticut. My work can be commissioned directly or purchased through a growing number of galleries from the East Coast to Hawaii.

## BILHENRY WALKER
Furniture
Page 65

I have added five new chairs to my line of sculptural furniture since being published in last year's Residential Sourcebook. I have also expanded my cocktail tables to dining table size and developed a new series of maquettes for conference tables. I am most interested in creating furniture that has ergonomic values, such as the backs of chairs which provide lumbar support and shaped arms onto which the arm and wrist fit comfortably. The Dining Tables are offered with 0.75" inch plate glass sitting atop a variety of sculptural bases. The new spectacular series of conference tables can be built in modular fashions to reach lengths of twenty feet, with many options for design. These challenge the design limits of aluminum plate and glass, and may be viewed at bilhenrygallery.com.

GUILD SOURCEBOOKS: *Architect's 12, 14; Residential Art 5*

## JUDITH WEBER
Murals, Tiles & Wall reliefs
Page 286

Since 1973 I have specialized in custom-designed dinnerware, accessories, and handmade tile for residential and commercial application. Driven by my constant search to explore new avenues of creativity, and being strongly influenced by Bauhaus and Asian Arts, I evolved from a studio potter to a product designer, ultimately developing dinnerware for Dansk. As an artist who thrives on challenge and diversity, my "other self" spends equal time exploring the techniques needed to create unusual and highly personal ceramic installations. I design work that reflects an individual aspect of my client, striving to capture the essence of an experience, an environment, a memory, and from that information, create a permanent and intimate work of art. *Tile Fish*, a 4' × 4' ceramic puzzle, creates an "aquarium" in my client's bathroom, which overlooks the sound. I recently completed the Donor Wall for the New Rochelle Public Library, a 13' bas relief that sculpturally portrays the vital life of the library.

## GEORGIA WALLER
Murals, Tiles & Wall Reliefs
Page 284

My *Rock Art* series meticulously reproduces the primitive line and form of ancient Indian cave art in colorful renditions. The contrast inherent in the use of modern materials and archaic images yields a powerful glimpse into the mystery and magic of the art of early man. These pieces add excitement and dramatic impact when placed among the subtle colors and hues inherent in the homes and businesses of the Southwest. For the last decade, I have worked and lived on my ranch in southwest Texas; the contrast of the vivid blooms of desert plant life with the vastness and subtly of the terrain have guided me to this venue. The blue-gray sage and the infinite variety of earth tones have revealed to me the impact that a dash of claret, a spark of brilliant orange, or the magentas of a desert sunset have on my horizons. I hand cut, grind, and fit stained glass and iridized tiles to form these images. The pieces fit so snugly that I do not use grout. Photographs of actual cave art and related information for each piece is available with your purchase. My website is georgiawallergallery.com.

## CANDONE M. WHARTON
Objects
Page 122

My finely crafted, hand-built vessels are uniquely carved with basket weave and block print designs. I am best known for my intricate work, fine luster glazes, and my development of a technique that produces a metallic-like gold luster. Using raku techniques to fire my coiled and carved vessels, I am able to create a striking combination of exciting surfaces that I intermix to create mystery. When viewing my work, you are transformed to a timeless place with its own language. My surfaces speak in this language, transmitting the effect of the influence of African potters and my love for this media. Having received a B.F.A. from the University of Georgia, living in Sweden for five years and with the Cuna Indians in Panama for one year, I arrived at the Spanish island of Ibiza. For fifteen years I made this island my home and developed many of the techniques I use today. Presently, I reside in Daytona Beach Shores, where I have a home and studio.

## LIBBY WARE
Murals, Tiles & Wall Reliefs
Pages 12, 285, 294

In using five sides of a cube as the basic statement of the picture plane, I hope to synthesize painting and sculpture, even though my cubes are characteristically attached to the wall. This confounding of two- and three-dimensional space is meant to present a visual puzzle. In addition, I intend for the depth and space of the cubes to engage the viewer in the work. As the viewer moves past the work, the image/illusion changes. Therefore, movement is a key characteristic of the multilevel installations. Another aspect of each piece is the owner's choice of involvement in the work. To help facilitate this involvement, each cube is individually mounted with hidden hardware. A person can choose to arrange the cubes to suit an aesthetic/space. Lusters, which radiate iridescent luminescence, help create the mystery of the material. Clay is an ancient material, which is soft and then hard, capturing both the organic nature and the handmade process. The cubes, separate and apart from each other, have subtle elements of difference from one to another. The choice of clay celebrates the use of non-industrial material in our electronic age.

GUILD SOURCEBOOKS: *Architectural & Interior Art 20, 21, 22; Residential Art 3, 4, 5*

## TIMOTHY WHITE
Furniture
Page 66

I am a contemporary studio furniture maker who works primarily with wood, adding occasional accents of steel, bronze, concrete, or glass. My skills have been honed over the past twenty-three years in a number of environments, including work at a pipe organ company and an eight-year tenure with Richard Scott Newman. I opened my own studio in 1997 in Crested Butte, Colorado, where I am constantly inspired by the awesome beauty that surrounds me. My work, while often commissioned for private collections, is shown in several galleries and occasional exhibitions around the country. It has won Best of Show and design awards, and been featured in publications including *American Art Collector, Woodworker West*, and *Woodwork*. Commission prices start at $2,000. For more information, please visit my website at www.spellboundfurnitureworks.com.

## CHERYL WILLIAMS
Sculpture
Pages 112, 123, 153

I took a pottery class in high school and fell in love instantly. I think I knew right then that this was what I wanted to do in my life. To this day I still enjoy the feeling of making large pieces on the potter's wheel. I love to create. It doesn't matter the medium. Over the years I've played in stone carving, painting, clay, jewelry, and fiber—sometimes in combinations. Many people ask me where my ideas come from. They come from living life and being open to that which shows itself to me. I love to make the ordinary appear extraordinary. My work is simple and elegant. It gives me great pleasure to share this with you. To see more of my work, please visit my website at www.cherylswilliams.com.

## MARY WILLIAMS
Mixed & Other Media Wall Art
Page 258

Seven years ago I left a successful career in advertising art and began exploring wood as an art form. I attended numerous workshops to learn carving techniques and woodworking skills. Soon after, I found myself creating sculptures from aspen trees. My aspen sculptures led me to explore other wood surfaces as canvases for my designs. Carved textures, lines, and shapes layered with color appear on custom-made wood panels and antique skis. Using wood as my medium allows me to explore many ideas, from small wood tiles to large totems. My work has a whimsical, organic, and truly unique style that is refreshing and makes people smile. Residential and commercial commissions are welcome. My work can be seen throughout Colorado in public places such as Vail Resorts, Kaiser Permanente medical facilities, The Children's Hospital, Platte Valley Medical Center, the Philip S. Miller Library, and numerous corporate offices.

## ELLEN WOODS
Paintings
Page 206

Falling between categories, my paintings and prints lie somewhere between the inner world of the imagination and the outer world of beauty and nature. Inspired by the Colorado landscape and a daily interaction with wildlife, I search for patterns and clues in my environment. Themes may evolve from shapes on a mountain hillside, the wings of a red-tailed hawk, or a cluster of dead leaves. Then I become an experimenter in the studio, trying new combinations of color, form, texture, and composition. Opposites often appear together, realism with abstraction or a sense of serious playfulness. I have received numerous grants and exhibit my work regionally and nationally. My work is included in many private collections, and I welcome commissions.

## XAVIER NUEZ CONTEMPORARY PHOTOGRAPHY
Fine Art Photography
Page 239

*Alleys & Fire Escapes* is an exploration of urban decay and of the elusive beauty and stories lurking within its dark corners. These are corners rich in history, which I sift through in an attempt to revive the past and to tell its tale in powerful yet subtle ways. Long after dark, I walk through desolate urban settings, seeking out the drama and intensity of these places. With the city humming in the background, I give myself the task of finding inspiration, beauty, and power where there shouldn't be any. It is a thrilling adventure in a risky setting. I've had to run from gangs, and I'm frequently questioned by the police, who never believe my story. Yet, ironically, in the alleys I find moments of peace in a hectic life. To see more images in the series, and for a list of collections, exhibitions, awards, and publications, please visit www.nuez.com.

## JEANNINE YOUNG
Sculpture
Page 154

I weld my original sculptures in steel and later have copies cast in bronze. I am drawn to the strength, flexibility, and luster of the metal. As I work, cutting, hammering, and welding the metal, the personality of the subject emerges. It can be dramatically affected by subtle changes in the angles and planes of the form. The contrast of the sharp smooth surfaces against the rounded textured surfaces is enhanced by the golden patina. My work is in private collections in the U.S. and Europe. For more information visit www.jeannineyoung.com.

EXHIBITIONS: Sculpture in the Park, 2007, Loveland CO; Face of Utah Sculpture, 2007, Salt Lake City, UT; Mesa Art on the Corner, 2006-2007, Mesa, AZ; Merit Award, Utah Spring Salon, 2007, Springville, UT; Industry Award, 2007, *Sculptural Pursuit,* fall issue

PUBLICATIONS: *Southwest Art,* August 2007; *Southwest Art,* July 2002; *Utah Painting and Sculpture,* 1999; *Artists of Utah,* 1997

GUILD SOURCEBOOKS: *Residential 4, 5*

## CHIN YUEN
Paintings
Pages 16, 156, 207

My acrylic paintings are an exploration and expression of beauty through abstraction. My approach is bold, intuitive, and playful, embracing my love for colors and the physicality of painting. I enjoy juxtaposing different textures and colors to create dynamic compositions that offer a sense of luxury and creativity. My abstract paintings have won the 2005 Herbert Siebner Practicing Artist Award (Canada) and the 2004 International Expo XXIII Award (USA), including earning positive reviews from *The New York Times* and other publications. My artworks are exhibited and collected internationally by private and corporate art lovers.

## LAURA ZINDEL
Home Accents
Pages 77, 86

I believe that some objects can carry a personal history through a family from year to year. I hope that I can make art that a family member can buy to be handed down the line. Something bought on a whim that becomes the platter for the family turkey or that sits on the mantel. I can hear it now: "Crazy old Uncle Larry bought that peculiar spider platter, and we just can't throw it out for some reason." I would like to be part of that. All work is handbuilt with earthenware and fired with nontoxic glazes.

## BARBARA ZINKEL
Prints
Page 219

It is my desire to create works of art that are dramatic in color, with a certain freedom and flow in movement, yet complex enough to be constantly interesting. My serigraph prints have been featured in decorators' show houses in Detroit, in the *Detroit News* (1994), *Hour Detroit* magazine (1999), and *Better Homes and Gardens Decorating* magazine (1987). My prints are in various collections in the Netherlands, Hong Kong, Venezuela, and Spain. My domestic collection placements include General Motors, DaimlerChryler Corporation Headquarters, Ford, Dupont, Steelcase, CBS, Chase Manhattan Bank, Texas Instruments, Honeywell, Ericcson, Verisign, Wyeth Pharmaceutical Headquarters, and ABN AMRO World Headquarters, Ann Arbor, MI.

## KURT DANIEL ZIVELONGHI
Paintings
Page 208

I was born in Barstow, California, in 1960 and earned my B.F.A. from the Pasadena Art Center College of Design in 1993. I spent 1988 and 1989 at the Art Student's League in New York and later toured Europe while studying in France at The Ecole D'Albert Defois near Anger. Artwork has always been my passion—its core deep within my soul. My work reflects passion focused on today's culture and tomorrow's reflection of a "truly artistic work." I currently reside in Midlothian, VA. My work has been displayed at Art Works Inc. and Crossroads Galleries, Richmond, VA; at Omma Gallery, Santa Barbara, CA.; Aaron Gallery, Washington, DC; Canvas Gallery, Dallas, TX.; various New York exhibits; and in collectors' homes throughout the world. You can see more of my work at www.kurtdanielgalleries.com or www.fineartstore.biz. My work has also appeared in *Style Magazine, Marquis' Who's Who in the World, America* (1997-2007), the *10th International Biennial Festival of Portraiture-Drawings and Graphics*, and Tulze Exhibition Catalogue.

## WILLIAM ZWEIFEL
Sculpture
Page 155

Shape, and structure used to evoke emotion summarize my work. Shapes that appear simple and smooth are in fact made up of individual lines, working on different planes, heading in different directions, yet interweaving in a way that they directly influence one another. I view life in much the same way. We are who we are as a result of the interweaving of many life experiences. How much we allow pressures to influence us will determine whether we will be in turmoil or at peace. The medium I have chosen for this work is glass. Beyond its obvious attributes of color and texture, it provides the ability to freeze a moment in time so that it can be explored. I find in its very fragility, a metaphor for the fragility of our existence. Being able to freeze these moments, in such a delicate medium offers me an opportunity to create the tranquility that I find so comforting.

# Rob Hare

*Essex Table and Chairs* ■ 2001 ■ Essex, CT
table: single-plank claro walnut and solid forged steel ■ 29"H x 88"L x 46"W
See more of Rob's work on page 59.

*"I met these clients at the Philadelphia Furniture show. They saw a table at the show they liked and asked me to create another for their kitchen dining table. They also ordered a set of chairs to go with it, but because they have children, they asked that the corners be rounded. I cut the seats and backs in half-el-lipses, to work with the ellipse of the table. The clients were really happy with the pieces."*

— Rob Hare, artist

Chris Kendall

# ORGANIZATIONS & PUBLICATIONS

## ORGANIZATIONS

### American Association of Woodturners

222 Landmark Center
75 West Fifth Street
St. Paul, MN 55102
TEL 651-484-9094
FAX 651-484-1724
www.woodturner.org

The American Association of Woodturners (AAW) is a nonprofit organization dedicated to the advancement of woodturning. Over 273 chapters throughout the United States provide education and information for those interested in woodturning. Members include hobbyists, professionals, gallery owners, collectors, and wood and equipment suppliers. Contact AAW for information on their annual symposium.

### American Craft Council

72 Spring Street
New York, NY 10012-4019
TEL 212-274-0630
FAX 212-274-0650
www.craftcouncil.org

American Craft Council is a national nonprofit educational organization founded in 1943 by Aileen Osborn Webb. The mission of the Council is to promote understanding and appreciation of contemporary American craft. Programs include the bimonthly magazine *American Craft*, annual juried craft shows presenting artists and their work, and other services to the public. Membership in the Council is open to all.

### American Tapestry Alliance

PO Box 28600
San Jose, CA 95159-8600
www.americantapestryalliance.org

The American Tapestry Alliance is a non-profit educational organization supporting the fine arts medium of contemporary handwoven tapestry. The purpose of the Alliance is to promote a widespread awareness of the development of contemporary tapestry in North America as an art form; educate the general public about tapestry techniques, materials, images, and meanings; coordinate exhibitions of tapestries to establish a professional networking system for tapestry designers and weavers throughout the world; and support its members by providing them with necessary information and resources.

### Architectural Woodwork Institute

46179 Westlake Drive Suite 120
Potomac Falls, VA 20165
TEL 571-323-3636
FAX 571-323-3630
www.awinet.org

The Architectural Woodwork Institute (AWI) is a nonprofit trade association whose mission is to be the authoritative resource for the advancement of architectural woodwork. The AWI publishes *Quality Standards Illustrated*, which is referenced by design professionals and woodwork manufacturers to define and describe the criteria for fine architectural quality grades and customer expectations. Membership is available to architectural woodworkers, manufacturers and suppliers, design professionals, and students in the woodworking field interested in helping to further public knowledge.

### Art Alliance for Contemporary Glass

PO Box 7022
Evanston, IL 60201
TEL/FAX 847-869-2018
www.ContempGlass.org

The Art Alliance for Contemporary Glass is a not-for-profit organization whose mission is to further the development and appreciation of art made from glass. The Alliance informs collectors, critics, and curators by encouraging and supporting museum exhibitions, university glass departments and specialized teaching programs, regional collector groups, visits to private collections, and public seminars. AACG maintains a calendar of glass-related events, links to artists and galleries, secondary market glass, and "house tours" of collections as regular features on its website.

### Artist-Blacksmiths' Association of North America

PO Box 3425
Knoxville, TN 37927-3425
TEL 865-546-7733
FAX 865-215-9964
www.abana.org

Artist-Blacksmiths' Association of North America (ABANA) is a nonprofit organization devoted to promoting the art of blacksmithing. ABANA serves to help educate blacksmiths, acts as a central resource for information about blacksmithing, and publishes two quarterly journals—*The Anvil's Ring* and *The Hammer's Blow*—for blacksmiths. These publications are included as a part of ABANA membership.

### Creative Glass Center of America

1501 Glasstown Road
Millville, NJ 08332-1566
TEL 800-998-4552
FAX 856-825-2410
www.wheatonvillage.org/creativeglasscenteramerica

The Creative Glass Center of America (CGCA) offers fellowships to artists working in glass and has serviced glass artists and the arts community for over twenty years. Over 250 professional and emerging artists, from twenty-five states and twenty foreign countries, have been recipients of a CGCA fellowship. Artists are encouraged to use their fellowships to develop and refine their work, while experimenting with both traditional and innovative glassmaking processes.

### The Furniture Society

111 Grovewood Road
Asheville, NC 28804
TEL 828-255-1949
FAX 828-255-1950
www.furnituresociety.org

The purpose of the Furniture Society is to advance the art of furniture making by inspiring creativity, promoting excellence, and foster-

# ORGANIZATIONS & PUBLICATIONS

ing understanding of this art and its place in society. The Furniture Society is open not only to professional furniture makers, but also to all who have an interest in the art of furniture making, including galleries, arts professionals, collectors, educators, students, the media, amateur furniture makers, and studio furniture enthusiasts.

## Glass Art Society

3131 Western Avenue Suite 414
Seattle, WA 98121
TEL 206-382-1305
FAX 206-382-2630
www.glassart.org

The Glass Art Society (GAS) is an international non-profit organization founded in 1971 whose purpose is to encourage excellence, to advance education, to promote the appreciation and development of the glass arts, and to support the worldwide community of artists who work with glass. GAS members are glass artists, students, educators, collectors, gallery and museum personnel, writers and critics, manufacturers and suppliers, and anyone interested in glass art.

## Handweavers Guild of America, Inc.

1255 Buford Highway Suite 211
Suwannee, GA 30024
TEL 678-730-001
FAX 678-730-0836
www.weavespindye.org

Founded in 1969 to inspire creativity and encourage excellence in the fiber arts, the Handweavers Guild of America, Inc., brings together weavers, spinners, dyers, basketmakers, fiber artists, and educators. HGA provides educational programs, conferences, and an award-winning quarterly publication, *Shuttle Spindle & Dyepot*, to its members as it seeks to increase awareness of, and appreciation for, the fiber arts.

## International Sculpture Center

19 Fairgrounds Road Suite B
Hamilton, NJ 08619
TEL 609-689-1051
FAX 609-689-1061
www.sculpture.org

The International Sculpture Center (ISC) is a nonprofit membership organization founded in 1960 to advance the creation and understanding of sculpture and its unique, vital contribution to society. Members include sculptors, collectors, patrons, architects, developers, journalists, curators, historians, critics, educators, foundries, galleries, and museums. The ISC publishes *Sculpture* magazine, and has an award-winning website, www.sculpture.org.

## National Council on Education for the Ceramic Arts

77 Erie Village Square Suite 280
Erie, CO 80516-6996
TEL 866-266-2322
FAX 303-828-0911
www.nceca.net

The National Council on Education for the Ceramic Arts (NCECA) is a nonprofit educational organization whose purpose is to promote and improve the ceramic arts through education, research, and creative practice. NCECA accomplishes this through an annual conference, publications, programs, exhibitions, and other services. Members include educators, ceramic artists, students, museum and gallery professionals, representatives of ceramic arts media, technicians and manufacturing professionals, collectors and patrons, and others interested in ceramic arts.

## National Ornamental & Miscellaneous Metals Association

1535 Pennsylvania Avenue
McDonough, GA 30253
TEL 888-516-8585
FAX 770-288-2006
www.nomma.org

Founded in 1958, the National Ornamental & Miscellaneous Metals Association (NOMMA) is the trade organization for those who produce ornamental gates, railings, doors, furniture, sculpture, restorations, and other structural and industrial fabricated metal products. NOMMA publishes a professional magazine, a newsletter, bulletins and technical materials, and various sales and educational aids, and produces educational videos. The association also holds an annual awards competition and a trade show and convention, which include an intensive education program.

## Society of American Mosaic Artists

PO Box 624
Ligonier, PA 15658-0624
TEL 866-902-7262
FAX 724-238-3973
www.americanmosaics.org

Founded in 1999, the Society of American Mosaic Artists (SAMA) is a non-profit organization dedicated to educating, inspiring, and promoting excellence in mosaic fine art. The organization educates artists and the public regarding contemporary and classical mosaic fine art and provides mosaic artists with opportunities for creative and professional growth. SAMA has over 900 members including mosaic artists from all levels, mosaic aficionados, collectors, materials suppliers, and art educators.

## Society of American Silversmiths

PO Box 72839
Providence, RI 02907
TEL 401-461-6840
FAX 401-461-6841
www.silversmithing.com

The Society of American Silversmiths (SAS) was founded in 1989 to preserve and promote contemporary silversmithing, specifically in the areas of hollowware, flatware, and sculpture. SAS provides its juried artisan members with support, networking, and greater access to the market. SAS also educates the public in demystifying silversmithing techniques, silver care, restoration and conservation, and the aesthetic value of this art form through its comprehensive website.

# ORGANIZATIONS & PUBLICATIONS

## Stained Glass Association of America

10009 East 62nd Street
Raytown, MO 64133
TEL 800-438-9581
www.stainedglass.org

Founded in 1903, the Stained Glass Association of America (SGAA) is a nonprofit national organization founded to promote and defend the finest in the stained and leaded art glass world. In addition to producing the *Stained Glass* quarterly, the oldest stained glass magazine in the world, and other publications, SGAA also sponsors educational programming and public awareness programs.

## Surface Design Association

PO Box 360
Sebastopol, CA 95473-0360
TEL 707-829-3110
FAX 707-829-3285
www.surfacedesign.org

The Surface Design Association is a nonprofit organization that promotes textile arts through education, encouragement of individual artists in all areas of textile/fiber, communication of technical information and information concerning professional opportunities, and the exchange of ideas through exhibitions, electronic media, educational opportunities, conferences, and publications. Members include studio artists, industrial designers, educators, technicians, curators, gallery owners, interior designers, students, and enthusiasts.

## Tile Heritage Foundation

PO Box 1850
Healdsburg, CA 95448
TEL 707-431-8453
FAX 707-431-8455
www.tileheritage.org

The Tile Heritage Foundation, founded in 1987 as a national nonprofit organization, is dedicated to promoting awareness and appreciation of ceramic surfaces in the United States. In addition to maintaining a reference and research library of information and materials, Tile Heritage Foundation publishes a biannual magazine, a monthly e-newsletter, and a resource directory for architects, designers, preservationists, historians, collectors, dealers, installers, tile artists, manufacturers, and others. It also conducts educational events, provides consultation in a variety of areas in the tile industry, and supports research in the field of ceramic history and conservation.

## PUBLICATIONS

## American Craft

72 Spring Street
New York, NY 10012-4019
TEL 212-274-0630
FAX 212-274-0650
www.craftcouncil.org

*American Craft*, a bimonthly magazine founded in 1941, focuses on contemporary achievements in the craft media—clay, fiber, metal, glass, wood, and other materials—through artist profiles, reviews of major exhibitions and solo shows, a portfolio of emerging artists, a national calendar and news section, book reviews, and illustrated columns reporting on commissions and gallery/museum shows.

## AmericanStyle

3000 Chestnut Avenue Suite 304
Baltimore, MD 21211
TEL 410-889-3093
www.americanstyle.com

Launched in 1995, the mission of *AmericanStyle* magazine is to inform craft enthusiasts and art collectors about the significance of handmade objects of art. *AmericanStyle* magazine provides art lovers with valuable tips on decorating, interior design, display and lighting ideas for everything from designer jewelry and art glass to collectible teapots, art furniture and sculptural ceramics. More than 250 arts festivals, gallery exhibitions and museum events are listed in the Datebook section of each issue.

## The Anvil's Ring

Artist-Blacksmiths' Association of North America
PO Box 3425
Knoxville, TN 37927-3425
TEL 865-546-7733
FAX 865-215-9964
www.abana.org

*The Anvil's Ring* provides a comprehensive overview of the artist-blacksmithing world, as well as inspiration. The quarterly publication includes tips, historical notes, photos of members' work, books reviews, and event information. It is included as part of membership in the Artist-Blacksmiths' Association of North America or can be purchased as back issues.

## Art Calendar

1500 Park Center Drive
Orlando, FL 32835
TEL 877-415-3955
FAX 407-563-7099
www.artcalendar.com

For over twenty years, Art Calendar has connected artists with income-generating opportunities and supplied educational articles on how to make a living producing their beloved craft.

## Ceramics Monthly

The American Ceramic Society
735 Ceramic Place Suite 100
Westerville, OH 43081
TEL 800-342-3594
www.ceramicsmonthly.org

Founded in 1952, *Ceramics Monthly*, an internationally distributed magazine, offers a broad range of articles—including artist profiles; clay and glaze recipes, kiln designs, and firing techniques; reviews of exhibitions, books and videos; and business and technical information—for potters, ceramic sculptors, educators, collectors, students, gallery and museum personnel, and interested observers.

# ORGANIZATIONS & PUBLICATIONS

## Clay Times

15481 Second Street
PO Box 365
Waterford, VA 20197
TEL 540-882-3576
FAX 540-882-4196
www.claytimes.com

*Clay Times* magazine is designed to inform ceramic enthusiasts at all levels of the latest developments in the clay world, while providing useful information and techniques to help our readers learn and grow in their individual pursuits in clay.

## Design Solutions

Architectural Woodwork Institute
46179 Westlake Drive Suite 120
Potomac Falls, VA 20165
TEL 571-323-3636
FAX 571-323-3630
www.awinet.org

*Design Solutions*, a quarterly magazine, focuses on fine architectural woodwork, including drawings and explanations of techniques, materials, installations, and restorations.

## Fabricator

National Ornamental & Miscellaneous Metals Association
1535 Pennsylvania Avenue
McDonough, GA 30253
TEL 888-516-8585
FAX 770-288-2006
www.nomma.org

Printed bimonthly, *Fabricator* is a resourceful guide to metalwork techniques, open forums, expert advice, business tips, new products, and industry news.

## Fiberarts Magazine

201 East Fourth Street
Loveland, CO 80537
TEL 800-875-6208
www.fiberartsmagazine.com

For thirty years *Fiberarts* has covered the best and most interesting work in weaving, surface design, quilting, needlework, basketry, fiber sculpture, knitting, papermaking, and wearable art. The readership includes artists, craftspeople, collectors, and curators.

## Fine Woodworking

The Taunton Press, Inc.
63 South Main Street
PO Box 5506
Newtown, CT 06470-5506
TEL 800-477-8727
FAX 203-549-0747
www.taunton.com/finewoodworking

*Fine Woodworking* is a bimonthly magazine for those who strive for and appreciate excellence in woodworking—veteran professional and weekend hobbyist alike. Articles by skilled woodworkers focus on everything from basics of tool use, to product reviews, step-by-step instructions, stock preparation and joinery, and specialized techniques and finishing.

## Glass Art

PO Box 630377
Highlands Ranch, CO 80163-0377
TEL 303-791-8998
FAX 303-791-7739
www.glassartmagazine.com

*Glass Art*, published bimonthly, includes the latest happenings in the art glass industry, artist profiles, and trends in art glass.

## Glass Craftsman Magazine

Arts & Media, Inc.
PO Box 678
Richboro, PA 18954
TEL 215-826-1799
FAX 215-968-4766
www.glasscraftsman.com

*Glass Craftsman* features articles on all aspects of the art, craft, design, fabrication, and business of contemporary and traditional decorative glass.

## GLASS Quarterly

Urbanglass
647 Fulton Street
Brooklyn, NY 11217-1112
TEL 800-607-4410
www.urbanglass.org

*GLASS Quarterly*, founded in 1979, is a full-color magazine with a global focus. It features profiles of new and emerging artists; important trends in making and collecting art; events; commissions; museum openings; news from the worlds of art, architecture, and design; and reviews of exhibitions and books.

## Metalsmith

SNAG/Metalsmith Business Office
540 Oak Street Suite A
Eugene, OR 97401
TEL 541-345-5689
FAX 541-345-1123
www.snagmetalsmith.org

*Metalsmith*, the award-winning publication of the Society of North American Goldsmiths (SNAG), is the premier publication of the metal artists in the United States. Recurring features include in-depth profiles of contemporary artists, provocative columns, relevant historical work, public and private commissions, and exhibition and book reviews.

# ORGANIZATIONS & PUBLICATIONS

**Public Art Review**

FORECAST Public Artworks
2324 University Avenue West
St. Paul, MN 55114
TEL 651-641-1128
FAX 651-641-1983
www.publicartreview.org

*Public Art Review* is a semi-annual journal founded in 1989 that explores the many dimensions of public art. Each issue provides coverage of growing trends, reflects on critical issues, and surveys many of the latest public art projects happening in the United States and around the globe. The readership includes artists, architects, curators, city planners, students, educators, design professionals, program administrators, community leaders, and writers.

**Sculpture Magazine**

1529 18th Street NW
Washington, DC 20036
TEL 202-234-0555
FAX 202-234-2663
www.sculpture.org

*Sculpture* is an international monthly magazine that focuses on established and emerging sculptors and contemporary sculpture. Each issue includes profiles, feature articles, interviews, reviews, and technical information. *Sculpture* also includes listings of opportunities for sculptors, including competitions, residencies, workshops, and other information.

**Shuttle Spindle & Dyepot**

Handweavers Guild of America, Inc.
1255 Buford Highway Suite 211
Suwannee, GA 30024
TEL 678-730-0010
FAX 678-730-0836
www.weavespindye.org

An award-winning quarterly publication, *Shuttle Spindle & Dyepot* features emerging artists and craftspeople, highlights innovative techniques and events, and honors established fiber artists and textile traditions.

**Stained Glass Quarterly**

The Stained Glass Association of America
10009 East 62nd Street
Raytown, MO 64133
TEL 800-438-9581
www.stainedglass.org

Since 1906 this quarterly publication has focused on expanding the use of stained glass as an architectural element. The *Stained Glass Quarterly* features descriptions of materials and techniques, artist profiles, trade news, and source information.

**Surface Design Journal**

Surface Design Association
PO Box 360
Sebastopol, CA 95473-0360
TEL 707-829-3110
FAX 707-829-3285
www.surfacedesign.org

The Surface Design Association (SDA), a nonprofit educational organization of artists, educators, designers, and lovers of beautiful textiles and quality design, publish *Surface Design Journal*, a full-color quarterly magazine. Each issue explores a theme, such as stitching or creative process, that allows for in-depth coverage of different aspects of surface design.

**Tile Heritage: A Review of American Tile History**

Tile Heritage Foundation
PO Box 1850
Healdsburg, CA 95448
TEL 707-431-8453
FAX 707-431-8455
www.tileheritage.org

*Tile Heritage: A Review of American Tile History*, a biannual publication, features informative articles on both historic and contemporary ceramic tiles, written from a humanistic perspective and enhanced with large black-and-white photographs.

**Woodshop News**

Soundings Publications, LLC
10 Bokum Road
Essex, CT 06426
TEL 860-767-8227
FAX 860-767-1048
www.woodshopnews.com

*Woodshop News*, published monthly, includes features and descriptions of new woodworking tools and technology, profiles and techniques, trade news and source information.

**World Art Glass Quarterly**

1650 The Alameda
San Jose, CA 95126
TEL 408-834-8945
FAX 408-317-0360
www.artglassquarterly.com

*World Art Glass Quarterly* features four high-quality issues annually. They are beautifully designed and printed, rich in color and detail, showcasing the most excellent artists and art glass in the world.

Lighting by Hubbardton Forge, see page 74.  Painting by Dorothy L. Martinez.  Photograph: Jim Westphalen Photography.

# FAVORITE ART FAIRS & FINE CRAFT SHOWS

## JANUARY

**Carefree Fine Art & Wine**
Carefree, AZ
www.thunderbirdartists.com

**Palm Beach³**
West Palm Beach, FL
www.palmbeach3.com

**Southwest Arts Festival**
Indio, CA
www.southwestartsfest.com

## FEBRUARY

**American Craft Council**
Baltimore, MD
www.craftcouncil.org

**ArtExpo**
New York, NY
www.artexpos.com

**Carefree Fine Art & Wine**
Carefree, AZ
www.thunderbirdartists.com

**Palm Beach Fine Craft Show**
West Palm Beach, FL
www.crafftsamericashows.com

## MARCH

**American Craft Council**
Atlanta, GA
www.craftcouncil.org

**Artrider Show**
Morristown, NJ
www.artrider.com

**Contemporary Crafts Market**
San Francisco, CA
www.contemporarycraftsmarket.com

**CraftBoston**
Boston, MA
www.craftboston.org

**La Quinta Art Festival**
La Quinta, CA
www.lqaf.com

**Paradise City Arts Festival**
Marlborough, MA
www.paradisecityarts.com

**The Philadelphia Invitational Furniture Show**
Philadelphia, PA
www.pffshow.com

**Scottsdale Art Festival**
Scottsdale, AZ
www.scottsdaleartsfestival.org

## APRIL

**American Craft Council**
St. Paul, MN
www.craftcouncil.org

**Art Chicago**
Chicago, IL
www.artchicago.com

**ArtWalk**
San Diego, CA
www.artwalksandiego.org

**Paradise City Arts Festival**
Philadelphia, PA
www.paradisecityarts.com

**Smithsonian Craft Show**
Washington, DC
www.smithsoniancraftshow.com

## MAY

**Affaire in the Gardens**
Beverly Hills, CA
www.beverlyhills.org

**Artrider Show**
Lyndhurst, NY
www.artrider.com

**Bethesda Fine Arts Festival**
Bethesda, MD
www.bethesda.org

**International Contemporary Furniture Fair**
New York, NY
www.icff.com

**Old Capitol Art Fair**
Springfield, IL
www.socaf.org

**Paradise City Arts Festival**
Northampton, MA
www.paradisecityarts.com

**Sculpture Objects & Functional Art (SOFA)**
New York, NY
www.sofaexpo.com

# FAVORITE ART FAIRS & FINE CRAFT SHOWS

## JUNE

**Affordable Art Fair**
New York, NY
www.aafnyc.com

**Contemporary Crafts Market**
Santa Monica, CA
www.contemporarycraftsmarket.com

**Des Moines Art Festival**
Des Moines, IA
www.desmoinesartsfestival.org

**Edmonds Arts Festival**
Edmonds, WA
www.edmondsartsfestival.com

**Lakefront Festival of the Arts**
Milwaukee, WI
www.lfoa.mam.org

## JULY

**Art Fair on the Square**
Madison, WI
www.mmoca.org

**Artrider Show**
Guilford, CT
www.artrider.com

**Bellevue Arts Museum ArtsFair**
Bellevue, WA
www.bellevuearts.org/fair

**Cherry Creek Arts Festival**
Denver, CO
www.cherryarts.org

**Geneva Arts Fair**
Geneva, IL
www.genevachamber.com/artfair.html

**Krasl Art Fair on the Bluff**
St. Joseph, MI
www.krasl.org

**Palo Alto Clay and Glass Festival**
Palo Alto, CA
www.acga.net

**Ruidoso Art Festival**
Ruidoso, NM
www.ruidosonow.com

**Sawdust Art Festival**
Laguna Beach, CA
www.sawdustartfestival.org

**Street Art Fair**
Ann Arbor, MI
www.artfair.org

## AUGUST

**American Craft Council**
San Francisco, CA
www.craftcouncil.org

**American Craft Exhibition**
Evanston, IL
www.americancraftexpo.org

**Loveland Sculpture Invitational**
Loveland, CO
www.lovelandsculpturegroup.org

**Port Clinton Art Festival**
Highland Park, IL
www.amdurproductions.com/port-clinton.html

**Sculpture in the Park**
Loveland, CO
www.sculptureinthepark.org

## SEPTEMBER

**Artrider Show**
Lyndhurst, NY
www.artrider.com

**Common Ground Art in the Park**
Birmingham, MI
www.artinthepark.info

**Fall in the Village Art Festival**
Freeport, ME
www.freeportusa.org/artfestival.html

**Fine Furnishings & Fine Craft Show–Milwaukee**
Milwaukee, WI
www.finefurnishingsshow.com

**Kings Mountain Art Fair**
Woodside, CA
www.kingsmountainartfair.org

**Long's Park Art & Craft Festival**
Lancaster, PA
www.longspark.org

**Sausalito Art Festival**
Sausalito, CA
www.sausalitoartfestival.org

# FAVORITE ART FAIRS & FINE CRAFT SHOWS

**St. Louis Art Fair**
St. Louis, MO
www.saintlouisartfair.com

## October

**Affaire in the Gardens**
Beverly Hills, CA
www.beverlyhills.org

**Bethesda Row Arts Festival**
Bethesda, MD
www.bethesdarowarts.org

**Fine Furnishings & Fine Craft Show–Providence**
Providence, RI
www.finefurnishingsshow.com

**Open Studios**
Boulder, Co
www.openstudios.org

**Paradise City Arts Festival**
Northampton, MA
www.paradisecityarts.com

**Westchester Craft Show**
White Plains, NY
www.craftsamericashows.com

**Wheaton Village Festival of Fine Craft**
Millville, NJ
www.wheatonvillage.org

## November

**American Craft Council**
Charlotte, NC
www.craftcouncil.org

**American Craft Council**
Sarasota, FL
www.craftcouncil.org

**Bad Girls of the North**
Anchorage, AK
www.badgirlsofthenorth.com

**Celebration of Craftswomen**
San Francisco, CA
www.celebrationofcraftswomen.org

**Contemporary Crafts Market**
Santa Monica, CA
www.contemporarycraftsmarket.com

**Homestead Craft Fair**
Waco, TX
www.homesteadcraftfair.com

**Paradise City Arts Festival**
Marlborough, MA
www.paradisecityarts.com

**Philadelphia Museum of Art Craft Show**
Philadelphia, PA
www.pmacraftshow.org

**Piedmont Craftsmen's Fair**
Winston-Salem, NC
www.piedmontcraftsmen.org

**Sculpture Objects & Functional Art (SOFA)**
Chicago, IL
www.sofaexpo.com

**Washington Craft Show**
Washington, DC
www.craftsamericashows.com

**Winter Fantasy**
Laguna Beach, CA
www.sawdustartfestival.org

## December

**Artrider Show**
Morristown, NJ
www.artrider.com

**Artrider Show**
New York, NY
www.artrider.com

**Crafts at the Castle**
Boston, MA
www.fsgb.org/catc.htm

**One of a Kind Show**
Chicago, IL
www.merchandisemart.com/oneofakindshow

# GLOSSARY OF ART TERMS

ACRYLIC
A water-soluble paint made with pigments and synthetic resin; used as a fast-drying alternative to oil paint.

ALABASTER
A fine-textured, usually white, gypsum that is easily carved and translucent when thin.

ALUMINUM
A lightweight, silver-colored metal used extensively in commercial applications, and occasionally by metal artists. In a process called anodizing, aluminum is given a tough porous coating that can be colored with dyes.

APPLIQUÉ
A technique whereby pieces of fabric are layered on top of one another and joined with decorative stitches.

AQUATINT
Printmaking process used to create areas of solid color, as well as gradations of white through black tones. Usually has the appearance of transparent water color.

BAS-RELIEF
Literally, "low-relief." Raised or indented sculptural patterns that remain close to the surface plane.

BATIK
A method of applying dye to cloth that is covered, in part, with a dye-resistant, removable substance such as wax. After dyeing, the resist is removed, and the design appears in the original color against the newly colored background.

BEADING
The process whereby decorative beads are sewn, glued, or otherwise attached to a surface.

BEVELED GLASS
Plate glass that has its perimeter ground and polished at an angle.

BONDED GLASS
Glass pieces that have been adhered together by glue, resin, or cement.

BRASS
An alloy of copper and zinc. Brass is yellow in color, and though harder than either of its constituents, it is appropriately malleable for jewelry making.

BRONZE
Traditionally, an alloy of copper and tin widely used in casting. The term is often applied to brown-colored brasses.

BURL
A dome-shaped growth on the trunk of a tree. Intricately patterned burl wood is often used by wood turners and furniture makers.

CASTING
The process of pouring molten metal or glass, clay slip, etc. into a hollow mold to harden. Some casting processes permit more than one reproduction.

CELADON
French name for a green, gray-green, blue-green, or gray glaze produced with a small percentage of iron as the colorant.

CERAMICS
The art and science of forming objects from earth materials containing or combined with silica; the objects are then heated to at least 1300°F to harden.

CHASING
A technique in which steel punches are used to decorate and/or texture a metal surface.

CHINA PAINT
A low-temperature overglaze fired onto previously glazed and fired ceramic.

DICHROIC GLASS
A thin metallic coating on any type of glass. The coating is applied at a high temperature in a vacuum chamber.

DIE FORMING
The process of placing metal between two steel dies or stamps and squeezing them together under high pressure. This process shapes and strengthens the metal.

DIGITAL IMAGING
Refers to the creation, manipulation, and production of images by use of computer technology, including software and printers.

Acrylic
Glenys Porter, *Quadrants 2.*

Aluminum
Louise Rauh, *Spring Rain.*

Celadon
Suzanne Crane, *Large Medusa Jars.*

Chasing
Eva Seid, *Hydrangea.*

# GLOSSARY OF ART TERMS

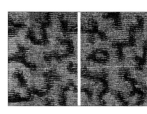

Diptych
Tim Harding, *Runes Diptych.*

Fused Glass
Martin Kremer, *Navajo Zig Zag Bowl.*

Giclée
Barbara Buer, *Gold Peony.*

Incalmo
Michael Trimpol, *Flattened Banded Vase.*

| | |
|---|---|
| DIPTYCH | Artwork on two panels that are hung together. Historically, a hinged, two-paneled painting or bas-relief. |
| EARTHENWARE | Ceramic ware with a permeable or porous body after firing (usually to a temperature of 1600°F to 1900°F). |
| ENAMELED GLASS | Glass decorated with particles of translucent glass or glass-like material, usually of a contrasting color, which fuses to the surface under heat. Multicolored designs can be created, as well as monochrome coatings. |
| ENCAUSTIC | A paint medium in which pigment is suspended in molten wax and resin. After applying the paint to a panel or canvas, the artist passes a heat element over the work to fuse the colors into a fixed, uniform film. |
| ENGRAVING | An intaglio printing process in which a design is incised into a metal plate. Characterized by sharp, clean lines and high definition. Also called line engraving. |
| ETCHED GLASS | Glass decorated, carved, or otherwise marked by sandblasting or the use of hydrofluoric acid. The glass is partially covered with an acid-resistant wax or gum and the exposed area is etched. |
| ETCHING | A printing process in which chemical agents are used to deepen lines drawn onto a printing plate. |
| FIRING | Heating clay, glaze, enamel, or other material to the temperature necessary to achieve a desired structural change. Most ceramics are fired in a kiln to temperatures ranging from 1600°F to 2300°F. |
| FORGED | A blacksmithing technique in which metal is shaped by hammering, usually while at red or white heat. |
| FUMING | A vapor deposition process in which a thin film of metal (usually silver, platinum, or gold) condenses on the surface of a hot piece of glass or clay, resulting in an iridescent surface. |
| FUSED GLASS | Glass that has been heated in a kiln to the point where two separate pieces are permanently joined as one without losing their individual color. |
| GICLÉE | French term meaning "sprayed." A process by which an image is rendered digitally by spraying a fine stream of ink onto archival art paper or canvas. Similar to an airbrush technique. |
| GLASSBLOWING | The process of gathering molten glass onto the end of a blowpipe and forming it into a variety of shapes by blowing and manipulating it as the glass is rotated. |
| GLAZE | Glassy melted coating on a clay surface. Glaze has a similar oxide composition to glass, but includes a binder. |
| GOUACHE | An opaque watercolor paint, or work so produced. Gouache is applied like watercolor, but reflects light due to its chalky finish. |
| HUE | The pure state of any color. |
| ILFOCHROME | A trademarked photographic paper and the process of making prints with such paper. Ilfochrome prints are produced from slides or transparencies, not color negatives. |
| IMPASTO | A thick, uneven surface texture achieved by applying paint with a brush or palette knife. |
| INCALMO | The glassblowing technique used to create horizontal or vertical bands of color by forming and connecting cylinders of colored glass. |

# GLOSSARY OF ART TERMS

**INCLUSIONS**  Particles of metal, bubbles, etc., that occur naturally within glass or are added for decorative effect.

**INLAY**  A decorating technique in which an object is incised with a design, a colorant is pressed into the incisions, and the surface is then scraped to confine the colored inlay to the incisions.

**INTAGLIO**  A printmaking process in which an image is created from ink held in the incised or bitten areas of a metal plate, below the surface plane. Engraving, etching, mezzotint, and aquatint are examples of the intaglio process.

**IRIDIZED GLASS**  Flat or blown glass sprayed with a vapor deposit of metal oxides for an iridescent finish. The iridized layer, which resembles an oil slick, can be selectively removed for a two-tone effect.

**IRIS PRINT**  The trademarked name for a digital print produced by an Iris Graphics inkjet printer. (See "Giclée.")

**KILN**  A furnace for firing clay, forming glass, or melting enamels; studio kilns can achieve temperatures up to 2500°F and can be fueled with gas, wood, or electricity.

**KILN-FORMING**  A glass-forming process that utilizes a kiln to heat glass in a refractory or heat-resistant mold, slump glass over a form, or fuse two or more pieces of glass together.

**KINETIC**  Active. Kinetic sculpture has parts that move, whether by air currents (as with a mobile) or by motors and gears.

**LAMINATED**  Composed of layers bonded together for strength, thickness, or decorative effect.

**LAMPWORK**  The technique of manipulating glass by heating it with a small flame. An open flame is advantageous in very detailed work.

**LEADED GLASS**  Glass containing a percentage of lead oxide, which increases its density and improves its ability to refract and disperse light. Leaded glass is used for ornaments and for decorative and luxury tableware.

**LIMITED EDITION**  Artworks produced in a deliberately limited quantity. All items in the edition are identical and each one is an original work of art. The limited size of the edition enhances the value of each piece.

**LINOCUT**  A relief print process similar to woodcut. Wood blocks covered with a layer of linoleum are carved with woodcut tools, coated with ink, and printed by hand or in a press.

**LITHOGRAPHY**  A planographic printmaking process based on the repellence of oil and water and characterized by soft lines and blurry shapes.

**LOW-FIRE GLAZES**  Low-temperature ceramic glazes, usually associated with bright, shiny colors.

**LUSTER**  A brilliant iridescent film used on ceramic glazes; formed from metallic salts.

**MAJOLICA**  An opaque glaze, usually white, with a glossy surface. Typically decorated with bright overglaze stains.

**MARQUETRY**  Decorative patterns formed when thin layers of wood (and sometimes other materials, such as ivory) are inlaid into the surface of furniture or other wood products.

**MEZZOTINT**  An intaglio printing process that produces areas of tone rather than clean lines.

Inclusions
Takuya Tokizawa, *Moonlit Vases*.

Intaglio
Harvey K. Littleton, *Undulation State II*.

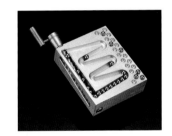

Kinetic
Bill Durovchic, *Archimedes Screw*.

Marquetry
Bonnie Bishoff and J.M. Syron,
*Sun and Shade Wall Hung Cabinet*.

357

# GLOSSARY OF ART TERMS

Mosaic
Carl and Sandra Bryant,
*Lotus Flower.*

Murrini
Trefny Dix and Bengt Hokanson,
*Black Murrini.*

Palladium
Dan Burkholder, *Egyptian on Pier.*

Porcelain
Lynne Meade, *Potential.*

| | |
|---|---|
| MONOPRINT | A print produced by painting directly onto an already-etched surface and printing the image by hand onto paper. |
| MONOTYPE | A print made when an artist draws or paints on a glass or metal plate and then prints the image onto paper. |
| MOSAIC | The process of creating a design or picture with small pieces of glass, stone, terra cotta, etc. |
| MURRINI | A small wafer of glass bearing a colored pattern. Formed by bundling and fusing colored glass rods together and then heating and pulling the resulting cylinder to a very small diameter. When cut into cross-sectioned wafers, each piece bears the original pattern in miniature. |
| OIL PAINT | A paint in which natural oil—usually linseed—is the medium that binds the pigments. |
| PALLADIUM | A photographic process in which the image is produced by palladium crystals deposited on the paper. |
| PASTEL | A crayon of ground pigment bound with gum or oil. Pastel crayons have varying ratios of pigment to chalk and gum; the more pigment, the more intense the color. |
| PATE DE VERRE | A "paste" of finely crushed glass that is mixed, heated, and poured into a mold. |
| PATINA | A surface coloring, usually brown or green, produced by the oxidation of bronze, copper, or other metal. Patinas occur naturally and are also produced artificially for decorative effect. |
| PHOTOETCHING | A printmaking technique in which a light-sensitive metal plate is exposed to photographic film under ultraviolet light. |
| PHOTOGRAVURE | A printing process based on the production, by photographic methods, of a plate containing small ink-receptive pits. |
| POLAROID TRANSFER | A trademarked name for the process by which an image recorded by the camera's lens is reproduced directly onto a photosensitive surface, which functions as both film and photograph. |
| PORCELAIN | A clay body that is white, strong, and hard when fired. When sufficiently thin, it is also translucent. |
| PRINT | An image made from an inked surface. Prints are usually, but not always, produced in multiples. |
| RAKU | The technique of rapidly firing low-temperature ceramic ware. Raku firings were used traditionally in Japan to make bowls for tea ceremonies. |
| RELIEF PRINT | A process in which a print is produced from the relief carving on a metal plate or a wood or linoleum block. |
| REPOUSSÉ | An ancient process in which sheet metal is hammered into contours from both the front and the back. |
| REVERSE PAINTING | A technique where paint is applied to the back side of a surface (typically glass) and viewed through the front. This process requires the painting to be done in reverse order; what appears closest to the viewer as a detail or highlight must be painted first rather than last. Any lettering must likewise be painted in the mirror image so it will appear right facing when viewed from the front. |

# GLOSSARY OF ART TERMS

SALT GLAZE — A glaze created during high-temperature firings. Sodium, usually in the form of rock salt, is introduced into the fully heated kiln and forms a clear coating on the clay, often with an orange-peel texture.

SAND CASTING — An ancient and still widely used casting method in which moistened sand is packed against a model to make a mold—usually for metal.

SANDBLASTING — A method of etching the surface of a material by spraying it with compressed air and sand.

SEPIA — Warm, reddish-brown pigment produced from octopus or cuttlefish ink, used in watercolor and drawing ink. In photography, some toning processes produce a similar color in the print.

Sandblasting
Lia Kass and Laurie Thal,
*Cobalt Ruby Leaves.*

SILKSCREEN PRINTING — A printing process in which paint, ink, or dye is forced through a fine screen onto the surface beneath. Different areas of the screen are blocked off with each layer of color. Also known as "serigraph."

SILVER GELATIN — A photographic process that uses silver halide crystals suspended within the photographic emulsion to produce the image. The most popular type of black-and-white photograph produced today.

SLUMPED GLASS — Preformed flat or three-dimensional glass that is reheated and shaped in a mold.

SPALTED — Wood that contains areas of natural decay, giving it distinctive markings. Spalted wood is used for its decorative effect.

Spalted
Michael Allison,
*Spalted Maple Hollow Form*

STILL LIFE — A depiction of a group of inanimate objects arranged for symbolic or aesthetic effect.

STONEWARE — A gray, red, or buff clay body that matures (becomes nonporous) between 1900°F and 2300°F.

TERRA COTTA — Low-fired ceramic ware that is often reddish and unglazed.

TERRA SIGILLATA — A thin coating of colored clay or clays applied like a glaze. A terra sigillata solution is composed of fine particles of decanted clay and water.

TRIPTYCH — A three-paneled artwork. Historically, triptychs were hinged together so that the two side wings closed over the central panel.

TROMPE L'OEIL — Literally, "fool the eye" (French). An object or scene rendered so realistically that the viewer believes he or she is seeing the real thing.

Terra Sigillata
Judith E. Motzkin, *Spirit Keeper, Large.*

TURNED — Wood or other materials shaped by tools while revolving around a fixed axis, usually a lathe. Cylindrical forms (dowels, rungs) and circular designs (bowls) are made in this way.

VITREOGRAPH — A print made from a glass plate that has been prepared by sandblasting or etching.

VITREOUS — Clay fired to maturity, so that it is hard, dense, and nonabsorbent.

WATERCOLOR — Watercolor paints are made with pigments dispersed in gum arabic and are characterized by luminous transparency.

WHITEWARE — A generic term for white clay bodies.

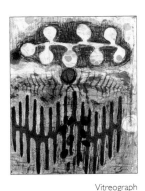

WOODCUT — A relief printing process in which a picture or design is cut in relief along the grain of a wood block.

Vitreograph
Karen Kunc, *Frond*

359

# Turn your passion into a living!

ART MARKETING • JURIED COMPETITIONS • GRANTS • FAIRS & FESTIVALS • CAREER ADVICE

*Art Calendar* provides visual artists with the most comprehensive source of opportunities available

| 2 YEAR SUBSCRIPTION | 1 YEAR SUBSCRIPTION |
|---|---|
| **44% OFF** | **33% OFF** |
| 22 ISSUES FOR ONLY $62 | 11 ISSUES FOR ONLY $37 |

Subscribe Today at www.artcalendar.com/specialoffer

17HSA

*Advertising Opportunities - Get Your Product into Every Artist's Studio!*
Contact David Trask at 407.515.2603 or dtrask@artcalendar.com
www.ArtCalendar.com

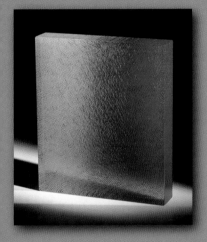

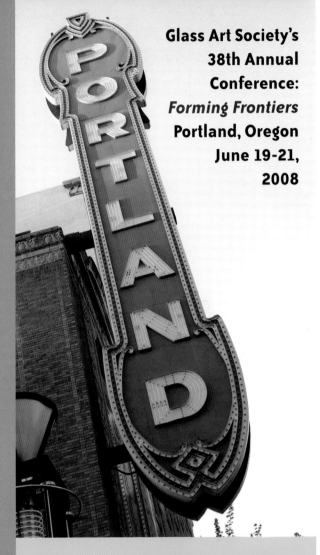

# Don't miss a single issue.

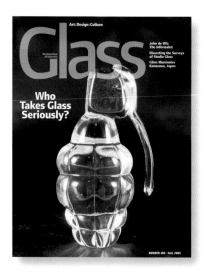

# www.glassquarterly.com

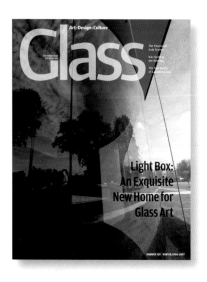

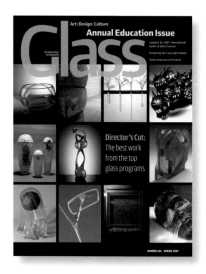

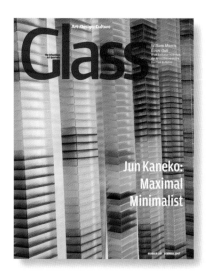

# Question: Should you join NCECA? (we know the answer...)

# National Council on

**YES.** We are a national member-organization of ceramic artists, educators, collectors, curators, art historians, manufacturers and suppliers, however our outreach and membership is truly international. For more than 40 years we have shaped and chronicled the clay world.

# Education for the

**YES.** Our Annual Conferences are legendary, but at the core our emphasis is education. Through workshops, lectures, demonstrations, scholarships, exhibitions, research, critical thinking, publishing and art making we define and drive the investigation of clay as an art medium. After all, Education is our middle name.

# Ceramic Arts

**YES.** It all comes down to Art. While we appreciate and celebrate the exciting role of ceramics in emerging technologies and industrial applications, we are all about clay, and we are an essential part of the art world. We are creators, purveyors and suppliers of the Ceramic Arts, and if you are a designer, art dealer, or collector you should join, network and grow with us.

# LOCATION INDEX

# LOCATION INDEX

# LOCATION INDEX

# INDEX OF ARTISTS & COMPANIES

# INDEX OF ARTISTS & COMPANIES

# INDEX OF ARTISTS & COMPANIES

# INDEX OF ARTISTS & COMPANIES